ELECTRICAL NETWORKS AND FILTERS
Theory and design

ELECTRICAL NETWORKS AND FILTERS

Theory and design

G H Tomlinson

Prentice Hall
New York London Toronto Sydney Tokyo Singapore

First published 1991 by
Prentice Hall Prentice Hall Europe |
66 Wood Lane End, Hemel Hempstead
Hertfordshire HP2 4RG
A division of
Simon & Schuster International Group

© Prentice Hall Europe 1991   (UK) Ltd, 1991

Typeset in 10 on 12 point Times
by MCS Typesetters, Salisbury, Wiltshire, England

Printed and bound in Great Britain at
Hartnolls Ltd, Bodmin, Cornwall

Library of Congress Cataloging-in-Publication Data

Tomlinson, G. H.
    Electrical networks and filters: theory and design with
interactive software/by G. H. Tomlinson.
      p. cm.
    Includes index.
    ISBN 0–13–248261–4; – ISBN 0–12–248253–3 (pbk.):
    1. Electric networks. 2. Electric filters. I. Title.
TK1005.T66 1991
621.319′2–dc20   91-20552
                                      CIP

British Library Cataloguing in Publication Data

Tomlinson, Gerry
  Electrical network and filters.
  I. Title
  621.319

  ISBN 0-13-248261-4 hbk. 0-13-248253-3 pbk.

---

3 4 5 6 7   00 99 98 97 96

CONTENTS

PREFACE

The subject of network and filter theory is an extensive one, with many books available which give in-depth treatment of particular aspects. However, there are few up-to-date books that give both broad coverage, including the more recent topics of switched-capacitor filters and digital filters, and make use of a supporting software package.

From many years of teaching experience at the University of Salford and industrial consultancy work in the area of filter design, I have gained sufficient knowledge of the relative importance of the various aspects of the subject to be able to present it in an interesting and coherent manner, and at a level that can be readily understood by the student. I have found also that the teaching of the subject can be greatly aided by computer graphics for class demonstration and student self-learning. It is on the methods developed and tested over many years that I have based this book and the supporting software package.

Scope of the book

The particular features of the text are as follows: broad coverage starts with the fundamental equations of circuit elements and transient analysis and proceeds through to the design of passive and active lumped constant networks, digital filters and switched-capacitor filters. New ideas are introduced by dealing with simple examples before moving on to generalized principles. The simplest possible mathematics are used. Computer exercises are included to aid student learning.

Particular emphasis is given to the complex frequency domain in order to provide a thorough understanding of the s-plane and its relationships with transient response and steady-state frequency response. These properties are related throughout to practical examples of circuits rather than being treated purely as mathematical abstractions. The theory is applied to the design of a wide variety of networks.

Readership

The book is suitable for students of electrical and electronic engineering, physics and applied acoustics as a senior undergraduate or beginning graduate level course in circuit theory, network and filter synthesis and signal processing. Used in conjunction with the supporting software package, the book should be useful for practising engineers engaged in filter design.

It is assumed that the student is already familiar with the basic principles and standard theorems of d.c. and steady-state a.c. circuit theory. An elementary knowledge of the Laplace transformation is also assumed although some revision of this topic is provided.

Structure of the book

Chapters 1 to 8 are written in integrated form, providing a step-by-step development of the theory for determining a system function to realize a specific characteristic. According to the student's needs, or the particular course, certain other parts may be omitted. For example, Chapters 9 and 10, which deal with passive network synthesis, are not essential for the understanding of the remaining chapters. Similarly, Chapters 11 and 12 on active *RC* synthesis, are not essential for an understanding of Chapter 13 on digital filters.

In more detail, Chapter 1 presents an introduction which explains the differences between network analysis and synthesis, and describes the overall general strategy employed in network synthesis. The practical considerations which influence the choice of the type of network which will be employed to achieve a given response are then discussed. Chapter 2 introduces the basic equations for network elements and the principles of transient analysis using the concept of generalized immittances. Analysis of the transient response of a number of first-order circuits is given, followed by a transient analysis of the second-order circuit. In Chapter 3, the concepts of the *s*-plane, poles, zeros and complex frequencies are introduced, initially with reference to the second-order circuit and then more generally for rational functions. Chapter 4 introduces the sinusoidal input function, leading to the steady-state frequency response function. The geometric relationship between the frequency response function and the *s*-plane is developed and a thorough analysis of the second-order response is given. In Chapter 5 it is shown how the zeros influence the steady-state frequency response. The concepts of minimum phase and nonminimum phase and the allpass function are introduced. Practical examples of simple circuits and their *s*-plane diagrams are given for lowpass, highpass, bandpass, bandstop and allpass networks. In Chapter 6 semilog frequency response plots, known also as Bode diagrams, are described. Straight line approximation methods for magnitude and phase plots are developed. Chapter 7 introduces the theoretical aspects of filter design. Some properties of the magnitude-squared function are derived, the approximation problem is introduced and the maximally flat criterion is described. This is then applied to derive the Butterworth filter function. The equiripple criterion is next described leading to the Chebyshev family of filters. The Bessel filter is next introduced followed by a brief description of the elliptic filter. Chapter 8 is concerned with impedance and frequency transformation, and includes the important topics of scaling and derivation of highpass, bandpass and bandstop filters from lowpass prototypes. Chapter 9 describes analysis and synthesis techniques for the passive ladder network, and develops methods of synthesis for realization of the all-pole filters described in the previous chapter. Chapter 10 introduces the constant-resistance network and describes the realization of allpass networks in passive unbalanced form. Chapter 11 introduces the topic of active RC networks which use operational amplifiers. The principles of negative feedback are considered and practical examples of the operational amplifier in simple feedback configurations are described. The methods of multiple feedback, Sallen–Key and the state-variable technique for realization of transfer functions with complex poles are described. In Chapter 12 we consider the practical operational amplifier, its effect on stability and the errors due to finite gain bandwidth. Chapter 13 introduces the principles of sampled-data systems and quantization. Some simple digital filters are described and the Z-transform is developed as an extension of the Laplace transform. A method of design for nonrecursive FIR filters is described. The methods of impulse invariance and bilinear z-transformation for design of FIR recursive filters are developed. Chapter 14 introduces the principle of the switched capacitor and describes the basics of SC filters.

Software package

The supporting software package ENTIS (Electrical Network Theory Integrated Software) provides animated demonstration programs and access to an unlimited number of characteristics, graphs, exercises and solutions. The programs are useful also to the lecturer for class demonstration purposes. The software may also be used as an aid to practical design of filters. However, ENTIS is not essential to the understanding of the book, as all necessary results and graphs are given and fully discussed in the main text. Further details of ENTIS, including ordering information, are given in Appendix B.

1 INTRODUCTION

An electrical network consists of an interconnection of certain types of elements, the basic ones being resistors, capacitors and inductors (including mutual coupling). In the analysis of electrical networks, the voltage–current relationships of the individual elements are idealized in that they are assumed to obey a set of simple mathematical laws. Firstly, the relationships are assumed to be linear and time invariant. Also, it is assumed here that the elements are lumped. That is, we exclude cases such as the microwave transmission line where the elements are distributed. These assumptions lead to the important result that all the currents and voltages in the network are related by ordinary differential equations with constant coefficients.

The mathematical tool for the analysis of systems governed by the above laws is the Laplace transformation. Application of the Laplace transformation leads to a function which relates the transforms of the time functions and is known as the system function. An ordinary differential equation with constant coefficients leads to a system function which is a rational function in s with constant coefficients, where s is the Laplace complex variable.

Many other types of system, such as electromechanical, mechanical and process control systems, are governed by system functions which are rational in s, and much of the theory developed is applicable to a wide range of systems. In such cases however, the relationships are not necessarily between voltage and current functions but may extend to other physical qualities such as angular and linear position, speed, temperature and pressure.

The subject of network theory encompasses not only analysis but also synthesis. Analysis is understood to mean the determination of the response of a given network with a prescribed excitation or input. Synthesis, on the other hand, can be regarded as the converse of analysis and involves the design of a network which will produce an output related to the input in some prescribed manner.

There are several important distinctions to be made regarding analysis and synthesis. Firstly, analysis is expected to lead to a unique solution. Further, general methods are available, which provide the response without any restriction on the complexity of the network. These methods are applicable to a wide variety of networks including power systems. Computer software packages for the analysis of complex networks have been in use for many years, and now

1

scaled-down but nevertheless powerful versions are available for use on personal computers.

In the case of synthesis, the excitation and response are assumed to be in the form of signals. That is, they contain information. The purpose of the network is then to process the signal in some way, the most common example being the recovery of a signal which has been corrupted by noise. Networks of this kind are generally known as *filters* and have a wide range of applications in such fields as instrumentation, communications and audio engineering.

Unlike analysis, there is no general method for synthesis, and unique solutions do not normally exist. In fact in many cases, no exact solution at all may be possible and a compromise approximate solution may have to be accepted.

The first systematic methods of filter synthesis that were developed were based on image-parameter theory. These techniques utilize a ladder-type passive structure. The constant-k and m-derived filters are examples of types that are designed using the image-parameter method. A particular merit of the method is the mathematical simplicity of the design algorithms where the requirement is for a conventional filter characteristic. These types of filter are often referred to as *wave filters*.

The methods that have been developed more recently are usually referred to under the heading of *modern synthesis*. These methods are much more flexible than the image-parameter methods, are suitable for a much wider range of applications and generally produce better characteristics. The advantage possessed by the image-parameter method, because of the mathematical simplicity of its design procedure, is generally no longer an important consideration owing to the availability of modern computing techniques. The image-parameter method has been extensively covered elsewhere, and only modern synthesis will be described in this book.

The procedure involved in the design of a network to meet a prescribed specification using modern synthesis techniques consists of two separate stages. The first stage consists of determining the mathematical description of a realizable system that will theoretically meet the specification. This is a purely mathematical problem and at this stage no reference need be made to the actual network. The mathematical description is usually in the form of a system function that is a rational function in s. In most practical cases, it is not possible to realize the exact requirements and a system function whose characteristics best approximate the requirements must be obtained. This area of mathematics is known as the approximation problem. The particular solution obtained depends upon the exact way in which the 'best approximation' is defined and also upon the order of the approximating system function. In general, an approximation can be improved by increasing the order of the approximating function, but this leads to an increase in the complexity of the corresponding network. A practical solution will thus represent a compromise between the conflicting requirements for an optimum approximation and a minimum-order network.

Once a realizable system function has been obtained, the second stage of the synthesis procedure consists of determining a practical network. Theoretical methods are available for achieving this by means of a network which may include resistors, capacitors, inductors and transformers. In practice, however, the transformer presents problems in terms of deviation from its idealized characteristics because of its inevitable stray capacitance, adjustment difficulties for the coupling, and losses and nonlinearities of the core. It has disadvantages in terms of cost and bulk which are particularly significant at low frequencies. Further, it cannot be realized in integrated circuit form. Fortunately, synthesis procedures can often be arranged to exclude the use of transformers.

For reasons similar to those applicable to the transformer, the inductor is also an unsatisfactory element, although to a lesser extent than the transformer. However, unlike transformers, inductors cannot simply be eliminated from a passive network without imposing serious limitations on the type of system function which can be obtained.

The restrictions imposed by the exclusion of inductors can be removed by the addition of electronic amplifiers in a feedback configuration, resulting in an active *RC* network. The relationships that govern the operation of active networks are similar in most respects to those of passive networks. In particular, the assumption that the active devices are linear ensures that the operation is still governed by ordinary linear differential equations and hence the system function is rational in s.

Active *RC* networks have a wide range of applications, particularly in the audio and sub-audio frequency ranges and, theoretically, can realize any system function that can be realized by a passive *RLC* network. However, in comparison with passive networks, active networks have a restricted upper frequency range and increased sensitivity to component value variations. Also, the problem of instability can occur in an active network. On the other hand, an advantage of active networks is that relatively straightforward general design procedures are available for the implementation of system functions with any order.

The networks referred to above are ones in which the signals are continuous. There are two other types of filter covered in this book which are finding an ever-increasing range of applications. These are the *switched-capacitor filter* and the *digital filter*, and both are based on sampling techniques. The advantages and applications of these types are discussed later. Although the concept of ordinary linear differential equations no longer holds, it is shown that the methods developed for the synthesis of continuous filters can be extended to cover the case of sample filters. Also, a further design method, applicable only to digital filters, is described.

A signal is a function of time and where the excitation and response are described in this form, the specification is referred to as being 'in the time domain'. Other forms of description are possible, the most common alternative being where the signals are described in terms of their spectra or sinusoidal components. Such a specification is said to be 'in the frequency domain'. Both domains will be considered here, although in accordance with current practice the emphasis will be on the frequency domain when considering filter design.

2 CIRCUIT FUNDAMENTALS

We begin by studying analysis since this leads on to synthesis methods. It is assumed that the reader is familiar with the techniques for analysis of d.c. circuits by means of Kirchhoff's laws and other related circuit theorems. An elementary knowledge of the Laplace transformation is also assumed, although some revision of this topic is included and a table of the most useful transform pairs is developed in Appendix A.

2.1 Basic equations

We first consider the equations that govern the behaviour of the three basic circuit elements, namely the resistor, the capacitor and the inductor. We adopt the convention of using lower-case italics to denote the current and voltage where these are specified as functions of time. These can be written $i(t)$ and $v(t)$ but where no ambiguity can occur we write simply i and v. We also need to define a reference direction for the current flow relative to the reference polarity of the voltage. We adopt the standard convention where the current flow is in the direction, say, from node 1 to node 2 and the polarity is then that of the voltage at node 1 with respect to node 2, as shown in Fig. 2.1. That is, the voltage is measured in the $+$ to $-$ sense. Using the above conventions, the relationships are now given.

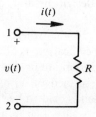

Figure 2.1 *Voltage polarity and current direction for resistor.*

Resistor

Here the relationship is

$$v(t) = Ri(t) \tag{2.1}$$

where R is the resistance in ohms. A positive voltage at node 1 with respect to node 2 causes a current flow through the resistor from node 1 to node 2.

Capacitor

Here the relationship is

$$i(t) = C \frac{\mathrm{d}v}{\mathrm{d}t} \tag{2.2}$$

where C is the capacitance in farads. A current from an external source flowing in at node 1 charges the capacitor and causes an increase in the voltage at node 1 with respect to node 2, as shown in Fig. 2.2.

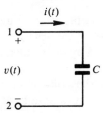

Figure 2.2 *Voltage polarity and current direction for capacitor*

Inductor

Here the relationship is

$$v(t) = L \frac{\mathrm{d}i}{\mathrm{d}t} \tag{2.3}$$

where L is the inductance in henries. An increase in the current flowing through the inductor from node 1 to node 2 causes the voltage at node 1 with respect to node 2 to be positive as shown in Fig. 2.3a.

In the case of the inductor, confusion sometimes arises concerning the voltage polarity. This is because the equation is often written as a relationship between current and back e.m.f., $e_b(t)$. This relationship is

$$e_b(t) = -L \frac{\mathrm{d}i}{\mathrm{d}t} \tag{2.4}$$

The negative sign is necessary to indicate that the direction of the e.m.f. is opposite to that of the current as shown in Figure 2.3b. However, it is seen that such an e.m.f. causes the voltage at node 1 to be positive with respect to node

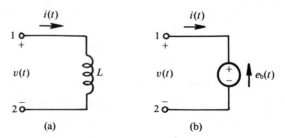

Figure 2.3 *Voltage polarity and current direction for inductor.*

2. That is, if we define a given direction in a circuit as being positive, a *positive* voltage source or e.m.f. in the given direction is equivalent to a *negative* voltage drop and vice versa.

2.1.1 Application to series circuit

We next consider a simple network consisting of a series arrangement of a resistor and an inductor. Suppose we wish to determine the voltage across the resistor when a voltage is applied by the sudden closure of a switch in series with an ideal constant voltage source, as shown in Fig. 2.4. For convenience we assume that the magnitude of the voltage source is unity; the linearity of the circuit ensures that the response to a source of any magnitude V_m is obtained simply by multiplying the response to a source of unit magnitude by V_m. The excitation applied to the series circuit is a voltage function which is zero until $t = 0$ and then abruptly rises to unity and subsequently remains constant as shown in Fig. 2.5. This is known as a unit step function and is denoted by $u(t)$.

Each element has the same current $i(t)$ flowing through it. The voltage $v(t)$ across the combination is the sum of the voltages $v_R(t)$ and $v_L(t)$ across R and L respectively.

We have

$$v(t) = v_L(t) + v_R(t)$$

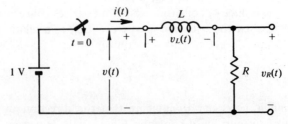

Figure 2.4 *Unit step voltage applied to series RL circuit.*

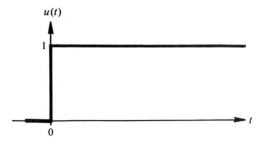

Figure 2.5 *Unit step function* u*(t).*

Hence

$$v(t) = L\frac{di}{dt} + Ri(t) \tag{2.5}$$

Thus the relationship between the voltage and current for the series RL circuit is a first-order differential equation. We will first determine the expression for the current i, from which the expression for the voltage across R can be readily obtained from the relationship

$$v_R(t) = Ri(t)$$

In order to determine the response to a unit step voltage we apply the Laplace transformation to (2.5). We adopt the convention of using upper-case letters to denote the Laplace transforms of time functions. Thus $I(s)$ and $V(s)$ denote the transforms of $i(t)$ and $v(t)$ respectively.

The Laplace transform of a derivative di/dt is given by (see Appendix A)

$$\mathscr{L}\frac{di}{dt} = sI(s) - i(0+) \tag{2.6}$$

where $i(0+)$ is the value of i immediately after $t = 0$. For the circuit under consideration the switch is open until $t = 0$ and hence $i(0+) = 0$.

Thus, transforming (2.5) we have

$$V(s) = (Ls + R)I(s) \tag{2.7}$$

i.e.

$$\frac{I(s)}{V(s)} = \frac{1}{Ls + R} \tag{2.8}$$

The transform of the unit step is $1/s$ (Appendix A, Table A.1) and hence substituting for $V(s)$ in (2.8) we obtain

$$I(s) = \frac{1}{(Ls + R)s} \tag{2.9}$$

To determine the response $i(t)$ by inverse transformation of (2.9) we perform a partial expansion of the right-hand side in the form

$$I(s) = \frac{A_0}{s} + \frac{A_1}{Ls + R} \tag{2.10}$$

We can determine the values of A_0 and A_1 by means of the cover-up rule (see Appendix A) and these are found to be

$$A_0 = \frac{1}{R}$$

$$A_1 = -\frac{L}{R} \tag{2.11}$$

Hence (2.10) can be written

$$I(s) = \frac{1}{R}\left[\frac{1}{s} - \frac{1}{s + R/L}\right] \tag{2.12}$$

and (2.12) can be inverse transformed to

$$i(t) = \frac{1}{R}\,[1 - e^{-t/T}] \tag{2.13}$$

where $T = L/R$.

The voltage $v_R(t)$ across the resistor is given by $v_R(t) = Ri(t)$ and therefore

$$v_R(t) = 1 - e^{-t/T} \tag{2.14}$$

The function $v_R(t)$ exhibits a decaying exponential form of response. The coefficient T is known as the time constant of the exponential function. Variation of T generates a family of curves as shown in Fig. 2.6.

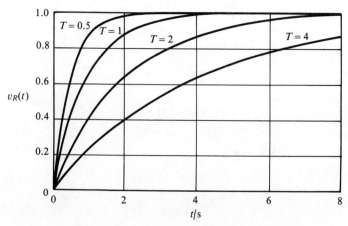

Figure 2.6 *Unit step response of circuit of Fig. 2.4.*

2.2 Generalized immittances

2.2.1 System function

In the analysis of the previous circuit, the expression for I/V (2.8) provides an example of a function known as a system function. In general, the system function can be defined as the ratio of the transform of the output or response function to the transform of the input or excitation function with all initial conditions set to zero. Thus if $c(t)$ is the excitation and $r(t)$ is the response then the system function $F(s)$ is given by

$$F(s) = \frac{R(s)}{C(s)} \tag{2.15}$$

For the electrical networks considered here, $c(t)$ and $r(t)$ can each be either a voltage or a current. In control system theory, many other physical quantities are possible such as position, speed, temperature and pressure.

To determine the response $r(t)$, we substitute for the transform of the input function in (2.15), perform a partial fraction expansion of the expression for $R(s)$ and finally perform an inverse Laplace transformation.

In the previous example, the differential equation relating the output and input was obtained by application of Kirchoff's laws to combine the separate equations of the individual elements. Transformation of the differential equation then provided the system function.

For more complex circuits however, the manipulation of the simultaneous differential and integral equations of the individual elements to obtain the overall differential equation using Kirchhoff's laws is less straightforward. An alternative approach which can lead to considerable simplification is one in which the fundamental equations of the individual R, L and C elements are transformed initially and are treated as simultaneous algebraic equations in s. In this way the system function is obtained directly without first determining the overall differential equation. This approach, which is known as *working in the s-domain* and which involves the concept of *generalized immittances*, is now described.

Consider the three basic equations (2.1) to (2.3) which relate i and v for the elements R, C and L respectively. For zero initial conditions, the equations can be transformed as follows:

$$\left. \begin{aligned} V(s) &= RI(s) \\ V(s) &= \frac{1}{Cs}\, I(s) \\ V(s) &= LsI(s) \end{aligned} \right\} \tag{2.16}$$

Each of the above three equations is of the form $V(s) = Z(s)I(s)$ where $Z(s)$ is known as the *generalized impedance* and is equal to R, $1/Cs$ and Ls for the elements R, C and L respectively. Each equation can also be written in the form

$I = Y(s)V$ where $Y(s) = 1/Z(s)$ is known as the *generalized admittance* of the element. The term *immittance* is used to denote a function that is either an impedance or an admittance and hence the set of equations (2.16) forms the basis for the method of generalized immittances.

It is assumed that the reader is familiar with the application of Kirchhoff's laws to a d.c. circuit. More generally, these laws can be applied to any circuit where the voltages and currents are expressed as functions of time. Application of the Laplace transformation to the equations which represent Kirchhoff's laws results in equations which relate the transforms of the voltages and currents. That is, (a) the algebraic sum of the transforms of the currents flowing into a node is zero and (b) the algebraic sum of the transforms of the voltage drops round any closed path is zero. In other words, Kirchhoff's laws can be extended into the s-domain and, as a consequence, it can be readily shown that generalized immittances can be combined using the same rules as those used for combining resistances in a d.c. circuit. For example, two generalized impedances $Z_1(s)$ and $Z_2(s)$ in series combine to a generalized impedance $Z_1(s) + Z_2(s)$. Similarly, two generalized admittances $Y_1(s)$ and $Y_2(s)$ in parallel combine to a generalized admittance $Y_1(s) + Y_2(s)$. Moreover, all the theorems derived from Kirchhoff's laws, with which the reader is likely to be familiar in application to d.c. circuits, can be applied to the s-domain, e.g. Thevenin, Norton, superposition and reciprocity.

We will demonstrate the use of generalized immittances by means of several examples. Provided that no ambiguity can occur, the term 'generalized' is subsequently omitted and for notational simplicity we write V, I, Z and Y in place of $V(s)$, $I(s)$, $Z(s)$ and $Y(s)$ respectively.

2.2.2 Series *RL* circuit

For the first example, we return to the circuit of Fig. 2.4. The impedance at the input for this series arrangement is $Z = Ls + R$ and the admittance is $Y = 1/(Ls + R)$. If the input or excitation is a voltage and the response is considered to be the current, the system function is an immittance function given by

$$\frac{I}{V} = \frac{1}{Ls + R} \tag{2.17}$$

which is identical to (2.8). The subsequent procedure for determining $i(t)$ is the same as previously given by (2.9) to (2.14).

The response $v_R(t)$ can be obtained without first determining $i(t)$ by substituting $I = V_R/R$ in (2.17). We have

$$\frac{V_R}{V} = \frac{1}{Ts + 1} \tag{2.18}$$

where

$$T = \frac{L}{R}$$

(2.18) defines a system function V_R/V which is dimensionless and is referred to as a *voltage transfer function*. Evaluation of $v_R(t)$ for $v(t) = u(t)$ is the same as the procedure of (2.8) to (2.13).

It is seen from the above that a system function can be in the form of an immittance function or a transfer function. The immittance function of (2.17) relates the voltage and current at the same pair of terminals and is therefore referred to as a *driving-point immittance*. In other circuits it is possible to relate a voltage and a current at different terminals, in which case the system function is a *transfer immittance*. Another possibility is that both the excitation and the response are currents, in which case the system function is dimensionless and is referred to as a *current transfer function*.

2.2.3 Inverted-L section

The network of the previous example is in the form of an inverted-L section, and it is useful to develop a simple formula for the voltage transfer function of such a section which is shown in general form using two impedances Z_1 and Z_2 in Fig. 2.7. The current through the series circuit is given by

$$I = \frac{V_i}{Z_1 + Z_2} \tag{2.19}$$

and since $V_o = Z_2 I$, the voltage transfer function is given by

$$\frac{V_o}{V_i} = \frac{Z_2}{Z_1 + Z_2} \tag{2.20}$$

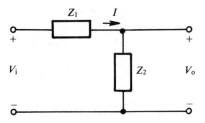

Figure 2.7 *Inverted-L section.*

2.2.4 First-order *RC* circuit

For the next example we consider the *RC* circuit shown in Fig. 2.8. We determine the voltage across the capacitor when a step input of voltage is applied to the circuit with the capacitor initially uncharged. As in the previous example, the network is in the form of an inverted-L section and therefore we can use (2.20) to determine the voltage transfer function. Letting $Z_1 = R$ and $Z_2 = 1/Cs$ gives

$$\frac{V_o}{V_i} = \frac{1}{Ts + 1} \tag{2.21}$$

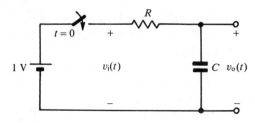

Figure 2.8 *Unit step voltage applied to series* RC *circuit.*

where

$$T = RC$$

Since the form of (2.21) is identical to that of (2.18) the solutions for a unit step input are the same and the response curves are as shown in Fig. 2.6.

2.2.5 Exponential response

The exponential form of response of a first-order system has two important properties which lead to two alternative definitions of the time constant. These definitions are as follows:

1. The time constant is the time required for the response to change by 0.63 of the difference between its initial and final values. This can be verified by substituting $t = T$ in (2.14).
2. The time constant is the time that would be required for the response to reach its final value if it continued to change at its initial rate. That is, the tangent to the curve at $t = 0$ intersects the final asymptote at $t = T$. This can be verified by differentiation of (2.14) and observing that the slope at $t = 0$ is equal to $1/T$.

Computer Exercise 2.1

Use Option A1 of ENTIS to display the unit step response of the transfer functions of (2.18) and (2.21) for various values of T and verify the above properties 1 and 2 of the exponential response. (Note: the significance of the *s*-plane diagram will be explained later.)

2.2.6 Lead network

For the next example we consider the circuit of Fig. 2.9. For reasons which will be explained in Chapter 4, this circuit is known as a 'lead network'. In this case

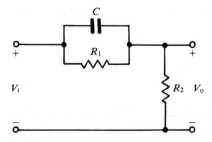

Figure 2.9 *Lead network.*

the series impedance Z_1 consists of a resistor and a capacitor in parallel, i.e.

$$Z_1 = \frac{R_1}{CR_1s + 1} \qquad (2.22)$$

Hence, using (2.19) we obtain

$$\frac{V_o}{V_i} = \alpha \frac{Ts + 1}{T\alpha s + 1} \qquad (2.23)$$

where

$$\alpha = \frac{R_2}{R_1 + R_2}$$

and

$$T = CR_1$$

For a unit step input, $v_i = u(t)$, we have $V_i = 1/s$ and hence

$$V_o = \frac{\alpha(Ts + 1)}{(T\alpha s + 1)s} \qquad (2.24)$$

This can be expanded in partial fraction form as

$$V_o = \frac{\alpha}{s} + \frac{1 - \alpha}{s + 1/(T\alpha)} \qquad (2.25)$$

Inverse transforming we have

$$v_o = \alpha + (1 - \alpha)e^{-t/(T\alpha)} \qquad (2.26)$$

As in the previous examples, variation of the exponential time constant generates a family of responses. This family can be reduced to a single curve by plotting against a normalized variable, say t/T as in Fig. 2.10 which shows the response for $\alpha = 0.25$.

The nature of the above response could have been deduced directly from the circuit by consideration of the initial and final values of the output voltage, and

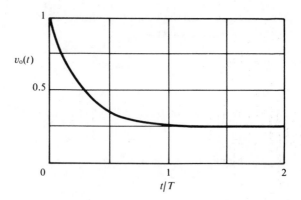

Figure 2.10 *Unit step response of lead network of Fig. 2.9 ($\alpha = 0.25$).*

by consideration of the paths for discharge of the capacitor. To determine the initial value we observe that the charge on the capacitor, and hence the voltage across it, cannot change instantaneously at $t = 0$, since any such change would imply an infinite current. We therefore know that the input step is transmitted to the output at $t = 0$. In the steady state when the capacitor is fully charged and therefore takes no current, the output voltage is determined by the resistors which act as a potential divider. There are two parallel paths for charge or discharge of the capacitor, that is, through each resistor. Therefore the time constant of the exponential is determined by the product RC where R is the equivalent resistance of R_1 and R_2 in parallel.

2.2.7 Initial and final value theorems

Another way in which the initial value of the output voltage can be readily determined without reference to the circuit is by means of a theorem that enables evaluation directly from the expression for V_o. The *initial value theorem* states that the initial value $f(0+)$ of a function of time $f(t)$ immediately after $t = 0$ is related to its transform $F(s)$ by

$$f(0+) = \lim_{s \to \infty} [sF(s)] \qquad (2.27)$$

This relationship is subject to the restriction that the degree of the numerator polynomial of $F(s)$ is less than the degree of the denominator polynomial.

Applying the above theorem to the expression given by (2.24) gives $v_o(0+) = 1$.

The final value of output voltage also can be determined without reference to the circuit. In this case the relevant theorem is known as the *final value theorem* which states that the steady-state value f_{ss} of a function $f(t)$ is given by

$$f_{ss} = \lim_{t \to \infty} [f(t)] = \lim_{s \to 0} [sF(s)] \qquad (2.28)$$

This relationship is subject to the restriction that $F(s)$ represents a stable system. The implications of this are discussed more fully in a later section.

Applying the above theorem to the expression given by (2.24) gives $v_o(\infty) = \alpha$.

2.2.8 Initial conditions

We now consider how the method of generalized immittances can be extended to include nonzero initial conditions. We return to the three basic equations (2.1) to (2.3) for R, C and L in the time domain. For R, the transformation into the s-domain is unaffected by initial conditions. We begin, therefore, by considering the capacitor.

Capacitor
Transforming (2.2) we have

$$I = CsV - Cv(0+)$$ (2.29)

where $v(0+)$ is the voltage across the capacitor at time $t = (0+)$.

(2.29) leads to the equivalent circuit of Fig. 2.11a which consists of a current source $Cv(0+)$, with direction as shown, in parallel with a generalized admittance $Y = Cs$. Alternatively, (2.29) can be rearranged as

$$V = \frac{I}{Cs} + \frac{v(0+)}{s}$$ (2.30)

(2.30) leads to the equivalent circuit of Fig. 2.11b which consists of a generalized impedance $1/Cs$ in series with a voltage source $v(0+)/s$ with polarity as shown.

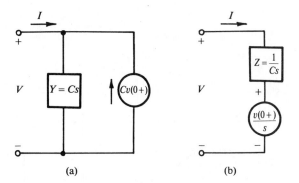

(a)   (b)

Figure 2.11 *Equivalent circuit of a capacitor with initial conditions: (a) using admittance and current source, (b) using impedance and voltage source.*

Capacitor discharge
To demonstrate the application of generalized immittances with nonzero initial conditions we consider the circuit of Fig. 2.12a where the switch is opened after

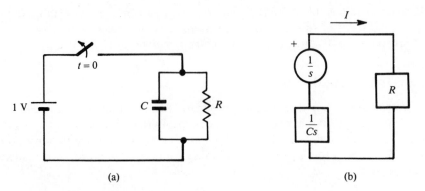

Figure 2.12 *Discharge of a capacitor: (a) network, (b) equivalent circuit using impedances and voltage source.*

steady-state conditions have been established, i.e. the capacitor is charged to 1 volt. Since the charge on the capacitor cannot change abruptly, we have that $v(0+) = 1$. The equivalent circuit is drawn as in Fig. 2.12b, which shows a voltage source $1/s$ in series with a total impedance $R + 1/Cs$. Hence we can write

$$I = \frac{C}{CRs + 1} \tag{2.31}$$

Inverse transforming we have

$$i(t) = \frac{1}{R} \, e^{-t/T} \tag{2.32}$$

where

$$T = CR$$

Fig. 2.13 shows the curve of $i(t)$ versus t/T.

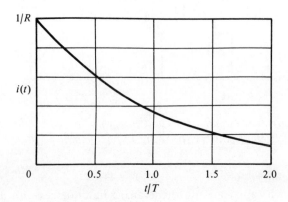

Figure 2.13 *Current versus normalized time for circuit of Fig. 2.12.*

Inductor

For an inductor L we can transform (2.3) and obtain

$$V = LsI - Li(0+) \qquad (2.33)$$

where $i(0+)$ is the current through the inductor at time $t = (0+)$.

(2.33) leads to the equivalent circuit of Fig. 2.14a which consists of a voltage source $Li(0+)$, with polarity as shown, in series with a generalized impedance $Z = Ls$. Alternatively, (2.33) can be rearranged as

$$I = \frac{V}{Ls} + \frac{i(0+)}{s} \qquad (2.34)$$

(2.34) leads to the equivalent circuit of Fig. 2.14b, which consists of a current source in parallel with a generalized admittance $Y = 1/Ls$.

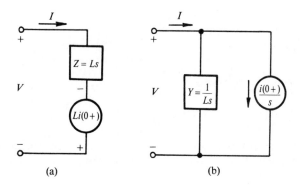

(a) (b)

Figure 2.14 *Equivalent circuit of an inductor with initial conditions (a) using impedance and voltage source, (b) using admittance and current source.*

Current decay through an inductor

To demonstrate the application of the equivalent circuit of Fig. 2.14a, we consider the response of the network of Fig. 2.15a. It is assumed that the switch has been closed for sufficient time to establish steady-state conditions and therefore the initial current through the inductor is $1/R_1$. Since the current cannot change abruptly, we have that $i(0+) = 1/R_1$. The equivalent circuit, valid after $t = 0$, can be drawn as in Fig. 2.15b, which consists of a voltage source L/R_1 in series with a total impedance $Ls + R_1 + R_2$. Hence the current I is given by

$$I = \frac{L/R_1}{Ls + R_1 + R_2}$$

$$= \frac{1/R_1}{s + 1/T} \qquad (2.35)$$

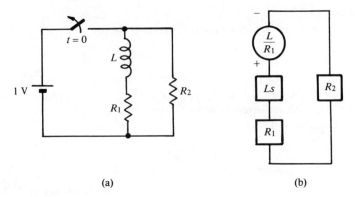

(a)   (b)

Figure 2.15 *Current decay through an inductor: (a) network, (b) equivalent circuit using impedances and voltage source.*

where

$$T = \frac{L}{R_1 + R_2}$$

Inverse transforming, we have

$$i(t) = \frac{1}{R_1}\, e^{-t/T} \tag{2.36}$$

Comparison of (2.32) and (2.36) indicates that the waveform of the inductor current is the same as that of the capacitor current shown in Fig. 2.13.

2.2.9 Mutual inductance

The technique of generalized immittances can be applied to networks in which there is mutual inductance between elements, as occurs for example with the use of transformers.

Fig. 2.16 shows two mutually coupled coils 1 and 2 with self inductances L_1

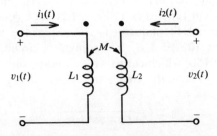

Figure 2.16 *Mutual inductance with* M *positive.*

and L_2 respectively and mutual inductance M related to L_1 and L_2 by

$$M = K\sqrt{(L_1L_2)} \qquad (2.37)$$

where K is known as the *coefficient of coupling*. The magnitude of K lies between 0 and 1. For the ideal transformer, where all the flux produced by one coil links the other, the magnitude of K is unity.

The equations relating the voltages and currents of the circuit of Fig. 2.16, in the time domain, are

$$\left.\begin{array}{l} v_1(t) = L_1 \dfrac{di_1}{dt} + M \dfrac{di_2}{dt} \\[3mm] v_2(t) = L_2 \dfrac{di_2}{dt} + M \dfrac{di_1}{dt} \end{array}\right\} \qquad (2.38)$$

The numerical value of M can be either positive or negative depending upon the reference polarities of the voltages and the reference directions of the currents relative to the physical layout of the coils. Dot symbols can be used to provide sign information by showing a dot on one terminal of each winding as in Fig. 2.16. The convention is as follows: an increase in current flowing into the dot terminal of either coil will induce a positive voltage at the dot terminal of the other coil. If the voltages $v_1(t)$ and $v_2(t)$ are defined as the voltages at the dotted terminals, and the directions of the currents are both defined as flowing into the dotted terminals as in Fig. 2.16, then M has a positive value. If the currents are both defined as flowing out of the dotted terminals then M is again positive. However, if one current is defined as flowing into the dotted terminal and the other is defined as flowing out of the dotted terminal then M will have a negative value.

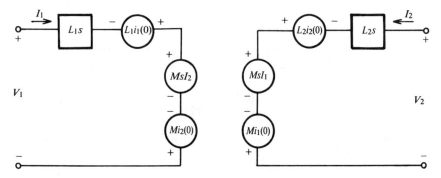

Figure 2.17 *Equivalent circuit of mutually coupled coils.*

(2.38) can be transformed as follows:

$$\left.\begin{aligned} V_1 &= L_1 sI - L_1 i_1(0) + MsI_2 - Mi_2(0) \\ V_2 &= L_2 sI - L_2 i_2(0) + MsI_1 - Mi_1(0) \end{aligned}\right\} \tag{2.39}$$

where $i_1(0)$ and $i_2(0)$ are the initial values of $i_1(t)$ and $i_2(t)$ respectively.

These equations lead to the equivalent circuit of Fig. 2.17 where the mutual coupling between the coils has been replaced by dependent voltage sources $MsI_2 - Mi_2(0)$ and $MsI_1 - Mi_1(0)$ in loops 1 and 2 respectively. That is, each source depends upon the current in the other loop.

2.2.10 Step response of mutually coupled circuits

To demonstrate the analysis of a circuit containing mutual inductance we consider the circuit of Fig. 2.18a with zero initial conditions: Fig. 2.18b shows the circuit in generalized immittance form.

We first determine a general expression for the function I_2/V_1 which is a transfer admittance. We then determine an expression for $i_2(t)$ subsequent to the switch being closed at $t = 0$.

The two loop equations are

$$\left.\begin{aligned} V_1 &= (L_1 s + R_1)I_1 + MsI_2 \\ 0 &= MsI_1 + (L_2 s + R_2)I_2 \end{aligned}\right\} \tag{2.40}$$

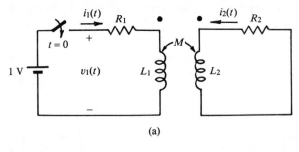

(a)

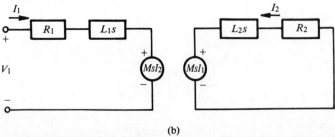

(b)

Figure 2.18 *Step response of mutually coupled circuits: (a) network, (b) equivalent circuit.*

Eliminating I_1, we have

$$\frac{I_2}{V_1} = \frac{-Ms}{(L_1L_2 - M^2)s^2 + (R_1L_2 + R_2L_1)s + R_1R_2} \tag{2.41}$$

For a case of a unity coupling coefficient

$$L_1L_2 - M^2 = 0$$

and (2.41) becomes

$$\frac{I_2}{V_1} = \frac{-Ms}{(R_1L_2 + R_2L_1)s + R_1R_2} \tag{2.42}$$

The closing of the switch at $t = 0$ imposes a unit step voltage and hence $V_1 = 1/s$. Therefore

$$I_2 = \frac{-M}{(R_1L_2 + R_2L_1)s + R_1R_2}$$

$$= \frac{-M/\alpha}{s + (1/T)} \tag{2.43}$$

where

$$\alpha = R_1L_2 + R_2L_1$$

and

$$T = \frac{\alpha}{R_1R_2}$$

Inverse transforming, we obtain

$$i_2(t) = \frac{-M}{\alpha} e^{-t/T} \tag{2.44}$$

2.3 Second-order networks

So far, the networks analyzed in the examples have all been first order and have exhibited a step response of a simple exponential form. For the network of the previous example, the admittance function of (2.40) is first order only for $K = 1$. For any other value of K the expression becomes second order, and the solution to determine i_2 could be achieved by factorization of the denominator of (2.40) followed by a partial fraction expansion. This method of solution is covered more fully in the following sections where we consider the second-order network in more detail.

2.3.1 *LC* section

We consider first the inverted-L series *LC* section of Fig. 2.19. Using (2.20), the voltage transfer function of this network is found to be

$$\frac{V_o}{V_i} = \frac{1}{LCs^2 + 1} \tag{2.45}$$

Suppose we require the response to a unit step input. We have that $V_1 = 1/s$ and (2.45) becomes

$$V_o = \frac{1}{(LCs^2 + 1)s} \tag{2.46}$$

(2.46) can be expanded in the following partial fraction form:

$$V_o = \frac{A_0}{s} + \frac{A_1 s + A_2}{LCs^2 + 1} \tag{2.47}$$

By means of the cover-up rule it is readily determined that $A_0 = 1$. To determine the values of A_1 and A_2 we can rewrite (2.47) as

$$V_o = \frac{LCs^2 + 1 + A_1 s^2 + A_2 s}{(LCs^2 + 1)s} \tag{2.48}$$

Comparing the coefficients of the corresponding powers of s in the numerators of (2.46) and (2.48), we obtain $A_1 = - LC$ and $A_2 = 0$. (2.47) then becomes

$$V_o = \frac{1}{s} - \frac{s}{s^2 + \omega_0^2} \tag{2.49}$$

where

$$\omega_0 = \frac{1}{\sqrt{(LC)}}$$

Using entries 1 and 6 in Table A.1 of Laplace transforms in Appendix A, we can inverse transform to obtain the following expression for $v_o(t)$:

$$v_o(t) = 1 - \cos \omega_0 t \tag{2.50}$$

Thus the response is continuously oscillatory and sinusoidal as shown in

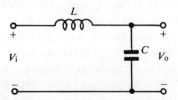

Figure 2.19 *Series LC section.*

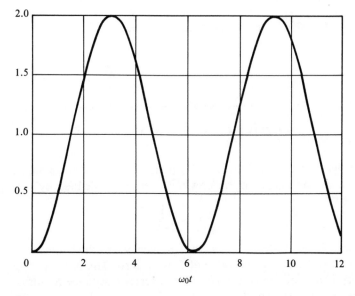

Figure 2.20 *Unit step response of series* LC *section* ($\omega_0 = 1/\sqrt{(LC)}$).

Fig. 2.20. The frequency ω_0 is known as the *resonant angular frequency* of the network. The transfer function of (2.45) can be written in terms of ω_0 in a standard form as

$$\frac{V_o}{V_i} = \frac{1}{s_2/\omega_0^2 + 1} \tag{2.51}$$

or

$$\frac{V_o}{V_i} = \frac{\omega_0^2}{s^2 + \omega_0^2} \tag{2.52}$$

Transfer functions of the above form arise in control system theory where, in preference to ω_0, the symbol ω_n is often used and is referred to as the *undamped natural frequency*.

2.3.2 *LCR* section

We consider next the effect of introducing a series resistance to the previous circuit, giving rise to the series *LCR* section of Fig. 2.21. Using (2.20), the voltage transfer function of this network is found to be

$$\frac{V_o}{V_i} = \frac{1}{LCs^2 + RCs + 1} \tag{2.53}$$

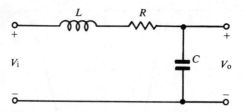

Figure 2.21 *Series LRC section.*

This transfer function can be expressed in a standard form in terms of the parameters ω_0 and Q. As in the previous case, ω_0 is defined by

$$\omega_0 = \frac{1}{\sqrt{(LC)}} \tag{2.54}$$

Here ω_0 can be considered to be the frequency at which the network would respond to a step input if the value of R were zero. The parameter Q represents the quality factor of the coil including the series resistance R, measured at the frequency ω_0. It is defined by

$$Q = \frac{\omega_0 L}{R} \tag{2.55}$$

(It is assumed that the reader is already familiar with the steady-state frequency response of the series resonant circuit.)

From (2.53), (2.54) and (2.55) we can write the transfer function in the standard form

$$\frac{V_o}{V_i} = \frac{1}{(s/\omega_0)^2 + s/(Q\omega_0) + 1} \tag{2.56}$$

or

$$\frac{V_o}{V_i} = \frac{\omega_0^2}{s^2 + \omega_0 s/Q + \omega_0^2} \tag{2.57}$$

The effect of the resistance R in the series RLC circuit corresponds mathematically in control theory to the introduction of damping in the control system. However, as well as the symbol ω_n being preferred to ω_0, a parameter ζ known as the *damping factor* is employed instead of Q. The damping factor is related to Q by

$$\zeta = 1/(2Q) \tag{2.58}$$

and hence in control theory (2.57) would be written

$$\frac{V_o}{V_i} = \frac{\omega_n^2}{s^2 + 2\zeta\omega_n s + \omega_n^2} \tag{2.59}$$

Step response

We consider next the unit step response of the circuit of Fig. 2.21. Writing

$V_1 = 1/s$ in (2.57) we have

$$V_o = \frac{\omega_0^2}{(s^2 + \omega_0 s/Q + \omega_0^2)s} \qquad (2.60)$$

The method of solution to determine the response V_o can be divided into three separate cases depending upon whether the quadratic expression in the denominator of (2.60) has the following factors:

1. Complex factors.
2. Real coincident factors.
3. Real distinct factors.

Using the well-known condition $b^2 < 4ac$ for a quadratic $ax^2 + bx + c$ to have complex factors it follows that the three conditions can be expressed as follows:

1. $Q > 0.5$
2. $Q = 0.5$
3. $Q < 0.5$.

In terms of the damping factor these conditions become:

1. $\zeta < 1$
2. $\zeta = 1$
3. $\zeta > 1$.

Case 1 Where the factors of the quadratic are complex (2.59) can be expanded in partial fraction form, using a procedure similar to that used in the previous example to determine the numerator coefficients, giving

$$V_o = \frac{1}{s} - \frac{(s + \omega_0/Q)}{s^2 + \omega_0 s/Q + \omega_0^2} \qquad (2.61)$$

Since the quadratic denominator has complex roots it can be rewritten in the form of the denominators of entries 8 and 9 in the Laplace transform Table A.1 of Appendix A by the process known as completing the square. This gives

$$V_o = \frac{1}{s} - \frac{(s + \omega_0/Q)}{(s + \omega_0/2Q)^2 + \omega_0^2(1 - 1/(4Q^2))}$$

$$= \frac{1}{s} - \frac{(s + \omega_0/Q)}{(s + \omega_0/2Q)^2 + \gamma^2\omega_0^2} \qquad (2.62)$$

where

$$\gamma = (1 - 1/(4Q^2))^{1/2}$$

We next partition the numerator in (2.62) as follows, in order to match entries 8 and 9 in the Table A.1 of Laplace transforms in Appendix A.

$$v_o = \frac{1}{s} - \frac{[(s + \omega_0/2Q) + \omega_0/2Q]}{(s + \omega_0/2Q)^2 + (\gamma\omega_0)^2} \qquad (2.63)$$

(2.63) can now be inverse transformed to

$$v_o(t) = 1 - e^{-\omega_0 t/2Q}[\cos \gamma\omega_0 t + (\sin \gamma\omega_0 t)/(2Q\gamma) \tag{2.64}$$

Using the relationship $a \sin x + b \cos x = (a^2 + b^2)^{1/2} \sin(x + \phi)$ where $\phi = \tan^{-1}b/a$, (2.64) can be written

$$v_o(t) = 1 - \frac{1}{\gamma} e^{-\omega_0 t/2Q} \sin(\gamma\omega_0 t + \phi) \tag{2.65}$$

where

$$\phi = \tan^{-1}2\gamma Q \tag{2.66}$$

The response is thus a sinusoid modulated by a decaying exponential envelope. If we consider the case for given values of both L and C (ω_0 constant), variation of R and hence Q generates a family of curves. For the case $R = 0$ ($Q = \infty$), the response becomes the undamped case of the previous example with frequency ω_0. For a nonzero value of R and therefore a finite value of Q, the frequency is $\gamma\omega_0$ and the time constant of the exponential envelope is $2Q/\omega_0$. Thus, as Q is decreased in the range from ∞ to 0.5, by increasing R, the frequency $\gamma\omega_0$ of the sinusoid decreases, and the time constant of the exponential envelope decreases. That is, the response becomes better damped as we approach the condition known as the critically damped case, where $Q = 0.5$. This is illustrated by the curves in Fig. 2.22.

Case 2   the response for $Q = 0.5$ can be obtained by taking the limits of the expressions of (2.65) as $Q \to 0.5$ and hence $\gamma \to 0$. From (2.66) we have that $\phi \to 2\gamma Q = \gamma$ which we can substitute in (2.65). We then replace $\sin(\gamma\omega_0 t + \gamma)$ by $(\gamma\omega_0 t + \gamma)$. Hence for $Q = 0.5$:

$$v_o(t) = 1 - (\omega_0 t + 1)e^{-\omega_0 t} \tag{2.67}$$

This response, is shown in Fig. 2.22. The condition $Q = 0.5$ is the critically damped condition and the response is seen to be non-oscillatory.

Case 3   We now consider the case where the roots of the quadratic are real, i.e. $Q < 0.5$. Let the roots be denoted by p_1 and p_2 respectively, i.e.

$$s^2 + \omega_0 s/Q + \omega_0^2 = (s - p_1)(s - p_2) \tag{2.68}$$

Expansion of the right-hand side of (2.68) and a comparison of the constant terms on each side indicates that $p_1 p_2 = \omega_0^2$ and hence (2.57) can be written

$$V_o = \frac{p_1 p_2}{(s - p_1)(s - p_2)s} \tag{2.69}$$

(2.69) can be expanded in partial fraction form as

$$V_o = \frac{1}{s} + \frac{A_1}{(s - p_1)} + \frac{A_2}{(s - p_2)} \tag{2.70}$$

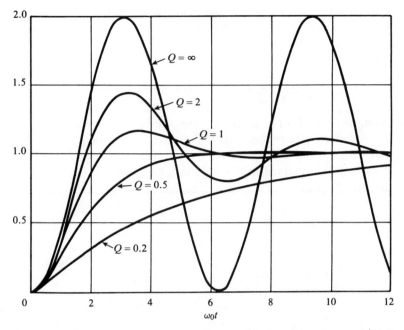

Figure 2.22 *Unit step response of series* LRC *section* ($\omega_0 = 1/\sqrt{(LC)}$; $Q = \omega_0 L/R$).

which can be inverse transformed to

$$v_o(t) = 1 + A_1 e^{p_1 t} + A_2 e^{p_2 t} \tag{2.71}$$

Using the cover-up rule we have

$$A_1 = \frac{p_2}{p_1 - p_2} \tag{2.72}$$

$$A_2 = \frac{p_1}{p_2 - p_1} \tag{2.73}$$

Hence (2.71) can be written

$$v_o(t) = 1 + \frac{1}{p_1 - p_2} \left[p_2 e^{p_1 t} - p_1 e^{p_2 t} \right] \tag{2.74}$$

where, from (2.68), p_1 and p_2 are given by

$$p_1 = -\frac{\omega_0}{2Q} + \omega_0 \left[\frac{1}{4Q^2} - 1 \right]^{1/2} \tag{2.75}$$

$$p_2 = -\frac{\omega_0}{2Q} - \omega_0 \left[\frac{1}{4Q^2} - 1 \right]^{1/2} \tag{2.76}$$

The response for a value of Q less than 0.5 is shown in Fig. 2.22. It is seen that for $Q < 0.5$ the response is non-oscillatory (aperiodic) and the response time increases as Q decreases.

Computer Exercise 2.2

Use Option B1 of ENTIS to display the unit step response of the second-order transfer function of (2.57). Use input mode 1 to select various values of ω_0 and Q. (Note: the significance of the s-plane diagram will be explained in the following chapter.)

---

3 POLES AND ZEROES

3.1 Second-order step response in terms of poles

In the previous chapter, we considered the solution of the step response of a second-order network and used different methods of analysis depending upon whether the factors of the denominator of the transfer function were real or complex. The method used for real factors can be applied to the case of complex factors and, as will be shown, provides an alternative method of solution to the one given in Section 2.3. We will consider the application of this method since it serves as a useful introduction to the important topic of the s-plane.

Adopting this alternative method we return to (2.71), observing that the steps taken in (2.68) to (2.71) are valid also for the case where $Q > 0.5$. Repeating (2.71):

$$v_o(t) = 1 + A_1 e^{p_1 t} + A_2 e^{p_2 t} \tag{3.1}$$

In this form, with p_1 and p_2 complex, (3.1) appears to contain imaginary parts. However, it will be shown that, because p_1 and p_2 are complex conjugate, the sum of the imaginary parts of (3.1) is zero and the equation can be manipulated to give the same solution as that of (2.65).

Since p_1 and p_2 are complex, (2.75) and (2.76) can be rewritten as

$$p_1 = -\frac{\omega_0}{2Q} + j\omega_0 \left[1 - \frac{1}{4Q^2} \right]^{1/2} \tag{3.2}$$

$$p_2 = -\frac{\omega_0}{2Q} - j\omega_0 \left[1 - \frac{1}{4Q^2} \right]^{1/2} \tag{3.3}$$

Since p_1 and p_2 are conjugate, we can more conveniently denote them as

$$p_1 = \alpha + j\beta \tag{3.4}$$

$$p_2 = \alpha - j\beta \tag{3.5}$$

where

$$\alpha = \frac{-\omega_0}{2Q} \tag{3.6}$$

$$\beta = \omega_0 \left[1 - \frac{1}{4Q^2} \right]^{1/2} \tag{3.7}$$

The constants A_1 and A_2 are given by (2.72) and (2.73). From these equations, or alternatively by means of the graphical method for evaluation of residues, described subsequently in Section 3.9, it can be readily established that A_1 and A_2 are complex conjugate, i.e.

$$A_2 = A_1^{\,*} \tag{3.8}$$

The separation of (3.1) into real and imaginary parts is facilitated if the terms are written in modulus argument form, i.e.

$$\left. \begin{array}{l} A_1 = |A_1| \, e^{j\theta} \\ A_2 = |A_1| \, e^{-j\theta} \end{array} \right\} \tag{3.9}$$

where

$$\theta = \angle A_1$$

(3.1) then becomes

$$v_0(t) = 1 + |A_1| \, (e^{p_1 t + j\theta} + e^{p_2 t - j\theta}) \tag{3.10}$$

Also we can write

$$\left. \begin{array}{l} e^{p_1 t + j\theta} = e^{\alpha t} e^{j(\beta t + \theta)} \\ \qquad = e^{\alpha t} [\cos(\beta t + \theta) + j \, \sin(\beta t + \theta)] \\ e^{p_2 t - j\theta} = e^{\alpha t} e^{-j(\beta t + \theta)} \\ \qquad = e^{\alpha t} [\cos(\beta t + \theta) - j \, \sin(\beta t + \theta)] \end{array} \right\} \tag{3.11}$$

By substituting into (3.10) we obtain

$$v_0(t) = 1 + 2|A_1| \, e^{\alpha t} \cos(\beta t + \theta) \tag{3.12}$$

It can be readily shown that substitution of the expressions for α and β from (3.6) and (3.7) leads to the expression of (2.65) derived in the previous chapter.

The main purpose of the inclusion of this alternative form of solution is to demonstrate the significance of the parameters p_1 and p_2 in determining the nature of the response. That is, the j-part of p_1 and p_2 determines the damped frequency of the sinusoid and the real part determines the rate of the exponential decay of the sinusoid. The parameters p_1 and p_2 are known as the *poles* of the transfer function. In general, the poles of a function in a given variable are defined as the values of the variable for which the function becomes infinite. Here we are concerned with functions of s. The *zeros* of a system function also play an important role in determining the response of a system. The zeros are defined as the values of the variable for which the function becomes zero. The significance of the zeros will become more apparent in the next chapter. The poles and zeros are known as the *singularities* of a function. The factored forms of the numerator and denominator polynomials of a function display the singularities. Thus a factor $(s - p_r)$ in the denominator implies a pole at p_r and a factor $(s - z_r)$ in the numerator implies a zero at z_r.

3.2 The *s*-plane

The locations of the singularities of a system function can be displayed graphically in a complex plane known as the *s*-plane. The position of a zero is shown by a circle and the position of a pole is shown with a cross. This will be demonstrated in the following examples.

EXAMPLE 3.1

Plot the singularities of the function $F(s)$ given by

$$F(s) = \frac{Hs(s^2 + 1)}{(s^2 + 2s + 2)(s^2 + 5s + 6)} \tag{3.13}$$

SOLUTION

$F(s)$ can be expressed in factored form

$$F(s) = \frac{Hs(s + j)(s - j)}{(s + 1 + j)(s + 1 - j)(s + 2)(s + 3)} \tag{3.14}$$

Hence $F(s)$ has zeros

$$z_1 = 0 \quad \text{(the origin)}$$

$$z_2 = -j$$

$$z_3 = +j$$

and poles

$$p_1 = -1 - j$$

$$p_2 = -1 + j$$

$$p_3 = -2$$

$$p_4 = -3$$

The *s*-plane diagram for $F(s)$ is shown in Fig. 3.1.

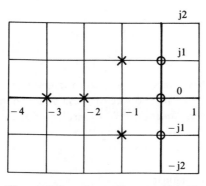

Figure 3.1 *s-plane diagram for Example 3.1.*

Note that the value of the constant multiplier H does not affect the pole–zero pattern and therefore a reconstruction of a transfer function from an s-plane diagram introduces an arbitrary constant multiplier as demonstrated by the next example.

EXAMPLE 3.2

Determine the transfer function represented by the s-plane diagram of Fig. 3.2.

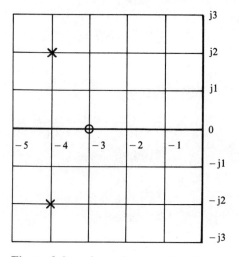

Figure 3.2 s-*plane diagram for Example 3.2.*

SOLUTION

The transfer function $F(s)$ has a zero

$$z_1 = -3$$

and poles

$$p_1 = -4 + j2$$

$$p_2 = -4 - j2$$

Hence the numerator has a factor $(s + 3)$ and the denominator has factors $(s + 4 - j2)$ and $(s + 4 + j2)$. The product of these two denominator factors is $(s^2 + 8s + 20)$. The transfer function $F(s)$ is therefore given by

$$F(s) = \frac{H(s + 3)}{s^2 + 8s + 20} \tag{3.15}$$

where H is an arbitrary multiplier.

3.3 The s-plane for a second-order network

We now return to the second-order network and examine its s-plane diagram. The pole locations are given by (3.6) and (3.7). Consider the loci of these poles as Q is varied. For $Q = \infty$ the poles are on the j-axis at $\pm j\omega_0$. For a finite value of Q greater than 0.5 the poles are in the left-half plane and the distance from the origin $|p_1|$ is given by

$$|p_1|^2 = \alpha^2 + \beta^2 \qquad (3.16)$$

Substituting for α and β from (3.6) and (3.7) we find that $|p_1| = \omega_0$. Thus as Q is reduced from infinity, with ω_0 constant, the poles move away from the j-axis on a circle of radius ω_0, becoming coincident on the real axis at $-\omega_0$ when $Q = 0.5$. As Q is decreased below 0.5, the two loci move in opposite directions along the negative real axis, tending to the origin and $-\infty$ respectively as Q tends to zero. The loci are shown in Fig. 3.3.

In general therefore, for a pair of complex poles, the associated value of ω_0 is given by the distance $|p_1|$ of either pole from the origin. From (3.6) we have

$$Q = \frac{-\omega_0}{2\alpha} \qquad (3.17)$$

Therefore the value of Q is given by the distance from the origin divided by twice the magnitude of the real part of either pole.

If we denote the angle of the position vector of the pole in the fourth quadrant with respect to the negative real axis as ψ, as shown in Fig. 3.4, then the magni-

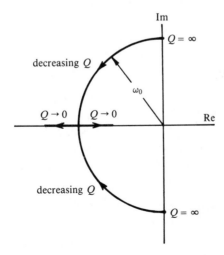

Figure 3.3 *Loci of poles of second-order transfer function.*

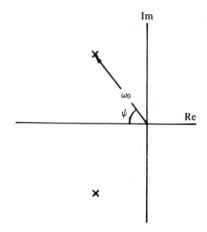

Figure 3.4 *Determination of* Q *and* ω_0 *in s-plane for complex poles;* $Q = 1/(2 \cos \psi)$.

tude of the real part is $\omega_0 \cos \psi$. Hence from (3.17) we have

$$Q = \frac{1}{2 \cos \psi} \tag{3.18}$$

We summarize these important relationships for a pair of complex poles p_1, $p_2 = \alpha \pm j\beta$ as follows:

$$\left. \begin{aligned} \omega_0 &= |p_1| = |p_2| = (\alpha^2 + \beta^2)^{1/2} \\ Q &= \frac{\omega_0}{2|\alpha|} = \frac{1}{2 \cos \psi} \end{aligned} \right\} \tag{3.19}$$

Computer Exercise 3.1

Repeat Computer Exercise 2.2 using Option B1 of ENTIS to display the unit step response of the second-order transfer function of (2.56) and (2.57) for various values of ω_0 and Q. Display the s-plane by means of User Key F5 and observe the locations of the poles

---

3.4 Rational functions

The system functions of the networks previously considered are all real rational functions in s. A rational function is one which can be expressed as the ratio of two polynomials, each having a finite number of terms and only integer powers. Examples of functions which are not rational are $s^{1/2}$, e^{Ts} and $\tan^{-1}Ts$.

It is obvious that analysis of a network containing generalized immittances which are rational in s, using for example Kirchhoff's laws, will always lead to a rational system function, since the mathematical operations involved are restricted to those of addition, subtraction, multiplication and division, and any combination of these operations on rational functions must result in another rational function. For each example analyzed so far, the transfer function has consisted only of a denominator polynomial, with the numerator being a constant term. As an example of a network whose transfer function includes a numerator polynomial, we can consider the network of Fig. 3.5. Using the formula of (2.20) for an inverted-L section it is readily established that the voltage transfer function $F(s)$ is given by

$$F(s) = \frac{RCLs^2 + Ls}{RCLs^2 + Ls + R} \tag{3.20}$$

The general form of a rational function $F(s)$ can be written

$$F(s) = \frac{N(s)}{D(s)} = \frac{a_m s^m + a_{m-1} s^{m-1} + \ldots + a_1 s + a_0}{b_n s^n + b_{n-1} s^{n-1} + \ldots + b_1 s + b_0} \tag{3.21}$$

If $F(s)$ represents a system function then there are further restrictions that apply. One such restriction is that all the a and b coefficients are real. Also, it will be shown subsequently that for a realizable transfer function, the power m of the numerator can not exceed the power n of the denominator. For a passive immittance function the difference between m and n must be zero or unity.

We can divide through the numerator and denominator polynomials by a_m and b_n respectively to express $F(s)$ in terms of monic polynomials $N_1(s)$ and $D_1(s)$. (A monic polynomial is one for which the coefficient of the term with the highest power is unity.) That is,

$$F(s) = \frac{a_m N_1(s)}{b_n D_1(s)} = H \frac{N_1(s)}{D_1(s)} \tag{3.22}$$

where $H = a_m/b_n$ is the scale factor.

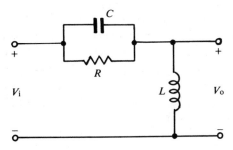

Figure 3.5 *Example of a network whose transfer function has zeros.*

(3.20) can be expressed in factored form to exhibit the poles and zeros as follows:

$$F(s) = H \frac{(s - z_1)(s - z_2) \dots (s - z_m)}{(s - p_1)(s - p_2) \dots (s - p_n)} \tag{3.23}$$

A third way in which $F(s)$ can be expressed is in the form of a partial fraction expansion. For the case $m < n$ and all the poles simple, this can be written

$$F(s) = \frac{A_1}{s - p_1} + \frac{A_2}{s - p_2} + \dots + \frac{A_r}{s - p_n} \tag{3.24}$$

where the constants $A_1, A_2, \dots$ are known as the *residues* of the respective poles $p_1, p_2, \dots$.

For the case $m \geqslant n$ the expansion can be achieved by first dividing $N(s)$ by $D(s)$ until the remainder has a numerator of order lower than that of its denominator.

3.5 Impulse response

Suppose that we require to evaluate the response $v_o(t)$ to some input function $v_i(t)$. Assuming that the transform of the input is a rational function, then the transform of the output is also rational, i.e. $V_o(s) = F(s)V_i(s)$. To determine $v_o(t)$ therefore, we perform a partial fraction expansion of $F(s)V_i(s)$, followed by an inverse transformation. This approach was adopted in the previous section for evaluation of the unit step response of a second-order system. In that case, the partial fraction expansion of (2.70) included a term $1/s$. This term was caused by the input function which introduced a factor s into the denominator of the expression for $V_o(s)$. That is, the step input function introduces a pole at the origin. There is one input function, namely the impulse function, which is of particular theoretical interest because it does not introduce any singularities into the output function. That is, if $v_i(t) = \delta(t)$, the unit impulse, then $V_i(s) = 1$ (see Appendix A). In this case, $V_o(s) = F(s)$ and therefore we can state that the unit impulse response is the inverse transform of the system function.

We can therefore inverse transform (3.24) to determine a general expression for the impulse response of a system governed by a rational system function. We obtain

$$v_o(t) = A_1 e^{p_1 t} + A_2 e^{p_2 t} + \dots + A_n e^{p_n t}$$

$$= \sum_{r=1}^{r=n} A_r e^{p_r t} \tag{3.25}$$

In general, some or all of the poles and their respective residues may be complex. In this case, (3.25) can be expressed in a more convenient form by writing each pole p_r in terms of its real and imaginary parts, i.e.

$$p_r = \alpha_r + j\beta_r \tag{3.26}$$

Note that there is no loss of generality in expressing each pole in this form since a real pole would have $\beta_r = 0$.

We can express the residues in modulus argument form, i.e.

$$A_r = |A_r| e^{j\theta_r}$$

where

$$\theta_r = \angle A_r \tag{3.27}$$

Also, we can expand

$$e^{j\theta_r} e^{p_r t} = e^{\alpha_r t} e^{j(\beta_r t + \theta_r)}$$

$$= e^{\alpha_r t} [\cos(\beta_r t + \theta_r) + j \sin(\beta_r t + \theta_r)] \tag{3.28}$$

Substituting (3.27) and (3.28) into (3.25) it can be readily established that the j-part of the right-hand side is zero provided that any complex poles occur in conjugate pairs. We can therefore write

$$v_0(t) = \sum_{r=1}^{r=n} |A_r| e^{\alpha_r t} \cos(\beta_r t + \theta_r) \tag{3.29}$$

In general, therefore, we can conclude that the impulse response of a system governed by a rational system function is a summation of terms each consisting of a sinusoid modulated by an exponential envelope. For each term, the frequency of the sinusoid is given by the imaginary part of the appropriate pole, and the time constant of the exponential decay or build-up is given by the reciprocal of the real part of the appropriate pole. For the case of a pole which is purely real ($\beta = 0$), the sinusoid has zero frequency and the term reduces to an exponential. For the case of a pole which is purely imaginary ($\alpha = 0$), the decay rate of the exponential is zero and the term reduces to an unmodulated sinusoid.

A signal which is the product of a sinusoid and an exponential is known in general as a *complex frequency*. A signal $e^{\alpha t} \sin(\beta t + \theta)$ is denoted by a complex frequency $\alpha + j\beta$. For example, a complex frequency $-2 + j5$ indicates a sinusoid of frequency 5 rad s^{-1} damped by an exponential with a time constant 0.5 s.

In the special case of an unmodulated sinusoid ($\alpha = 0$), the signal is referred to as a *real frequency*. This terminology can sometimes cause confusion, since a pole on the imaginary axis gives rise to a real frequency. An explanation for this apparent contradiction is provided in the following chapter. Further confusion can arise where the pole is on the real axis, since in this case the frequency can be referred to as an *imaginary frequency* but fortunately this terminology is not in common use.

It can be concluded from the above that the poles represent the natural complex frequencies of a system and the impulse response is the sum of these frequencies. The relative magnitudes of the complex frequency terms in the response are determined by the respective residues of the poles.

3.6 Forms of complex frequency

We now consider the various forms that can be taken by the complex frequency terms as in (3.29) and investigate how such terms combine to determine the overall response.

The first consideration regarding a complex frequency is that the sign of the numerical value of the real part determines whether the signal decays or builds up. A positive value indicates a build-up and hence an overall response which tends to infinity, as shown in Fig. 3.6a. This condition indicates instability which, of course, can occur only in the case of an active network. We can conclude therefore that for a passive network or a stable active network, every pole must have a negative real part. In the s-plane this condition implies that there are no poles in the right-half plane.

A pair of poles on the j-axis corresponds to a response that is a sinusoid of constant amplitude, as shown in Fig. 3.6b. This is theoretically possible for a passive network, but implies that the network has no loss. For an active network this condition indicates that the system is on the limit of stability.

Consider next a pair of poles in the left-half plane but close to the j-axis. We have that $\beta_r \gg |\alpha_r|$ as shown in Fig. 3.6c. This indicates a lightly damped response, since the frequency is relatively large and the rate of decay is slow.

Fig. 3.6d shows the effect of moving the poles away from the j-axis and towards the real axis. This increases the rate of decay and reduces the frequency, thus producing a more damped response.

Finally, a pole on the negative real axis indicates a nonperiodic exponential decay as shown in Fig. 3.6e.

3.7 Dominant poles

To determine how the complex frequencies add to produce the overall response, consider first the case of a second-order transfer function with both poles on the negative real axis as shown in Fig. 3.7. The decay rate for the pole p_1 close to the origin is very much less than that of the pole p_2 further away, and the response, which is the sum of the two exponentials, is determined principally by p_1, particularly when $t \gg -1/p_2$. The pole close to the origin is referred to as the *dominant pole* and the response approximates to a first-order response with a time constant $-1/p_1$.

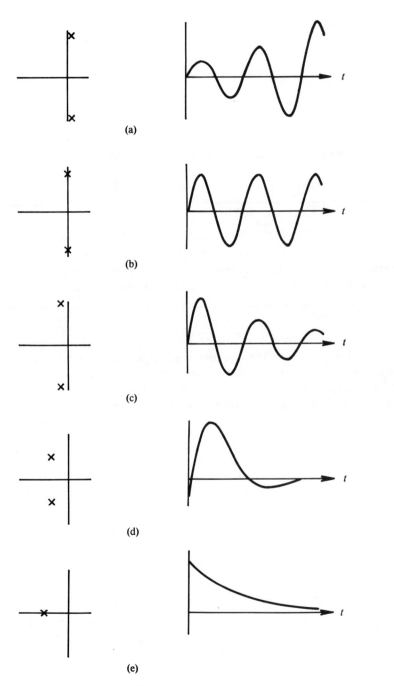

Figure 3.6 *Complex frequencies.*

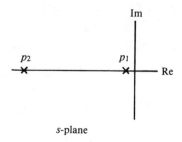

Figure 3.7 *Pair of real poles with one pole dominant.*

Computer Exercise 3.2

Use Option B8.1 of ENTIS to display the unit step response of the second-order transfer function for various locations of poles on the negative real axis. In each case compare the response with the first-order response obtained by neglecting the nondominant pole.

Consider next a fourth-order transfer function with the *s*-plane diagram as shown in Fig. 3.8. Here the complex frequencies, corresponding to the pair of poles closer to the j-axis, have the slower rate of decay. The response which is the sum of the two complex frequencies, is determined principally by the poles closer to the j-axis and these poles are the dominant poles.

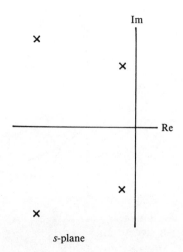

Figure 3.8 *Two pairs of complex poles with one pair dominant.*

Computer Exercise 3.3

Use Option B8.2 of ENTIS to display the unit step response of the fourth-order transfer function for various locations of complex poles, and investigate the locations for which the response approximates to a second-order response determined by the dominant poles.

In general, the nature of the response is determined principally by the pole or poles that represent the most oscillatory complex frequency and the slowest rate of decay. For example, a system with poles in the right-half plane is unstable regardless of the location of any left-half plane poles. Similarly, a system with a pair of complex poles will always have an oscillatory response regardless of any poles on the real axis; for a non-oscillatory (aperiodic) response all the poles must be real.

It is thus concluded that the locations of the poles in the s-plane give a useful pictorial representation of the complex frequencies that combine to produce the overall response. Where there is a single dominant pole or a single pair of dominant poles, then it is possible to determine the general nature of the overall response simply by inspection.

3.8 Response to other inputs

For any other input functions with a rational transform, evaluation of the response follows the same procedure as that of (3.23) to (3.29) for the unit impulse, but the partial fraction expansion must be performed on $F(s)V_i$ instead of $F(s)$. For example, in the case of a unit step input, following the above procedure we obtain

$$v_o(t) = B_0 + \sum_{r=1}^{r=n} |B_r| e^{\alpha_r t} \cos(\beta_r t + \theta_r) \tag{3.30}$$

The residues B_r in (3.30) are the residues of the poles of the function $F(s)/s$ and therefore do not have the same values as the residues A_r in (3.29). However, the step response displays the same natural complex frequencies as the impulse response but with different residues. Note the presence of the complex frequency of the input signal, which for a step input is simply a constant term. Note also that in the time domain, a unit impulse function is the derivative of a unit step function and therefore the impulse response can be obtained by differentiation of the step response.

For an input signal whose transform is rational, the poles of the output function consist of the system function poles and the poles of the input function. The system function poles are known as the *natural complex frequencies* and the input function poles are known as the *forced complex frequencies*. For the special case of the impulse response, there are no forced complex frequencies.

The system function zeros represent the complex frequencies that the system would eliminate or reject. Any input poles that coincide with system zeros produce cancellation. An example of this cancellation arises in the following chapter on steady-state frequency response. Even where cancellation does not take place, the zeros still play a part in determining the residues. As will be shown in Section 3.9, the presence of a zero close to a pole results in a small value for the residue of that pole.

3.9 Graphical evaluation of residues

We next show how the residue of any pole p_r of a rational function $F(s)$ can be determined by a simple graphical method in the s-plane. We assume that p_r is simple. To demonstrate the method we take a transfer function having two zeros and three poles. Let

$$F(s) = H \frac{(s - z_1)(s - z_2)}{(s - p_1)(s - p_2)(s - p_3)} \tag{3.31}$$

$$= \frac{A_1}{s - p_1} + \frac{A_2}{s - p_2} + \frac{A_3}{s - p_3} \tag{3.32}$$

To determine the residue A_1, say, we use the cover-up rule (see Appendix A), that is, we cover-up the factor $(s - p_1)$ in the denominator of the right-hand side of (3.31) and replace s by p_1 in the rest of the function. We obtain

$$A_1 = H \frac{(p_1 - z_1)(p_1 - z_2)}{(p_1 - p_2)(p_1 - p_3)} \tag{3.33}$$

To evaluate A_1, as given by (3.33), using a graphical procedure we observe that each factor in the numerator and denominator can be drawn as a phasor in the s-plane. For example, $(p_1 - z_1)$ can be drawn as a phasor from the zero z_1 to the pole p_1 as shown in Fig. 3.9a with direction as shown. Similarly, each of the other factors can be drawn from the appropriate singularity to p_1 as shown. The magnitude M_{z_1} of the factor $(p_1 - z_1)$ is the length of the phasor from z_1 to p_1 and the argument θ_{z_1} is the angle of the phasor with respect to the positive real direction. Similarly, the magnitude and argument of each of the other factors can be determined from the respective phasor.

Let each factor in the numerator and each factor in the denominator of (3.33) be expressed in modulus argument form, e.g.

$$(p_1 - z_1) = M_{z_1} e^{j\theta_{z_1}} \tag{3.34}$$

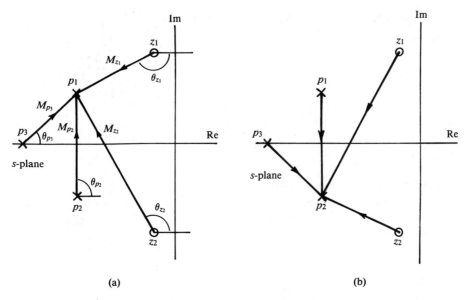

(a)   (b)

Figure 3.9 *Graphical determination of residues: (a) residue A_1, (b) residue A_2.*

(3.33) can then be written

$$A_1 = H \frac{M_{z_1} e^{j\theta_{z_1}} M_{z_2} e^{j\theta_{z_2}}}{M_{p_2} e^{j\theta_{p_2}} M_{p_3} e^{j\theta_{p_3}}}$$

$$= H \frac{M_{z_1} M_{z_2}}{M_{p_2} M_{p_3}} e^{j(\theta_{z_1} + \theta_{z_2} - \theta_{p_2} - \theta_{p_3})} \tag{3.35}$$

(3.35) is in the form

$$A_1 = |A_1| e^{j\phi} \tag{3.36}$$

where

$$|A_1| = H \frac{M_{z_1} M_{z_2}}{M_{p_2} M_{p_3}} \tag{3.37}$$

and

$$\phi = \arg A_1 = (\theta_{z_1} + \theta_{z_2}) - (\theta_{p_2} + \theta_{p_3}) \tag{3.38}$$

Therefore, to determine the residue A_1 in terms of its magnitude and angle, we draw phasors to the pole p_1 from all the other singularities. We measure the lengths of the phasors and determine $|A_1|$ from (3.37). We measure the angles of the phasors and determine the angle ϕ of A_1 from (3.38). We can determine the residues A_2 and A_3 by drawing phasors to p_2 and p_3 respectively and following a similar procedure to the above.

3.9.1 Residues of complex conjugate poles

It can be readily established from the above procedure that if p_1 and p_2 are complex conjugate then A_1 and A_2 are also complex conjugate. Fig. 3.9b shows the diagram for evaluation of A_2, where it is observed that for each phasor in the diagram of Fig. 3.9a there is a phasor in Fig. 3.9b which has the same length but whose angle is of opposite sign. Thus we have that $|A_1| = |A_2|$ and $\angle A_1 = -\angle A_2$. Therefore A_1 is the complex conjugate of A_2.

3.9.2 Pole close to a zero

It is clear from the above procedure that if a zero, say, z_1 is close to a pole, say, p_1 then the length of the phasor $p_1 - z_1$ is small. Since $|p_1 - z_1|$ appears in the numerator of the expression for $|A_1|$ it follows that the magnitude of the residue A_1 is small.

4 FREQUENCY RESPONSE

4.1 Introduction

In the previous chapter, input functions in the form of a step and impulse were considered, and it was shown how the response could be related to the location of the poles and zeros in the *s*-plane. Another very useful form of input, which will be considered in this chapter, is the sinusoidal function, which leads to the extremely powerful frequency response method of design and analysis. The usefulness of the sinusoidal function arises from its special mathematical properties, which are as follows:

1. The derivative of a sine wave is another sine wave of the same frequency as the original.
2. The addition of two sine waves with the same frequency ω results in another sine wave of frequency ω.

When a sinusoidal input function is applied to a linear network, the response consists of a transient component determined by the poles of the system function, i.e. the natural complex frequencies, and a component due to the poles introduced by the input function, i.e. the forced complex frequencies. For a stable system the natural component due to the system poles decays to zero. However, as will be shown, the forced component due to the input function does not decay. This is therefore known as the steady-state component which, for every signal throughout the system, is sinusoidal and has the same frequency as the input signal. The various signals differ from each other only in magnitude and phase. The relationship between the input and the steady-state component of the output is known as the *steady-state frequency response*.

The design and/or analysis of a system by means of the steady-state frequency response is known as the *frequency domain method*, in contrast to the use of a nonrepetitive form of input such as a step or impulse and which is known as the *time domain method*. Working in the frequency domain has the advantage that analytically it is usually much easier to determine the steady-state frequency response than it is to determine the impulse response. The disadvantage is that where the time domain response is required this cannot always be readily determined from the frequency response.

45

We consider first the use of the Laplace transformation to determine the complete response to a sinusoidal input function, and then show how simplification is achieved if only the steady-state component is required.

4.2 Complex sinusoid

Consider a network with a voltage transfer function $F(s)$, i.e.

$$V_o(s) = F(s)V_i(s) \tag{4.1}$$

We assume that the sine wave can be applied by, say, closing a switch and at the instant the switch is closed the waveform can be at any point in the cycle. In general therefore, the expression for the input signal takes the form

$$v_i(t) = \sin(\omega t + \theta) \tag{4.2}$$

To solve (4.1) by inverse transformation, we require the expression for $V_i(s)$. This can be obtained by first expanding (4.2) using the following formula:

$$\sin(A + B) = \sin A \cos B + \cos A \sin B \tag{4.3}$$

This leads to

$$v_i(t) = \sin \omega t \cos \theta + \cos \omega t \sin \theta \tag{4.4}$$

Using entries 5 and 6 from Table A.1 (Appendix A) we can transform (4.4) and obtain

$$V_i(s) = \sin \theta \, \frac{s + \omega \cot \theta}{s^2 + \omega^2} \tag{4.5}$$

Substitution of the above expression into (4.1) followed by a partial fraction expansion and an inverse transformation then leads to the expression for $v_o(t)$. However, an alternative method, which in most cases leads to simplified analysis, is to use the complex sinusoid, and this method is now described.

The complex sinusoid approach involves determining the response to an input function $e^{j(\omega t + \theta)}$ rather than $\sin(\omega t + \theta)$. The real part of the solution then gives the response to $\cos(\omega t + \theta)$ and the imaginary part gives the response to $\sin(\omega t + \theta)$. The justification is as follows.

Let the response to $\cos(\omega t + \theta)$ be denoted by A, and let the response to $\sin(\omega t + \theta)$ be denoted by B. It follows from the principle of linearity that the response to an input $k \sin(\omega t + \theta)$ is given by kB, where k is any constant. Consider next a signal $v_i(t)$ given by

$$v_i(t) = \cos(\omega t + \theta) + k \sin(\omega t + \theta) \tag{4.6}$$

It follows from the principle of superposition that the response $v_o(t)$ is given by

$$v_o(t) = A + kB \tag{4.7}$$

Consider the case where $k = j$. By Euler's formula the input is given by

$$v_i(t) = \cos(\omega t + \theta) + j \sin(\omega t + \theta) = e^{j(\omega t + \theta)} \tag{4.8}$$

This is the complex sinusoid, and from (4.7) it follows that the response to the complex sinusoid is given by

$$v_o(t) = A + jB \tag{4.9}$$

Although it is, of course, not possible in practice to generate a signal of this form, it is mathematically valid to determine the expression for the response to $e^{j(\omega t + \theta)}$ in the form $A + jB$. The real part A can be selected as the response to $\cos(\omega t + \theta)$ and the imaginary part B will yield the response to $\sin(\omega t + \theta)$. Therefore, to determine the response to an input voltage signal as given by (4.2) we first determine the response to an input of the form

$$v_i(t) = e^{j(\omega t + \theta)} \tag{4.10}$$

and then select the imaginary part of the solution. (4.10) can be expanded and transformed as follows:

$$v_i(t) = e^{j(\omega t + \theta)} = e^{j\theta} e^{j\omega t} \tag{4.11}$$

Therefore

$$V_i(s) = e^{j\theta} \frac{1}{s - j\omega} \tag{4.12}$$

and (4.1) becomes

$$V_o(s) = e^{j\theta} \frac{F(s)}{s - j\omega} \tag{4.13}$$

4.3 First-order network

We now apply the above method to determine the response of a simple circuit. The first-order RC network in Fig. 4.1 has been shown to have a voltage transfer function

$$F(s) = \frac{1}{Ts + 1} \tag{4.14}$$

where

$$T = RC$$

Suppose we wish to determine the output voltage waveform when a sinusoidal input voltage, as given by (4.2), is applied with zero initial conditions, i.e. the capacitor is initially uncharged. Using the complex sinusoid approach we can

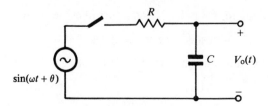

Figure 4.1 *Application of a sinusoidal input function to a first-order* RC *network.*

substitute $F(s)$ into (4.13) and obtain

$$V_o(s) = e^{j\theta} \frac{1}{(s - j\omega)(Ts + 1)} \tag{4.15}$$

Expanding the right-hand side of (4.15) into partial fractions

$$V_o(s) = e^{j\theta} \left(\frac{A_1}{s - j\omega} + \frac{A_2}{Ts + 1} \right) \tag{4.16}$$

Using the cover-up rule (see Appendix A) the residues A_1 and A_2 are found to be

$$\left. \begin{aligned} A_1 &= \frac{1}{1 + j\omega T} \\ A_2 &= \frac{-T}{1 + j\omega T} \end{aligned} \right\} \tag{4.17}$$

Substituting these values into (4.16) and inverse transforming we obtain

$$v_o(t) = \frac{e^{j\theta}}{1 + j\omega T} (e^{j\omega t} - e^{-t/T}) \tag{4.18}$$

It now remains to select the imaginary part of the right-hand side of (4.15) to determine the response to the sinusoidal input of (4.2). This is facilitated by expressing $1/(1 + j\omega T)$ in its modulus argument form, i.e.

$$\frac{1}{1 + j\omega T} = \frac{1}{(1 + \omega^2 T^2)^{1/2}} e^{j\phi} \tag{4.19}$$

where

$$\phi = -\tan^{-1}\omega T \tag{4.20}$$

(4.18) can now be rewritten

$$v_o(t) = \frac{1}{(1 + \omega^2 T^2)^{1/2}} [e^{j(\omega t + \theta + \phi)} - e^{-t/T}e^{j(\theta + \phi)}] \tag{4.21}$$

Selecting the imaginary part gives the response as

$$v_0(t) = \frac{1}{(1 + \omega^2 T^2)^{1/2}} \, [\sin(\omega t + \theta + \phi) - \sin(\theta + \phi)e^{-t/RC}] \qquad (4.22)$$

The above expression can be considered as the sum of two parts. The first part is a decaying exponential with a time constant determined by the product of circuit component values and is known as the *natural part* of the response. The natural part tends to zero as t tends to infinity and therefore this part of the response is also known as the *transient part*. This is because of the system pole at $-1/T$. It should be recalled that a term of this form appeared in the expression for the step response of the network in Chapter 2. For the present case the magnitude of the transient part depends upon the instant at which the switch is closed, i.e. it is a function of $(\theta + \phi)$, and vanishes for $\theta = -\phi$. From (4.20) therefore, the condition for the transient term to vanish is

$$\theta = \tan^{-1}\omega T \qquad (4.23)$$

The second part of the solution is a sine wave of the same frequency as the input signal and is known as the *forced part* of the response. The forced part remains as long as the input signal is present. This part is therefore known as the *steady-state part* of the response. It is the result of the pole at $j\omega$ that is introduced into the right-hand side of (4.10) by the input signal. The magnitude and phase of the steady-state part, relative to the magnitude and phase of the input, are determined by the circuit component values and the input frequency. A typical sketch of $v_0(t)$ is shown in Fig. 4.2.

It should be noted that whereas the complex sinusoid introduces only one pole,

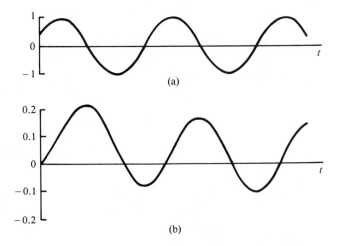

(a)

(b)

Figure 4.2 *Transient response of the* RC *network of Figure 4.1 to a sinusoidal input voltage: (a) input, (b) output.*

at jω, the sine function introduces a pole at jω together with the complex conjugate at $-$jω. However, by taking the imaginary part of the response to a complex sinusoid, the response to the two poles is obtained.

Note also that the condition for the transient term to vanish can be obtained by determining the condition for cancellation of the system function pole and the input function zero. From (4.5), the zero of the input function is at $-\omega \cot \theta$, and equating this to $-1/T$ we obtain

$$\tan \theta = \omega T \qquad (4.24)$$

which agrees with (4.23).

Computer Exercise 4.1

Option A3 of ENTIS displays the response $v_o(t)$ as given by (4.22). To show clearly the input and output waveforms on the same graph a normalized output voltage $v_o(t)/V_m$ is displayed. Run the program for various values of ω, T and ϕ, observing in particular how these parameters can be chosen to make the transient part vanish by making $(\theta + \phi) = 0$. A suitable value for ω is, say, 2 to show approximately three cycles of the steady-state sine wave. It should be observed that if a large value of T is used, say $T = 8$, the the transient does not decay appreciably over the first cycle. If, for this value of T, the transient is maximized by making $(\theta + \phi) = \pm \pi/2$, then over the first cycle the output voltage reaches a peak of almost twice its steady-state value.

4.4 General expression for steady-state response

The evaluation of the complete response to a sinusoidal input for second and higher order system functions follows the same procedure as the first-order function but, as in the case of impulse response, requires the factorization of the characteristic polynomial. It will now be shown that where only the steady-state part of the solution is required, it can be obtained very much more simply.

Consider a system function, say a voltage transfer function $F(s)$, expressed in the general form of (3.23), i.e.

$$F(s) = H \frac{(s - z_1)(s - z_2) \dots (s - z_m)}{(s - p_1)(s - p_2) \dots (s - p_n)} \qquad (4.25)$$

The transform of the output voltage when a sinusoidal input is applied is given by substituting for $F(s)$ in (4.13) giving

$$V_o(s) = e^{j\theta} G(s) \qquad (4.26)$$

where

$$G(s) = \frac{F(s)}{(s - j\omega)} \tag{4.27}$$

The singularities of $G(s)$ are those of the transfer function $F(s)$ but with the additional pole at $j\omega$. As in the case of the impulse response (see Section 3.5) it will be assumed that the poles of $G(s)$ are simple, and that the order of the numerator of $G(s)$ is lower than the order of the denominator.

$G(s)$ can be expanded in partial fraction form and becomes

$$G(s) = \frac{F(s)}{s - j\omega} = \frac{A_0}{s - j\omega} + \frac{A_1}{s - p_1} + \frac{A_2}{s - p_2} + \dots + \frac{A_n}{s - p_n} \tag{4.28}$$

A_0 is the residue of the pole at $j\omega$ which has been introduced by the input function. The residues $A_1 \dots A_n$ are those of the poles $p_1 \dots p_n$ (i.e. the natural complex frequencies) of $G(s)$.

Using the partial fraction expansion of $G(s)$, (4.26) can now be inverse transformed as follows:

$$v_o(t) = e^{j\theta}(A_0 e^{j\omega t} + A_1 e^{p_1 t} + \dots + A_n e^{p_n t}) \tag{4.29}$$

For a stable system, the terms corresponding to the system poles (i.e. those containing $A_1 \dots A_n$) all decay to zero as t tends to infinity, leaving the steady-state term containing A_0. Thus the steady-state response is given by

$$v_o(t) = A_0 e^{j(\omega t + \theta)} \tag{4.30}$$

We can determine the residue A_0 by applying the cover-up rule to (4.28). We multiply each side of the equation by $(s - j\omega)$ and let $s = j\omega$ giving

$$A_0 = F(j\omega) \tag{4.31}$$

It now remains to select the imaginary part of (4.30) in order to determine the steady-state response to an input $v_i(t) = \sin(\omega t + \theta)$. It should be observed that, in general, $F(j\omega)$ is complex and can be written in modulus argument form as

$$F(j\omega) = |F(j\omega)| e^{j\phi} \tag{4.32}$$

(4.30) now can be written

$$v_o(t) = |F(j\omega)| e^{j(\omega t + \theta + \phi)} \tag{4.33}$$

and selecting the imaginary part gives

$$v_o(t) = |F(j\omega)| \sin(\omega t + \theta + \phi) \tag{4.34}$$

Comparison of (4.34) with the expression for the input

$$v_i(t) = \sin(\omega t + \theta)$$

yields an extremely important result which can be stated as follows: when a sinusoidal signal is applied to a stable linear network, the steady-state output is a sine

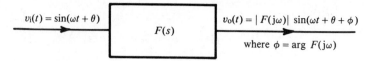

Figure 4.3 *Steady-state frequency response of a system with a transfer function* F(s).

wave of the same frequency but with altered magnitude and phase. To determine how the magnitude and phase are altered, we replace s by $j\omega$ in the transfer function $F(s)$ to obtain the frequency response function $F(j\omega)$. The magnitude of the output is determined by multiplying the magnitude of the input by the magnitude function $|F(j\omega)|$; the phase of the output is determined by adding ϕ to the phase of the input where the phase function $\phi = \arg F(j\omega)$. This steady-state relationship is shown in block diagram form in Fig. 4.3.

It should be noted that although the general result just derived may seem unfamiliar, it is likely that the reader has used formulae that are based on the above theory. For example, the formula $j\omega L$ for the impedance of an inductor L in a.c. circuit theory is the frequency response function obtained by replacing s by $j\omega$ in the expression Ls for the generalized impedance.

4.5 Frequency response plots

A graphical display of frequency response indicates how the magnitude and phase functions vary with frequency and there are several ways in which this can be shown. We first consider the use of separate graphs on linear scales of magnitude versus frequency and phase versus frequency.

Returning to the first-order RC network of Section 4.3, the transfer function $F(s)$ is given by

$$F(s) = \frac{1}{Ts + 1} \tag{4.35}$$

and therefore the frequency response function is given by

$$F(j\omega) = \frac{1}{1 + j\omega T} \tag{4.36}$$

Hence the magnitude and phase functions are respectively

$$|F(j\omega)| = \frac{1}{(1 + \omega^2 T^2)^{1/2}} \tag{4.37}$$

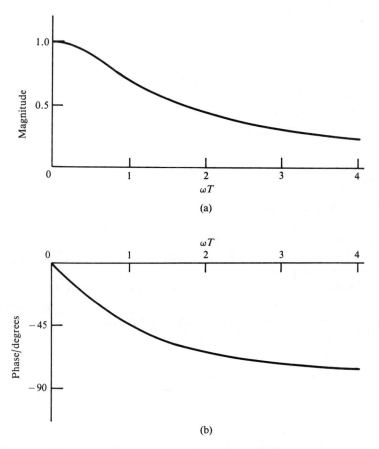

Figure 4.4 *Display on linear scales of steady-state frequency response for the first-order* RC *section of Figure 4.1: (a) magnitude versus frequency, (b) phase versus frequency.*

and

$$\phi = -\tan^{-1}\omega T \tag{4.38}$$

which agree with the results obtained in Section 4.3.

It can be seen from (4.37) that the magnitude function is unity at zero frequency and falls as the frequency increases, tending to zero as the frequency tends to infinity. This is illustrated in Fig. 4.4a. This form of response is known as a *lowpass response* since the filter passes low frequencies and attenuates high frequencies. The network is known as a *first-order lowpass filter*.

It can be seen from (4.38) that the phase function is zero at zero frequency and tends to -90° as the frequency tends to infinity. The negative sign signifies that the output lags the input. The phase response is shown in Fig. 4.4b.

Computer Exercise 4.2

Use Options A4 and A5 of ENTIS to display the magnitude and phase responses respectively of the first-order lowpass networks. The curves are shown on linear scales. Display the responses for a range of values of T. Observe in particular that at the angular frequency $\omega = 1/T$ the magnitude is $1/\sqrt{2}$ and the phase lag is $45°$.

4.5.1 Polar plots

Another way in which the frequency response can be displayed graphically is by means of a polar plot. In this case the locus of $F(j\omega)$ is plotted in the complex plane as ω is varied from zero to infinity. Thus, at each frequency $F(j\omega)$ is represented as a phasor quantity. The distance of the point on the locus from the origin represents the magnitude of $F(j\omega)$. The angle between the real positive axis and the line from the origin to the point on the locus determines the phase. This is illustrated in Fig. 4.5 which shows the locus for the first-order lowpass network. For this case it can be readily established that the locus of $F(j\omega)$ is a semicircle as shown with centre $(1/2, 0)$.

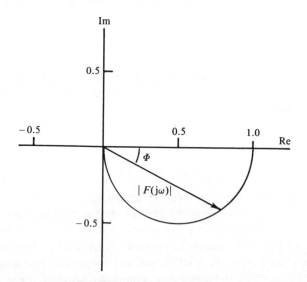

Figure 4.5 *Display in polar form of steady-state frequency response for the first-order* RC *section of Figure 4.1.*

4.6 Graphical evaluation of frequency response in *s*-plane

The frequency response in both magnitude and phase can be evaluated graphically on a point-by-point basis in the *s*-plane. This geometric interpretation is very useful for estimating the frequency response of a network simply by inspecting the pole–zero diagram.

The frequency response function $F(j\omega)$ is the residue of the pole at $-j\omega$ of the function $G(s)$ in (4.28), and can therefore be determined by the method previously described in Section 3.6 for the graphical evaluation of residues. Because of the importance of the method it will be briefly described again for the particular case of $F(j\omega)$.

We consider a system function $F(s)$ expressed in factored form

$$F(s) = H \frac{(s - z_1)(s - z_2)\dots(s - z_m)}{(s - p_1)(s - p_2)\dots(s - p_n)} \tag{4.39}$$

The frequency response function can be written as

$$F(j\omega) = H \frac{(j\omega - z_1)(j\omega - z_2)\dots(j\omega - z_m)}{(j\omega - p_1)(j\omega - p_2)\dots(j\omega - p_n)} \tag{4.40}$$

Consider the factors in the numerator. Each may be expressed in terms of its modulus and argument in the following form:

$$(j\omega - z_1) = M_{z_1} e^{j\theta_{z1}} \tag{4.41}$$

The factors in the denominator may be expressed in similar form:

$$(j\omega - p_1) = M_{p_1} e^{j\theta_{p1}} \tag{4.42}$$

Therefore (4.40) can be written

$$F(j\omega) = H \frac{M_{z_1} e^{j\theta_{z1}} M_{z_2} e^{j\theta_{z2}} \dots M_{z_m} e^{j\theta_{zm}}}{M_{p_1} e^{j\theta_{p1}} M_{p_2} e^{j\theta_{p2}} \dots M_{p_n} e^{j\theta_{pn}}}$$

$$= H \frac{M_{z_1} M_{z_2} \dots M_{z_m}}{M_{p_1} M_{p_2} \dots M_{p_n}} e^{j(\theta_{z1} + \theta_{z2} \dots + \theta_{zm} - \theta_{p1} - \theta_{p2} \dots - \theta_{pn})} \tag{4.43}$$

(4.43) is in the form

$$F(j\omega) = |F(j\omega)| e^{j\phi} \tag{4.44}$$

where

$$|F(j\omega)| = H \frac{M_{z_1} M_{z_2} \dots M_{z_m}}{M_{p_1} M_{p_2} \dots M_{p_n}} \tag{4.45a}$$

and

$$\phi = \arg F(j\omega) = (\theta_{z_1} + \theta_{z_2} + \dots + \theta_{zm}) - (\theta_{p_1} + \theta_{p_2} + \dots + \theta_{pn}) \tag{4.45b}$$

In the s-plane the factor $(j\omega - z_1)$ can be represented as a vector as shown in Fig. 4.6, i.e. it is the sum of the vectors $j\omega$ and $-z_1$. The vector $j\omega$ is the line OP from the origin to the point P on the j-axis, distance ω from the origin, where ω is the specific frequency. The length of the vector from P to z_1 is the magnitude M_{z_1} of the factor $(j\omega - z_1)$. The angle between the vector and the positive real axis is the argument θ_{z_1} of $(j\omega - z_1)$. Similarly, the magnitudes and arguments of the other factors can be represented in the s-plane by drawing vectors from each singularity to the point P on the j-axis as shown in the figure.

The response at different frequencies from zero to infinite frequency is therefore determined by moving the point P along the j-axis in the positive direction, starting at the origin, and at each frequency measuring the distances and angles as shown in the figure. The magnitude and phase are then given by (4.45a) and (4.45b) respectively. Since every point on the j-axis corresponds to a real frequency, the j-axis in the s-plane is known also as the *real frequency axis*.

The name 'real frequency axis' for the imaginary axis of the s-plane can sometimes be confusing. It should be remembered however, that the frequency response function is determined by replacing s by $j\omega$ in the system function and therefore when ω is real, s is imaginary.

The foregoing theory can be generalized to determine the forced part of the response to a signal of the form $e^{\sigma t} \sin(\omega t + \theta)$, which is a complex frequency

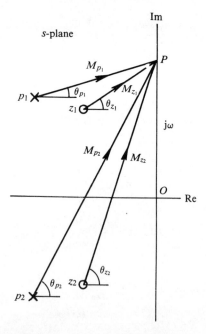

Figure 4.6 *Graphical evaluation of steady-state frequency response from the pole–zero diagram.*

$s_1 = \sigma + j\omega$. In this case it can be shown in a similar manner to the above that the frequency response function is given by replacing s by s_1 in the system function $F(s)$. The modulus and argument of $F(s_1)$ determine the magnitude and phase respectively of the forced part of the response. The modulus and argument can be determined graphically in the s-plane in exactly the same way as for a real frequency, except that the point P is positioned at the point s_1 and not on the real frequency axis. Note that the forced part of the response to a *complex* frequency cannot be referred to as the steady-state response, since its magnitude is exponentially decaying or increasing depending upon whether σ is negative or positive respectively. The concept of complex frequency response is an extremely powerful one, but because of the practical difficulties associated with the measurement of a signal of this form in the presence of the natural complex frequencies of the system, its use is normally limited to theoretical applications.

4.7 Second-order network

We now consider the frequency response of a second-order system function. The two-pole system function written in the standard form of (2.56), and which is the voltage transfer function of the *LCR* network of Fig. 2.21, is given by

$$F(s) = \frac{1}{s^2/\omega_0^2 + s/(Q\omega_0) + 1} \tag{4.46}$$

The network is shown again in Fig. 4.7.

Replacing s by $j\omega$ to obtain the frequency response function, we have

$$F(j\omega) = \frac{1}{1 - \omega^2/\omega_0^2 + j\omega/(Q\omega_0)} \tag{4.47}$$

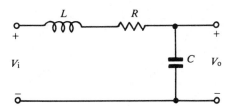

Figure 4.7 *Second-order lowpass LRC section.*

4.7.1 Magnitude

The magnitude function is given by

$$|F(j\omega)| = \frac{1}{[(1 - \omega^2/\omega_0^2)^2 + \omega^2/(Q\omega_0)^2]^{1/2}} \tag{4.48}$$

It is convenient to plot the characteristics against a frequency variable ω/ω_0, since this generates a family of characteristics independent of the value of ω_0. Variation of Q then generates a family of characteristics. To determine the general shape of the characteristics we observe the following:

1. The magnitude is unity at zero frequency.
2. The magnitude is Q at $\omega = \omega_0$.
3. The magnitude tends to zero as the frequency tends to infinity.

From the above, if Q is greater than 1 then the magnitude at $\omega = \omega_0$ is greater than the magnitude at $\omega = 0$ and therefore the characteristic must exhibit a maximum at some frequency, say $\omega = \omega_p$. This is illustrated in Fig. 4.8 which shows the family of characteristics of magnitude versus normalized frequency. It is observed that, as expected, for $Q = \infty$ the maximum occurs at $\omega = \omega_0$. As Q is decreased the value of ω_p decreases and below a certain value of Q no peak occurs.

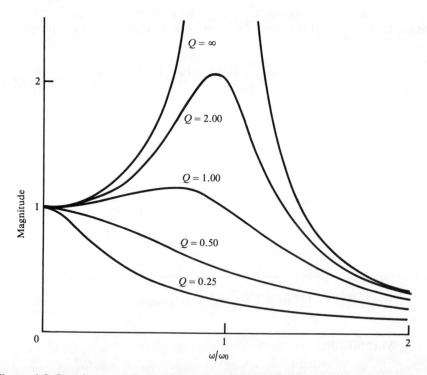

Figure 4.8 *Steady-state characteristics on linear scales of magnitude versus normalized frequency for the second-order network of Fig. 4.7.*

Computer Exercise 4.3

Use Option B4 of ENTIS with Input Mode 1 to display the magnitude response on linear scales for the second-order transfer function of (4.46) with various values of Q. Observe in particular that there is a limiting value of Q below which no peak occurs.

4.7.2 Phase

From (4.47) the phase function is given by

$$\phi = -\tan^{-1} \frac{\omega/\omega_0}{Q[1 - (\omega/\omega_0)^2]} \qquad (4.49)$$

From the above expression the following are observed for all values of Q:

1. The phase lag is zero at $\omega = 0$.
2. The phase lag is $90°$ at $\omega = \omega_0$.
3. The phase lag tends to $180°$ as the frequency tends to infinity.

Variation of Q generates a family of characteristics all of which pass through the above three points. This is illustrated in Fig. 4.9 which shows the family of characteristics of phase versus normalized frequency.

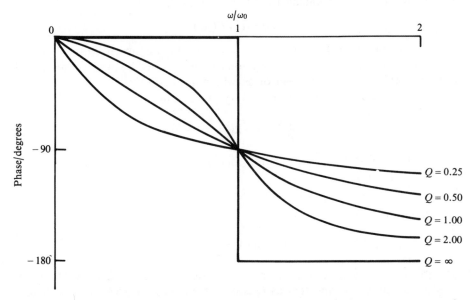

Figure 4.9 *Steady-state characteristics on linear scales of phase versus normalized frequency for the second-order network of Fig. 4.7.*

> ## Computer Exercise 4.4
>
> Use Option B5 of ENTIS with Input Mode 1 to display the phase
> response on linear scales for the second-order transfer function of (4.46)
> with various values of Q.

> ## Computer Exercise 4.5
>
> Use Option B3.2 of ENTIS to provide an animated display of the
> graphical relationship between the frequency response and the s-plane
> for a second-order system. Select the case of No Finite Zeros by means
> of User Key F1. Animate the display by means of the space bar and
> observe the magnitude and phase characteristics for various values of
> Q.

4.7.3 Peak frequency

The frequency at which the maximum magnitude occurs can be determined by
differentiating the expression given by (4.48) and setting the result to zero.
Simplification can be obtained by differentiating the function

$$G(\omega) = 1/\,|\,F(\mathrm{j}\omega)\,|^{\,2}$$

since the magnitude will be maximum when $G(\omega)$ is minimum. Since $G(\omega)$ is a
function of $(\omega/\omega_0)^2$, further simplification can be achieved by differentiating with
respect to the variable u instead of ω, where $u = (\omega/\omega_0)^2$.

Applying the above procedure to (4.48) we obtain

$$\frac{\mathrm{d}G(\omega)}{\mathrm{d}u} = -2(1-u) + \frac{1}{Q^2} \tag{4.50}$$

Setting the derivative to zero we find that the peak frequency is given by

$$u = 1 - \frac{1}{2Q^2} \tag{4.51}$$

and therefore

$$\omega_p = \omega_0\left(1 - \frac{1}{2Q^2}\right)^{1/2} \tag{4.52}$$

The above expressions confirm the previously observed results that for $Q = \infty$ the
peak occurs at $\omega = \omega_0$ and that as Q is decreased the peak frequency decreases.
It can be further observed that there is a critical value $Q = 1/\sqrt{2}$ for which the
peak occurs at $\omega = 0$. For values of Q below this critical value, (4.52) has no real
solution.

4.7.4 Peaking circle

The position of ω_p on the real frequency axis can be determined by a simple graphical procedure known as the *peaking circle construction*. For complex poles at $\alpha \pm j\beta$, where it is assumed that α has a negative value, the circle has its centre at the point N, which is the intersection of the negative real axis and a line through the poles, i.e. the point N is at $(\alpha, 0)$. The radius of the circle is β as shown in Fig. 4.10. The intersection of the circle with the positive real frequency axis at point P gives the frequency ω_p.

The validity of this construction can be established by rewriting (4.52) in terms of the real and imaginary parts of the poles. It has been shown previously (Section 3.2, (3.19)) that Q and ω_0 can be written in terms of α and β as

$$Q = - \frac{(\alpha^2 + \beta^2)^{1/2}}{2\alpha} \tag{4.53}$$

and

$$\omega_0 = (\alpha^2 + \beta^2)^{1/2} \tag{4.54}$$

Substituting these expressions into (4.52) gives

$$\omega_p^2 = \beta^2 - \alpha^2 \tag{4.55}$$

The right-angled triangle PNO in Fig. 4.10 has sides PN and ON with lengths β and $|\alpha|$ respectively. Hence the length of the side OP is given by the expression of (4.55) for ω_p.

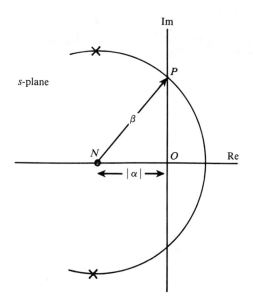

Figure 4.10 *Peaking circle construction.*

Computer Exercise 4.6

Option B3.3 of ENTIS provides a display of the peaking circle construction. Run the program for different pole locations. Note that it can be readily observed from the peaking circle construction that intersection of the circle with the real frequency axis will occur only if $\beta \geqslant |\alpha|$.

4.7.5 Filter characteristic

The second-order magnitude characteristics of Fig. 4.8 all provide a form of lowpass filtering. In most practical lowpass filter applications the requirement is for a magnitude characteristic that remains as near constant as possible over the pass band from d.c. up to a specified cut-off frequency and then falls off as rapidly as possible at higher frequencies. In the case of a second-order filter, the characteristic can be specified by two parameters such as Q and ω_0. The value of ω_0 would normally be chosen to be equal to, or in the region of, the cut-off frequency in order to obtain a well-defined transition from pass band to stop band. Choice of a value for Q could be determined by the requirements for a constant magnitude over the pass band. Inspection of the characteristics of Fig. 4.8 and/or the characteristics generated by Option B5 of ENTIS, as in Computer Exercise 4.3, indicates approximately the value of Q to provide best approximation to a flat pass band. The exact value of Q to provide an optimum characteristic depends upon the criterion adopted to define the best approximation; this is discussed more fully in Chapter 7. One possible criterion is to choose the largest value of Q for which no peak occurs. This has been shown in Section 4.7.3 to be the value $Q = 1/\sqrt{2}$. For reasons which are explained in Chapter 7, this value defines a characteristic which is said to be *maximally flat* and is known as the Butterworth second-order filter.

5 TRANSMISSION ZEROS

In Chapter 3 it was shown how both poles and zeros represent complex frequencies of a system, with the all-important difference that the poles are the natural frequencies whereas the zeros represent the frequencies which are not transmitted. Another important distinction is that for a passive or a stable active system the poles are restricted to lie in the left-half plane whereas for the zeros no such restriction occurs.

In the case of transient response, the effect of zeros is not generally very dramatic unless a zero coincides with a pole of the input function, in which case pole–zero cancellation occurs. For a sinusoidal input, the poles of the input function lie on the real frequency axis. Therefore the effect of zeros on the steady-state frequency response is most significant when the zeros of the system function are on the real frequency axis.

For some cases, the zero locations can be obtained directly by inspection of the network. For example, in the case of the inverted-L network (see Fig. 2.7) of Section 2.2.3, a transfer function zero is caused by either (a) a pole of the series impedance Z_1 or (b) a zero of the shunt impedance Z_2. That is, for case (a) it is clear that there is no transmission when the series impedance is infinite since this effectively creates an open circuit in the series path. For case (b) it is clear that there is no transmission when the shunt impedance is zero since this effectively creates a short circuit in the shunt path. A zero at the origin, for example, is caused by either a capacitor in the series arm or an inductor in the shunt arm. This is discussed more fully in relation to ladder networks in Chapter 9.

In this chapter we examine the part that zeros play in determining the nature of steady-state frequency response characteristics. Examples of simple networks with various zero locations are considered.

5.1 Zeros at the origin

If a system function has a single zero on the j-axis of the s-plane then this must be at the origin since complex singularities can occur only in conjugate pairs. Fig. 5.1 shows the s-plane for a function with a pole on the negative real axis

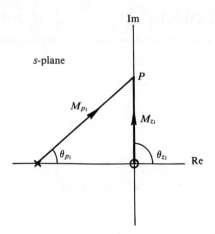

Figure 5.1 *Graphical determination in* s-*plane of a first-order highpass response.*

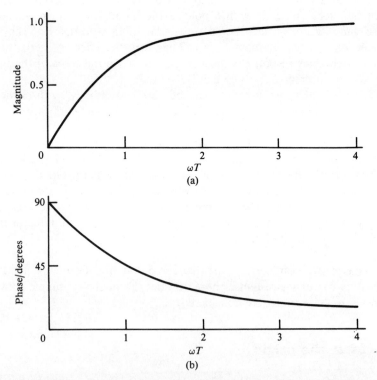

Figure 5.2 *Display on linear scales of the first-order highpass response for the p–z diagram of Fig. 5.1: (a) magnitude versus frequency, (b) phase versus frequency.*

and a zero at the origin. The relevant vectors for graphical evaluation of the frequency response at a point P on the real frequency axis are shown.

5.1.1 Magnitude

The magnitude is given by HM_{z_1}/M_{p_1} where M_{z_1} is the distance from P to the origin, M_{p_1} is the distance from P to the pole and H is an arbitrary constant.

Consider the effect of moving the point P towards the origin. The length M_{z_1} will tend to zero and therefore the magnitude of the response at zero frequency will be zero. Thus for any system with a magnitude function which tends to zero at zero frequency, and therefore rejects d.c., the system function must have at least one zero at the origin.

Fig. 5.2a shows the magnitude response corresponding to the p–z diagram of Fig. 5.1. This is known as a first-order highpass response.

5.1.2 Phase

It can be seen from Fig. 5.1 that the phase lead contribution of the zero is 90° at all frequencies. The phase lag contribution of the pole is zero at zero frequency and tends to 90° as the frequency tends to infinity. Therefore the overall phase response is one which has a 90° lead at zero frequency and tends to zero at high frequencies as shown in Fig. 5.2b.

5.1.3 Highpass network

The p–z pattern of Fig. 5.1 can be realized by the networks of Fig. 5.3a and Fig. 5.3b which show first-order highpass RC and LR sections respectively. The zero at the origin is introduced by the series capacitor for the RC network and by the shunt inductor for the LR network. In each case the voltage transfer

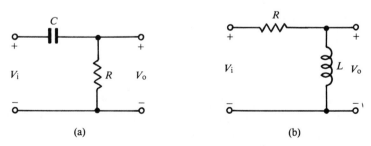

(a)   (b)

Figure 5.3 *Realization of a first-order highpass transfer function: (a)* RC *section, (b)* RL *section.*

function $F(s)$ is readily shown to be

$$F(s) = \frac{Ts}{Ts + 1} \tag{5.1}$$

where $T = RC$ for the RC section and $T = L/R$ for the LR section.

Computer Exercise 5.1

In general, for a highpass response the following conditions apply: (a) the transfer function has at least one zero at the origin in order to provide a magnitude characteristic which becomes zero at d.c. (b) the number of zeros equals the number of poles in order to ensure that the magnitude characteristic does not tend to zero at high frequencies.

Verify these properties for the second-order case using Option B3.2 of ENTIS. Select the case of *two zeros at the origin* by means of User key F2.

5.2 Bandpass characteristic

Consider next the case of a system function with a single zero at the origin and two poles. Fig. 5.4 shows the s-plane with the relevant vectors for determining

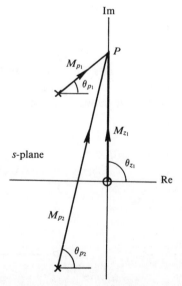

Figure 5.4 *Graphical determination in* s-*plane of a second-order bandpass response.*

the response at a point P on the real frequency axis. The figure shows complex poles although the following is generally applicable also to the case of poles on the negative real axis.

5.2.1 Magnitude

The magnitude is given by $HM_{z_1}/(M_{p_1}M_{p_2})$. The presence of the zero at the origin causes the magnitude to be zero at zero frequency, i.e. when P is at the origin the length M_{z_1} is zero. As P moves along the real frequency axis towards infinity, the distances M_{z_1}, M_{p_1} and M_{p_2} all tend to the same large value, say, D. Therefore as the frequency and D both tend to infinity the magnitude tends to H/D, which becomes zero at infinity. Since the characteristic rejects low and high frequencies but transmits an intermediate band of frequencies, it is known as a *bandpass response*.

At intermediate frequencies the shape of the characteristic depends upon the Q-factor of the poles. Fig. 5.5a shows the magnitude response corresponding to

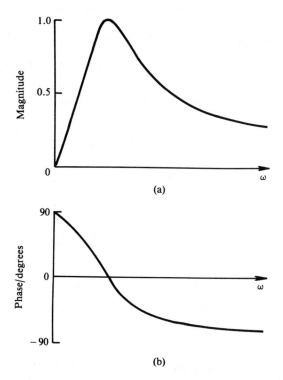

(a)

(b)

Figure 5.5 *Display on linear scales of the second-order bandpass response for the p–z diagram of Fig. 5.4.: (a) magnitude versus frequency, (b) phase versus frequency.*

the *p–z* diagram of Fig. 5.4 for which $Q = 1$. The effect of variation of the *Q*-factor is covered in Computer Exercise 5.2.

5.2.2 Phase

The zero at the origin contributes a phase lead of $90°$ at all frequencies. The phase lag contributed by the poles is the same as for the two-pole transfer function considered in Section 4.7 and illustrated in Fig. 4.9. The phase characteristic is therefore obtained by adding $90°$ lead to the appropriate lag characteristic of Fig. 4.9 and is shown in Fig. 5.5b.

Computer Exercise 5.2

Use Option B3.2 of ENTIS to verify the magnitude and phase responses of Fig. 5.5. Run the program for various values of *Q*-factor and observe in particular how the bandwidth or selectivity of the characteristic is related to the value of *Q*.

5.2.3 Bandpass network

The *p–z* pattern of Fig. 5.4 can be realized by the network of Fig. 5.6, which shows a second-order *LCR* bandpass section. The zero at the origin is introduced by the series capacitor. The voltage transfer function $F(s)$ of this network is readily shown to be

$$F(s) = \frac{RCs}{LCs^2 + RCs + 1} \tag{5.2}$$

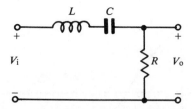

Figure 5.6 *Realization of a second-order bandpass transfer function by an* RCL *section.*

5.3 Bandstop characteristic

Consider next the case of a system function with a pair of conjugate zeros on the real frequency axis at, say, $\pm j\omega_1$ together with two complex poles. Fig. 5.7

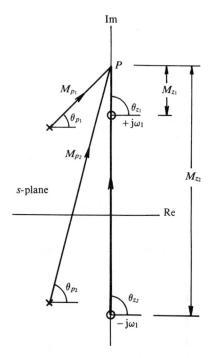

Figure 5.7 *Graphical determination in s-plane of a second-order bandstop response.*

shows the *s*-plane for such a case with the relevant vectors for determining the response at a point *P* on the real frequency axis.

5.3.1 Magnitude

The magnitude is given by $HM_{z_1}M_{z_2}/(M_{p_1}M_{p_2})$. As the point *P* moves from the origin along the real frequency axis towards $j\omega_1$, the distance M_{z_1} decreases and becomes zero at $j\omega_1$ and then increases. Hence the magnitude falls to zero at frequency ω_1 and then increases. Above the frequency ω_1, as *P* moves along the real frequency axis towards infinity, the distances M_{z_1}, M_{z_2}, M_{p_1} and M_{p_2} all tend to the same value, say, *D*. Therefore as the frequency tends to infinity the magnitude tends to *H*.

Fig. 5.8a shows the magnitude response corresponding to the *p*–*z* diagram of Fig. 5.7 for which $Q = 1$. Since the characteristic transmits low and high frequencies but rejects an intermediate band of frequencies it is known as a *bandstop response*.

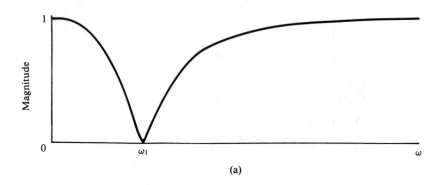

(a)

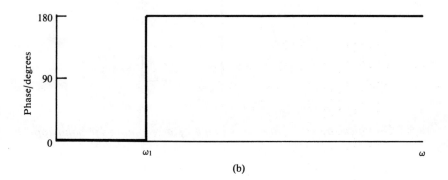

(b)

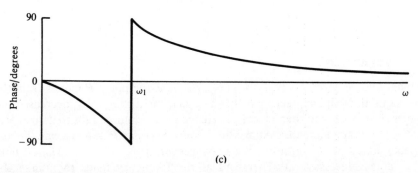

(c)

Figure 5.8 *Display on linear scales of the second-order bandstop response for the* p–z *diagram of Fig. 5.7: (a) magnitude characteristic, (b) phase characteristic of zeros only, (c) overall phase characteristic.*

5.3.2 Phase

The zero z_2 contributes a phase lead of $90°$ at all frequencies. The phase contributed by the zero z_1 at frequencies up to ω_1 is a lead of $-90°$ (i.e. a $90°$ lag), which cancels the contribution of z_1. At frequencies above ω_1 however, the contribution of z_1 is a $90°$ lead. Therefore the resultant contribution of the two zeros is zero phase shift up to ω_1 and $180°$ above ω_1 as shown in Fig. 5.8b. The lag contributed by the poles is the same as for the two-pole transfer function considered in Section 4.7 and illustrated in Fig. 4.9. The phase characteristic is therefore obtained by adding the characteristic of Fig. 5.8b to the appropriate lag characteristic of Fig. 4.9, resulting in an abrupt transition at frequency ω_1. The resultant characteristic is shown in Fig. 5.8c.

Computer Exercise 5.3

Use Option B3.2 of ENTIS to verify the magnitude and phase responses of Fig. 5.8. Run the program for various values of the Q-factor of the poles and observe in particular how the width of the rejection or stop band is related to the value of Q.

5.3.3 Bandstop networks

Twin-T network

A pair of transmisson zeros on the real frequency axis can be realized by the network shown in Fig. 5.9 which is known as a twin-T or parallel-T network.

The voltage transfer function of this network is third order but can be reduced to second order through pole–zero cancellation. Analysis of the network can be carried out by a star-mesh transformation of each T-section with the branches expressed as admittances. The poles of the admittances of the two π-sections

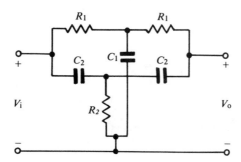

Figure 5.9 *Realization of zeros on the real frequency axis by an* RC *twin-T network.*

become coincident for the following condition:

$$R_1 C_1 = 4 R_2 C_2 \qquad (5.3)$$

If the above condition is satisfied the two parallel π-sections readily combine. The admittance from input to ground does not affect the voltage transfer function and the circuit reduces to an inverted L. The transfer function is then found to be

$$F(s) = \frac{2 C_2^2 R_1 R_2 s^2 + 1}{2 C_2^2 R_1 R_2 s^2 + C_1 (R_2 + R_1/2) s + 1} \qquad (5.4)$$

Bridged-T network

As is the case for all RC networks, the poles of the transfer function of the twin-T network are restricted to the negative real axis. However, as demonstrated in Computer Exercise 5.3, where a narrow stopband is required, this necessitates complex poles.

A pair of transmission zeros with complex poles can be realized by the network of Fig. 5.10 which is known as a bridge-T network. As in the previous case, the transfer function is third order but can be reduced to second order by pole–zero cancellation. Analysis follows a similar procedure to the previous case using a star-mesh transformation on the T-section with the branches expressed in admittance form. The poles of the admittances of the resultant π-section become coincident with the pole of the admittance of the series RL branch for the following condition:

$$2 C R r = L \qquad (5.5)$$

If the above condition is satisfied, the transfer function is found to be

$$F(s) = \frac{C^2 R r s^2 + 1}{C^2 R r s^2 + C r s + 1} \qquad (5.6)$$

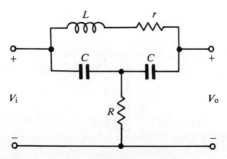

Figure 5.10 *Realization of zeros on the real frequency axis together with complex poles by an* RCL *bridged-T network.*

5.4 Singularities at infinity

Consider a system function with a single pole, e.g. $F(s) = 1/(s + a)$. If the zeros of a function $F(s)$ are defined as the values of s for which $F(s)$ becomes zero, then, since $F(s)$ tends to zero as s tends to infinity, it can be said that $F(s)$ has a zero at infinity. Similarly, a two-pole function can be said to have two zeros at infinity. For a function with n poles and m zeros where $m < n$, there are $n - m$ zeros at infinity. In other words, if the zeros at infinity are included, the total number of zeros is equal to the number of poles.

The concept of zeros at infinity is useful when considering frequency transformations (see Chapter 8), and also arises in the root locus method for determining the stability of feedback systems, which is outside the scope of this book.

When using the graphical method of evaluating frequency response in the s-plane, it must be remembered that the vectors to the zeros at infinity are not included. Inclusion of such vectors would correspond to a factor in the system function numerator of the form $(s - z_r)$ with z_r tending to infinity, and would cause the magnitude to be infinite. It is preferable to consider the factor in the numerator to be the limit of $(1 - s/z_r)$ as z_r tends to infinity.

Returning to the general expression of (4.45a) for the magnitude function

$$| F(\mathrm{j}\omega) | = H \frac{M_{z_1} M_{z_2} \dots M_{z_m}}{M_{p_1} M_{p_2} \dots M_{p_n}} \tag{5.7}$$

it is clear that at high frequencies the lengths of all the vectors tend to the same value D and hence

$$| F(\mathrm{j}\omega) | \to HD^{-q} \tag{5.8}$$

where $q = n - m$ is the number of zeros at infinity. Thus for $m < n$ the magnitude tends to zero and for $m = n$ the magnitude tends to a finite value.

It can be concluded therefore that for a magnitude response which tends to zero at high frequencies, as would often be the case for a lowpass or bandpass filter, the system function must have at least one zero at infinity. For a highpass response there must be no zeros at infinity.

If $m > n$ then the system function has a pole or poles at infinity, and the magnitude tends to infinity at high frequencies. Clearly this is not possible for the magnitude of a voltage or current transfer function of a realizable network, therefore these functions cannot have poles at infinity. In practice, stray capacitance ensures that the response always tends to zero as the frequency approaches infinity, since even resistors have stray capacitance. This implies that a transfer function must always have at least one zero at infinity. It is convenient, however, to consider theoretically pure resistors, which leads to transfer functions having no zeros at infinity. In active network synthesis, the assumption of perfect active devices can lead to theoretical transfer functions with poles at infinity, e.g. a transfer function $F(s) = Ts$, which is that of a differentiator, is considered in

Chapter 11. Here, however, the implication is that in practice the pole is sufficiently far away to be negligible over the frequency range of interest.

Since driving-point immittance functions can be expressed in impedance or admittance form, it is clear that singularities of either type can occur at infinity, e.g. $Z = Ls$ has a pole at infinity and $Y - 1/Ls$ has a zero at infinity.

The behaviour of the phase characteristic of a system at high frequencies can conveniently be expressed in terms of the number of singularities at infinity. We return to the general expression of (3.38) for phase:

$$\phi = (\theta_{z_1} + \theta_{z_2} + \dots + \theta_{z_m}) - (\theta_{p_1} + \theta_{p_2} + \dots + \theta_{p_n}) \tag{5.9}$$

It is clear that for all singularities in the left-half plane, all the angles tend to the value $\pi/2$ at high frequencies. Therefore the resultant phase at high frequencies tends to the value $(m - n)\pi/2 = -q\pi/2$ where q is the number of zeros at infinity.

5.5 Right-half plane zeros

As previously stated, the zeros of a system function are not restricted to the left-half plane. We now examine the effect on the frequency response of right-half plane zeros. This is best done by investigating how the response changes when zeros are moved from the left-half plane to positions in the right-half plane that are the mirror-images in the j-axis of the original positions.

Figure 5.11a shows an s-plane consisting of two poles and left-half plane zero and with the frequency response evaluated at an arbitrary point P on the real frequency axis. Let $(-a, 0)$ be the position of the zero. Figure 5.11b shows the p–z diagram when the zero is moved to the right-half plane to the position $(a, 0)$. We must compare the characteristics of the two cases.

It can be seen that the magnitude response is the same for both cases since the length of the vector from the point P to the zero is the same. A similar argument holds for complex zeros, and therefore it can be concluded that the magnitude response is unaffected by moving zeros from the left-half to the right-half plane in the manner described.

For the phase characteristics, the situation is not quite so straightforward. The phase characteristics for both a real pole and two complex poles in the left-half plane have already been examined in Sections 4.5 and 4.7.2 respectively. It has been shown that in all cases the characteristics exhibit lag at all frequencies. The phase characteristics for zeros in the left-half plane are the same as for poles but with opposite sign; i.e the characteristics exhibit lead at all frequencies.

The above result can be summarized by stating that in the left-half plane the poles always contribute phase lag and the zeros contribute phase lead to the overall phase response.

Consider now the zero in the right-half plane on the real axis at $(a, 0)$ as in Fig. 5.11b. It might at first be supposed that the angle which determines the phase contribution of the zero is δ_1. Note, however, that this angle has a value

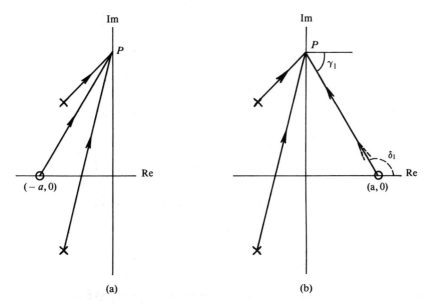

Figure 5.11 *Comparison of characteristics for a zero in (a) the left-half plane and (b) the right-half plane.*

of 180° at zero frequency. Now it should be remembered that a factor in the numerator of the transfer function which introduces a zero at $(a, 0)$ can be in the form either $(s - a)$ or $(a - s)$. In the former case the relevant vector is $(j\omega - a)$ which has direction from the zero to P; the angle is then given by $\delta_1 = \tan^{-1} \omega / (- a)$. In the latter case the relevant vector is $(a - j\omega)$ which has direction from P to the zero; the phase angle is then given by $\gamma_1 = \tan^{-1}(- \omega / a)$ where γ_1 is as shown and has a value of zero at zero frequency.

This ambiguity is present also for the case of left-half plane singularities since an inversion of the signal, which corresponds to multiplication of the transfer function by $- 1$, introduces a phase shift of 180° without affecting the singularities. In other words, for any specified pole–zero diagram an additional arbitrary phase shift of 180° can always be included. However, it is convention when plotting phase characteristics to assume normally that, excluding singularities at the origin, the phase shift is zero at zero frequency. Therefore, in the case of the real zero in the right-half plane, it is appropriate to take the phase as given by γ_1, and this value is always negative for frequencies other than $\omega = 0$ thus indicating that the zero contributes phase lag.

For a complex-conjugate pair of right-half plane zeros such as z_2 and z_3, as shown in Fig. 5.12, we obtain the same result by taking either the pair of angles δ_2 and δ_3 or the pair γ_2 and γ_3. That is, the algebraic sum of δ_2 and δ_3 is equal to the algebraic sum of γ_2 and γ_3, and this sum is zero at zero frequency. As the frequency is increased, the algebraic sum decreases indicating that the resultant

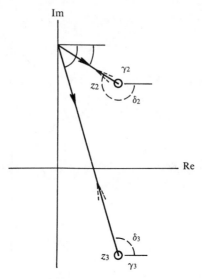

Figure 5.12 *Graphical determination of phase for the case of complex zeros in the right-half plane.*

phase is lagging for $\omega > 0$. Thus it can be concluded that, in all cases, zeros in the right-half plane contribute phase lag at all frequencies.

5.5.1 Minimum and nonminimum phase

Returning to Fig. 5.11, we have seen that the magnitude response is the same for both cases. However, the two functions have different phase characteristics. Whereas in (a) the zero contributes phase lead, in case (b) it contributes lag. Therefore the phase lag of (b) is greater than that of (a). The same argument applies for complex zeros. For the above reasons, a system function with all its singularities in the left-half plane is known as a *minimum phase function*.

A very important property of minimum phase systems is the one-to-one relationship that exists between the magnitude and the phase characteristics. In other words, once a magnitude response is specified the phase response is uniquely determined, and vice versa. The mathematics of this relationship is discussed further in Chapter 12 where it is relevant to the Bode stability criterion. The relationship has relevance also in filter theory, since the implication is that the designer is not free to specify the magnitude and phase characteristics independently. This restriction in the frequency domain corresponds to the more obvious restriction in the time domain that a system response cannot occur before the input is applied.

The restriction on the phase characteristic that can be obtained once a magnitude characteristic has been specified can be partly removed by the use of a nonminimum phase system. However, it follows from the foregoing theory that the use of such a system will always produce a phase characteristic which has greater lag than would be obtained by using a minimum phase system to achieve the same magnitude response.

5.5.2 Allpass functions

The best known example of a nonminimum phase function is the allpass function. The allpass function can have any number of left-half plane poles but must have no left-half plane zeros. In the right-half plane there are zeros equal in number to the poles in the left-half plane. The pattern of the zeros is the reflection in the j-axis of the pattern of the poles. This is illustrated in Fig. 5.13, which shows the frequency response evaluated at an arbitrary point P. From the symmetry of the diagram it is seen that $M_{z_1} = M_{p_1}$, $M_{z_2} = M_{p_2}$, etc., and therefore the magnitude remains constant at all frequencies. However, the zeros introduce a phase lag equal to the lag contributed by the poles and hence the overall phase lag is twice that of the poles alone. The allpass network has several applications. For example, it can be used where the frequency of the input signal is constant, and the requirement is for a variable phase shift without change in magnitude. This would be obtained by varying a time constant of the network. Another application arises in filter synthesis where an allpass network can be cascaded with a filter to modify the overall phase characteristic without changing

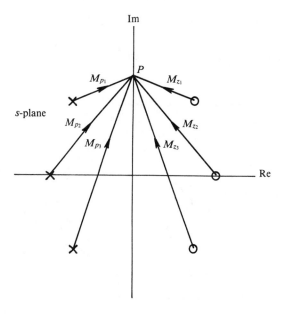

Figure 5.13 *Graphical determination in* s-*plane of an allpass response.*

the magnitude response. This technique is, of course, appropriate only where an increase in phase lag is acceptable.

Computer Exercise 5.4

Use Option B3.2 of ENTIS to investigate the magnitude and phase characteristics of a second-order allpass function. Select the case of *right-hand plane zeros* by means of User Key F6. Ensure that the values of Q for the poles and zeros are equal.

5.5.3 Nonminimum phase network

A nonminimum phase voltage transfer function can be realized by the bridge network of Fig. 5.14. Note that the input and output do not have a common terminal. This is usually undesirable in practice, and passive realizations with a common ground are given in Chapter 10. An active realization with a common ground terminal is given in Chapter 11.

To analyze the network we observe that

$$V_A = V_i/n \tag{5.10}$$

where

$$n = (R_1 + R_2)/R_2$$

and

$$V_B = \frac{Z_2}{Z_1 + Z_2} \, V_i \tag{5.11}$$

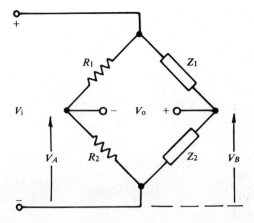

Figure 5.14 *Realization of a nonmininum phase transfer function.*

The output voltage is given by

$$V_o = V_B - V_A \tag{5.12}$$

From this the voltage transfer function is found to be

$$F(s) = \frac{(n-1)Z_2 - Z_1}{n(Z_1 + Z_2)} \tag{5.13}$$

5.5.4 First-order allpass network

Consider the case where $R_1 = R_2$, i.e. $n = 2$. (5.13) becomes

$$F(s) = \frac{Z_2 - Z_1}{2(Z_1 + Z_2)} \tag{5.14}$$

An allpass characteristic is achieved by choosing the impedances Z_1 and Z_2 such that one is purely resistive and the other is purely reactive. For example if $Z_1 = R$ and $Z_2 = 1/Cs$ then (5.14) becomes the first-order transfer function

$$F(s) = \frac{1 - CRs}{2(1 + CRs)} \tag{5.15}$$

The network for the above case is shown in Fig. 5.15.

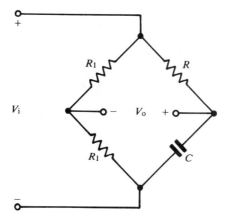

Figure 5.15 *Realization of a first-order allpass transfer function.*

5.5.5 Second-order allpass network

Realization of a second-order allpass transfer function with complex poles could theoretically be achieved using the network of Fig. 5.14 with $n = 2$, by letting Z_2 be a series LC impedance. However, this would require a lossless inductor. A more realistic representation would include a resistance r in series with L.

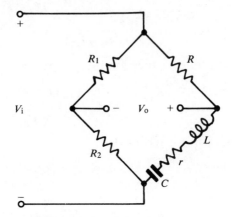

Figure 5.16 *Realization of a second-order allpass transfer function.*

In this case, by letting $Z_2 = r + Ls + 1/Cs$, (5.13) becomes

$$F(s) = \frac{n-1}{n} \frac{LCs^2 + [r - R/(n-1)] Cs + 1}{LCs^2 + (r + R) Cs + 1}$$ (5.16)

The condition for an allpass characteristic is therefore

$$n = 1 + \frac{R}{R + 2r}$$ (5.17)

i.e.

$$\frac{R_1}{R_2} = \frac{R}{R + 2r}$$ (5.18)

The network for the above case is shown in Fig. 5.16.

6 LOGARITHMIC FREQUENCY RESPONSE CHARACTERISTICS

The various ways in which frequency response can be displayed graphically were discussed briefly in Chapter 4. In this chapter we consider in more detail the most common method, known as the semilog or Bode plot. With this method, we display separate phase-versus-frequency and magnitude-versus-frequency characteristics. Logarithmic scales are used for magnitude and frequency. A linear scale is used for phase.

There are a number of advantages to be gained by the use of logarithmic scales which will become more apparent at a later stage but which can be stated briefly as follows:

1. The use of a logarithmic scale for magnitude enables a magnitude response to be determined by summation of the individual characteristics of the separate singularities. A linear scale would require multiplication of the characteristics.
2. A logarithmic scale for magnitude is more appropriate than a linear one in some applications. This is the case, for example, in audio signal processing, because the sensitivity of the ear is logarithmic.
3. The use of logarithmic scales for both magnitude and frequency leads to the straight line approximation method for magnitude response which is described in the following section.
4. The straight line approximation for phase characteristics to be described in Section 6.8 is based on a linear phase versus logarithmic frequency characteristic.
5. When using frequency transformations, as described subsequently in Chapter 8, there are a number of properties that relate to a logarithmic frequency scale. For example, the standard transformation for changing the cut-off frequency of a filter corresponds to a translation along the frequency axis without changing the shape of the characteristic if the frequency scale is logarithmic. Also, the standard transformations to obtain bandstop and bandpass filters produce symmetrical characteristics on logarithmic frequency scales.
6. For a minimum phase network the relationship between the magnitude and

the phase characteristics is considerably simplified by the use of logarithmic scales.

6.1 Scales

There are two ways in which a variable or function can be scaled logarithmically for a graphical plot. Either (a) the value of the logarithm of the function can be indicated on the axis, in which case the scale or grid is linearly spaced, or (b) the actual value of the function can be indicated on the axis, in which case the scale or grid is logarithmically spaced.

In the case of magnitude, the convention is to use a logarithmic unit, namely the neper, which is based on natural logarithms, or the decibel (dB) derived from logarithms to the base 10. The latter is the more common for lumped constant networks and will be used here. Thus a magnitude-squared function $|F(j\omega)|^2$ expressed in terms of decibels is $10 \log |F(j\omega)|^2 = 20 \log |F(j\omega)|$.

In the case of frequency, the convention is to indicate the actual value expressed in hertz or radians per second. Thus the plots require a semilog grid where the logarithmic scale is used for frequency along the horizontal axis, and the linear scale is used for magnitude expressed in dB or phase shift expressed in radians or degrees. The diagrams are known as *semilog plots* and the semilog magnitude diagrams are known as *Bode diagrams*, named after H. W. Bode who used them in the study of feedback amplifiers.

It is useful at this stage to review some of the properties of a logarithmic scale as used for the frequency axis. Figure 6.1 shows a semilog grid for a magnitude versus frequency plot. It should be noted that the point $\omega = 0$ cannot be shown on a logarithmic scale since $\log 0 = -\infty$. An important property of a logarithmic scale, which can be observed from the figure, is that the distance in, say, centimetres between any two frequencies is determined by the ratio of the frequencies. For example, the distance between $\omega = 1$ and $\omega = 3$ is the same as that between $\omega = 3$ and $\omega = 9$. Similarly the distance from any frequency ω_1 to $k\omega_1$ is the same as the distance from $k\omega_1$ to $k^2\omega_1$. Therefore $k\omega_1$ is midway between ω_1 and $k^2\omega_1$. In other words, the midpoint between any two frequencies is given by the geometric mean of the two.

Two terms in common use to represent logarithmic distance between frequencies are as follows:

1. The distance between two frequencies that are in the ratio of $2:1$ is referred to as an *octave*. This name is derived from the musical scale where a distance of eight notes corresponds to a change in frequency by a factor of 2. Note that a change in gain by a factor of 2 expressed in decibels is 6.021 dB which is usually rounded to 6 dB.
2. The distance between two frequencies that are in the ratio of $10:1$ is referred to as a *decade*. Note that a change in gain by a factor of 10 expressed in deci-

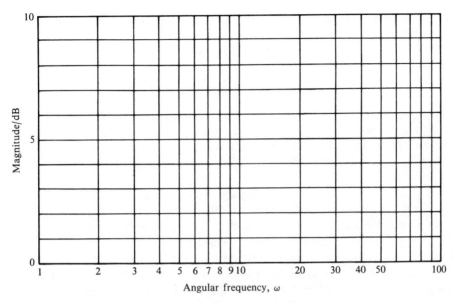

Figure 6.1 *Semilog grid for a magnitude versus frequency plot.*

bels is exactly 20 dB. Semilog graph paper has the logarithmic scale divided into cycles, each cycle consisting of one decade. The scale of the grid in Fig. 6.1 extends over two cycles. Scales having up to six cycles are commonly available.

6.2 Straight line approximation method

We first examine the Bode diagram for a transfer function with a simple pole on the negative real axis and with unity d.c. gain, i.e.

$$F(s) = \frac{1}{Ts + 1} \tag{6.1}$$

and the magnitude function is

$$|F(j\omega)| = \frac{1}{(1 + \omega^2 T^2)^{1/2}} \tag{6.2}$$

Expressed in dB the magnitude is

$$20 \log|F(j\omega)| = -10 \log(1 + \omega^2 T^2) \tag{6.3}$$

Consider the behaviour of this function as $\omega \to 0$, remembering that $\omega = 0$ is at an infinite distance in the negative direction along the frequency axis. The magnitude tends to 0 dB as $\omega^2 T^2$ becomes negligible compared to 1. The 0 dB line is therefore said to be the *low frequency asymptote* and the actual value of the magnitude is always below this asymptote.

Consider next the high frequency behaviour. Where $\omega T \gg 1$ the magnitude in dB approximates to

$$-20 \, \log(\omega T) = -20 \, \log \omega - 20 \, \log T \qquad (6.4)$$

Since the magnitude is plotted on a logarithmic frequency scale (6.4) is seen to be a straight line; that is, it is of the form $y = mx + c$ where $x = \log \omega$ and the constant $c = 20 \log T$. Therefore the high frequency asymptote is a straight line with a negative slope. The actual value of magnitude is always below this asymptote.

The high frequency and low frequency asymptotes intersect at the frequency where the right-hand side of (6.4) has a value of 0 dB, i.e. $\omega = 1/T$. At this frequency the true value of the magnitude is found from (6.3) to be -3 dB. A straight line approximation to the actual characteristic consists of two segments. One segment is the low frequency asymptote from d.c. to $\omega = 1/T$; the other is the high frequency asymptote from $\omega = 1/T$ to $\omega = \infty$ as shown in Fig. 6.2. The maximum deviation between the curve and the straight line approximation is 3 dB and occurs at $\omega = 1/T$. This frequency is known by a variety of terms including the 3 dB frequency, the corner frequency, the cut-off frequency, the break frequency and the asymptote intersection frequency. Note that the curve of error between the actual magnitude and the asymptote approximation is symmetrical about the break frequency, as shown in Fig. 6.3, where it is observed that at an octave away from the break frequency the error is approximately 1 dB. Use of the asymptote approximation simplifies considerably the determination of

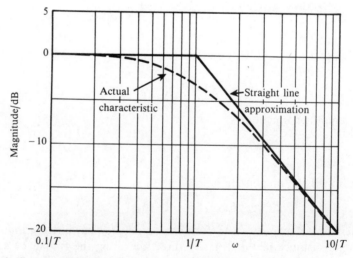

Figure 6.2 *Bode magnitude plot for a single pole on the real axis.*

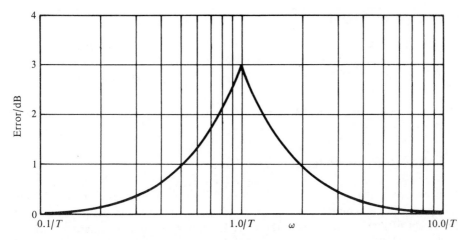

Figure 6.3 *Error in dB between the Bode magnitude plot and the straight line approximation for a single pole on the real axis.*

magnitude characteristics and is sufficiently accurate for many purposes. Where greater accuracy is required, a correction can be added.

There are several ways in which the slope of the high frequency asymptote can be expressed. The expression for this asymptote is $1/\omega T$. In other words, when the frequency increases by any factor, the gain falls by that same factor. It can be stated therefore that the asymptote has a slope of -1. The slope can also be expressed in terms of dBs and decades. Since the gain falls by a factor of 10 for an increase in frequency by a factor of 10 the slope can be expressed as -20 dB/decade. Similarly, the slope can be expressed as -6 db/octave. The units 'dB/octave' and 'dB/decade' are both in common use. However, dB/decade is sometimes preferred because 6 dB/octave is an approximation to unit slope whereas 20 dB/decade is exact. Here the unit dB/decade is used.

Note that the shapes of both the asymptote approximation and the actual curve are unchanged by changing T. As T is varied, the approximation and the actual curve move horizontally.

Suppose a multiplying factor H is introduced into the transfer function of (6.1). This then becomes

$$F(s) = \frac{H}{Ts + 1} \tag{6.5}$$

and the logarithmic magnitude function of (6.5) is

$$20 \log |F(\mathrm{j}\omega)| = 20 \log H - 10 \log(1 + \omega^2 T^2) \tag{6.6}$$

From a comparison of (6.3) and (6.6), it is observed that the effect of variation of H is simply to move the characteristic up or down without change of shape.

Computer Exercise 6.1

Use Option C of ENTIS to display the characteristic of Fig. 6.2. Observe the straight line approximation and the actual curve. Observe how the shapes of the characteristics are unchanged when T and H are varied.

6.3 Addition of characteristics

Consider next a transfer function with two poles on the negative real axis. The d.c. gain will be assumed to be unity although, as observed in the previous case, the effect of introducing a gain factor H is simply to move the characteristic up by $20 \log H$ dB.

The transfer function can be written

$$F(s) = \frac{1}{(T_1 s + 1)(T_2 s + 1)} \tag{6.7}$$

and the magnitude is given by

$$|F(j\omega)| = \frac{1}{(1 + \omega^2 T_1^2)^{1/2}(1 + \omega^2 T_2^2)^{1/2}} \tag{6.8}$$

The magnitude in dB can be expressed as

$$20 \log |F(j\omega)| = -10 \log(1 + \omega^2 T_1^2) - 10 \log(1 + \omega^2 T_2^2) \tag{6.9}$$

It is seen that the magnitude in dBs is the sum of the separate magnitudes resulting from each pole of the transfer function. If we take the asymptote approximation characteristic for each magnitude, these straight line characteristics can be readily added as shown in Fig. 6.4 where it is assumed that $T_1 > T_2$. At frequencies up to $1/T_1$ the resultant characteristic is flat. Between frequencies $1/T_1$ and $1/T_2$ the slope is -20 dB/decade. Above $1/T_2$ the two characteristics combine to give a slope of -40 dB/decade.

Computer Exercise 6.2

Use Option C of ENTIS to observe the straight line approximation and the actual magnitude characteristic for the transfer function of (6.7) using various values of T_1 and T_2. Observe that the worst case for error occurs when $T_1 = T_2$ and that the maximum error is then 6 dB.

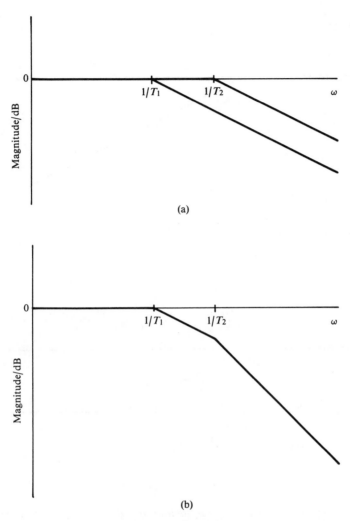

Figure 6.4 *Determination of the straight line approximation to the magnitude characteristic of a transfer function with two real poles: (a) separate approximations, (b) combined characteristic.*

6.4 Real zeros

Consider next a transfer function with a single pole and a single zero on the negative real axis. This can be written

$$F(s) = \frac{T_1 s + 1}{T_2 s + 1} \tag{6.10}$$

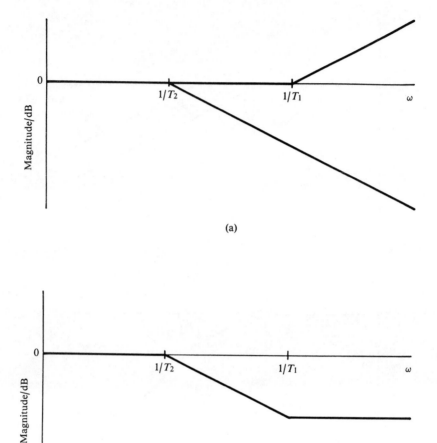

Figure 6.5 *Determination of the straight line approximation to the magnitude characteristic of a transfer function with one pole and one zero: (a) separate approximations, (b) combined characteristic.*

The magnitude expressed in dB is

$$20 \log |F(j\omega)| = 10 \log(1 + \omega^2 T_1^2) - 10 \log(1 + \omega^2 T_2^2) \qquad (6.11)$$

The characteristic for the zero is the same as for a pole but with altered sign. The two characteristics can be combined as shown in Fig. 6.5 for the case $T_2 > T_1$. The error characteristics for the pole and the zero are of opposite sign and therefore combine to an error which is always smaller in magnitude than either of the separate characteristics. The error is a function of the distance between the two

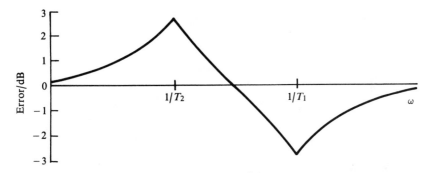

Figure 6.6 *Error characteristic for the straight line approximation of Fig. 6.5* ($T_2 = 4T_1$).

corner frequencies and decreases as the separation is decreased. The error curve for a separation of two octaves is shown in Fig. 6.6.

Computer Exercise 6.3

Use Option C of ENTIS to observe the straight line approximation and the actual magnitude characteristic for the transfer function of (6.10) using various values of T_1 and T_2.

6.5 Singularities at the origin

Up to now we have considered the contribution of singularities on the real axis to the overall magnitude characteristic. We now consider the particular case of singularities at the origin.

A factor s in the numerator of a transfer function produces a magnitude expressed in dB as 20 log ω. In this case no approximation is required since this characteristic is a straight line. The slope is 20 dB/decade and the line intersects the 0 dB line at $\omega = 1$. Sometimes it is convenient to include a multiplying factor, say T, with the zero. A function Ts produces a straight line with a slope of 20 dB/decade which intersects the 0 dB line at $\omega = 1/T$.

The characteristic for a pole at the origin is the same as that for a zero but with altered sign, i.e. a factor $1/Ts$ produces a line with a slope of -20 dB/decade which intersects the 0 dB line at $\omega = 1/T$.

Fig. 6.7 shows how the approximation for a transfer function with a zero at the origin and a pole on the real axis is obtained by combining the separate characteristics.

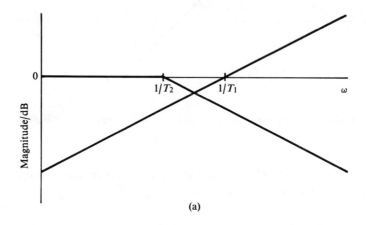

(a)

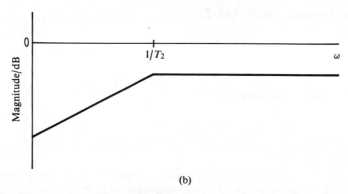

(b)

Figure 6.7 *Determination of the straight line approximation to the magnitude characteristic of a transfer function with a pole on the real axis and a zero at the origin: (a) separate approximations, (b) combined characteristic.*

Computer Exercise 6.4

Make a sketch of the straight line approximation to the magnitude characteristics of each of the following transfer function specifications (a) to (e). Choose a value for H to meet the conditions for the magnitude of the straight line approximation at the specified frequency. Verify your sketches by means of Option C of ENTIS and in each case observe the actual characteristic.

The transfer function is specified as

$$F(s) = Hs^r \, \frac{N(s)}{D(s)} \tag{6.12}$$

where:

(a) $N(s) = (25s + 1)$; $D(s) = (s + 1)$; $r = 0$.
Magnitude $= 0$ dB at high frequencies.
(b) $N(s) = (s + 1)$; $D(s) = (20s + 1)$; $r = 0$.
Magnitude $= 0$ dB at low frequencies.
(c) $N(s) = 1$; $D(s) = (2s + 1)(50s + 1)$; $r = 1$.
Magnitude $= 0$ dB at $\omega = 0.1$.
(d) $N(s) = 1$; $D(s) = (4s + 1)(20s + 1)$; $r = 2$.
Magnitude $= 0$ dB at high frequencies.
(e) $N(s) = (s + 1)(0.02s + 1)$; $D(s) = (5s + 1)(0.005s + 1)$; $r = 0$
Magnitude $= 0$ dB at $\omega = 1$.

6.6 Synthesis procedure

The determination of an approximating transfer function for a specified magnitude characteristic is the first stage in the modern approach to network synthesis. The straight line approximation method provides a simple means of determining a transfer function in a restricted, but nevertheless useful, range of applications. The limitation is that the method is suitable only for determining transfer functions with real singularities, and therefore is applicable only when the specified characteristic does not have abrupt changes in slope.

The procedure is as follows: a 'best' segmented straight line approximation is fitted to the specified curve using lines whose slopes are integer multiples of 20 dB/decade. The transfer function is then determined in the form of (6.12).

The number of singularities at the origin is determined by examining the slope of the low frequency asymptote. A slope of $20r$ dB/decade indicates r zeros at the origin. A negative slope indicates poles at the origin. The remaining singularities are then determined by starting at the low frequency end and locating each break or corner frequency ω_p. If the slope increases algebraically by

20 dB/decade, this indicates a factor $(s/\omega_p + 1)$ to be assigned to $N(s)$. If the slope decreases algebraically by 20 dB/decade this indicates that the factor is to be assigned to $D(s)$. A change in slope by a multiple of 20 dB/decade can be accommodated by multiple singularities, but it should be remembered that in this case the deviation between the straight line approximation and the actual curve can be of the order of $3m$ dB, where m is the multiplicity of the singularities, and this magnitude of deviation may not be acceptable. Large deviations can occur also where several poles or several zeros are close together. Best approximation is achieved when the poles and zeros alternate, since the errors introduced by poles and zeros are of opposite sign and produce some cancellation.

Finally, the factor H is determined. If the transfer function has no singularities at the origin then H is equal to the d.c. gain. Otherwise, it can be readily established that the intersection of the low frequency asymptote with the 0 dB line occurs at a frequency ω_0 which is related to H by

$$H = \omega_0^{-r} \tag{6.13}$$

where r can be either (a) the number of zeros at the origin, or (b) the negative of the number of poles at the origin.

Computer Exercise 6.5

Figure 6.8 shows a specified characteristic for a magnitude function. Determine an approximating characteristic using the straight line approximation method as outlined above. Verify your answer using Option C of ENTIS by observing both the straight line and the exact characteristics.

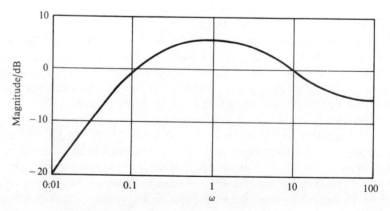

Figure 6.8 *Specified magnitude characteristic for Exercise 6.5.*

6.7 Magnitude for complex singularities

The remaining type of factor to be considered is that for complex singularities. This factor F_1 can be written

$$F_1 = [s^2/\omega_0^2 + s/(Q\omega_0) + 1] \qquad (6.14)$$

The low frequency asymptote for this characteristic is the 0 dB line. At high frequencies the magnitude of this factor approximates to $(\omega/\omega_0)^2$ which is a straight line whose slope is 40 dB/decade and which intersects the low frequency asymptote at $\omega = \omega_0$. In the case of poles, the slope is of course negative.

The family of characteristics plotted on linear scales was considered in Section 4.7 for the case of a two-pole transfer function. Figure 6.9 shows a set of semilog characteristics. It is observed that the deviation between the asymptote approximation and the exact response depends on the value of Q. At the break frequency the deviation is 20 log Q. For $Q = 1/\sqrt{2}$ the deviation is only 3 dB, but for much larger values of Q the asymptotes do not provide an adequate approximation.

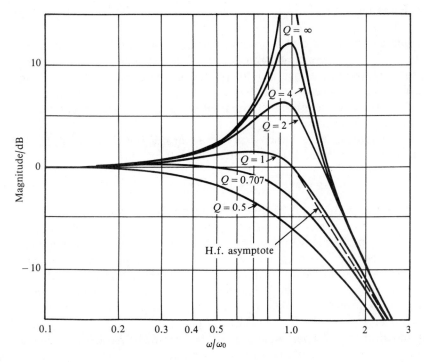

Figure 6.9 *Family of semilog magnitude characteristics for a two-pole transfer function.*

The procedure, outlined in the previous section, for transfer function estimation for a specified magnitude characteristic can be extended to include complex singularities. The complex singularities are used where the straight line approximation changes in slope by 40 dB/decade. The frequency where the break occurs determines the value of ω_0. The value of Q is estimated from the deviation between the straight line approximation and the specified curve. This technique may not always initially provide an accurate approximation, but can be useful for determining a starting point for a computer-aided optimization procedure.

Computer Exercise 6.6

Use Option B6 of ENTIS to display the semilog magnitude characteristics of a two-pole transfer function. Observe the deviation in dB between the asymptotes and the actual curve for different values of Q. Observe also how, for a given value of Q, the characteristic moves along the frequency axis without change in shape as ω_0 is varied.

6.8 Phase plots

The phase characteristic of a system is the algebraic sum of the separate phase characteristics of the separate factors of the transfer function. It is therefore not appropriate to take the logarithm of phase. However, several of the advantages of using a logarithmic scale for frequency for magnitude plots apply also in the case of phase, and therefore the display of phase characteristics on semilog plots will now be considered.

We first consider the characteristic for a transfer function with a simple pole on the negative real axis. If this is written in the form of (6.1) the phase ϕ is given by

$$\phi = -\tan^{-1}\omega T \qquad (6.15)$$

This function tends to zero at low frequencies and to $-90°$ at high frequencies. Thus the low frequency and high frequency asymptotes are both straight lines with zero slope. However, these two lines do not provide an adequate approximation over the whole frequency range, since the actual value of the phase at $\omega = 1/T$ is $-45°$ and the maximum error between the actual curve and a straight line approximation using the asymptotes would be $45°$. The semilog plot of the phase function of (6.15) is shown in Fig. 6.10 and it is seen that the curve has antisymmetry about the frequency $\omega = 1/T$.

A much improved approximation can be obtained by using a three-segment approximation. The additional segment is a straight line which, because of the antisymmetry of the curve, is chosen to pass through the point on the curve at $\omega = 1/T$, where the phase is $45°$. Different values have been proposed for the slope of the middle segment. For example, if the slope is chosen to make the

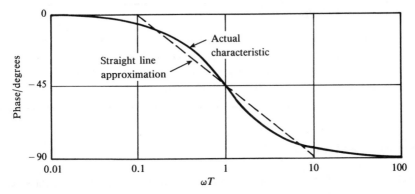

Figure 6.10 *Semilog phase characteristic for a transfer function with a single pole on the negative real axis.*

segment intersect the low frequency and high frequency asymptotes at $1/5T$ and $5/T$ respectively, then a good approximation is obtained at frequencies in the region of $1/T$, but at the expense of larger errors in the region of the corner frequencies. A more even approximation over the whole frequency range can be obtained if the segment is chosen to intersect the low frequency and high frequency asymptotes at frequencies $1/10T$ and $10/T$ respectively. This approximation is used here, and in this case the middle segment extends over two decades and has a slope of $45°$ per decade. This is shown in Fig. 6.10 where the maximum deviation from the actual characteristic occurs at the corner frequencies $1/10T$ and $10/T$ and has a value of $6°$.

For transfer functions whose singularities are restricted to the real axis, the determination of a straight line approximation to the phase characteristic is achieved by addition of the separate approximations of the individual singularities in a similar manner to that for the magnitude characteristics. An important difference, however, is that in the case of phase, the characteristic for each singularity consists of three segments.

For a zero on the negative real axis, the characteristic is the same as that for a pole but is lead instead of lag, and therefore is positive instead of negative. Each singularity at the origin contributes a constant $90°$ phase at all frequencies. Therefore the overall approximation can be determined as follows: the low frequency asymptote is first determined and has zero slope and a value $90r°$ where r is the number of singularities at the origin. The phase is positive (lead) in the case of zeros, and negative (lag) in the case of poles. The lower and upper corner frequencies ω_U and ω_L for each singularity are next determined and arranged in ascending order. Starting at the lowest corner frequency, the slope at each corner frequency increases or decreases by $45°$ per decade. For a corner frequency ω_L which relates to a zero the slope increases, and for one which relates to a pole the slope decreases. For a corner frequency ω_U the converse applies.

Computer Exercise 6.7

Sketch the straight line approximations for the phase plots of the transfer functions given in Computer Exercise 6.4. Verify your answers using Option C of ENTIS. Observe and compare the straight line approximations and the actual characteristics.

6.9 Lag transfer function

Consider a transfer function with a single pole and a single zero on the negative real axis, and with the pole positioned nearer to the origin than the zero. The

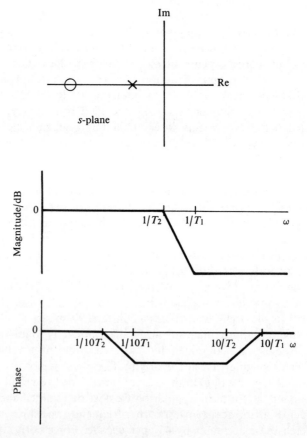

Figure 6.11 *Straight line approximations to the magnitude and phase characteristics of a lag network.*

transfer function can be written as

$$T(s) = k \frac{T_1 s + 1}{T_2 s + 1} \qquad (6.16)$$

where $T_2 > T_1$.

The straight line characteristics of magnitude and phase for the case $k = 1$ are shown in Fig. 6.11 where it is seen that the dominance of the pole results in a lag characteristic.

Computer Exercise 6.8

Use Option C of ENTIS to observe the characteristics of the transfer function of (6.16) for various values of T_1 and T_2. Observe in particular the symmetry of the phase characteristic and how the maximum value of phase lag is related to the ratio T_2/T_1.

6.10 Lag network

The transfer function of (6.16) can be realized by the lag network of Fig. 6.12, for which it can be readily shown that $T_1 = CR_2$ and $T_2 = C(R_1 + R_2)$. A network of this type has applications in certain feedback systems where its inclusion in the loop can improve system performance. An example of this application is given in Chapter 12.

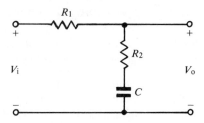

Figure 6.12 *Lag network.*

6.11 Lead network

If the positions of the pole and zero of the above transfer function are interchanged, the phase response becomes a lead instead of a lag characteristic, but otherwise is unchanged in shape. Such a characteristic can be realized by the network of Fig. 6.13, for which it can be readily shown that $k = R_2/(R_1 + R_2)$, $T_1 = CR_1$ and $T_2 = kCR_1$. The lead network has applications in certain feedback

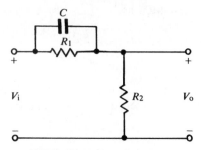

Figure 6.13 *Lead network.*

control systems where its inclusion in the loop can reduce the overall phase lag characteristic, thereby improving stability.

Computer Exercise 6.9

Use Option C of ENTIS to verify the characteristics of the lead network.

6.12 Synthesis

The straight line approximation method for phase can be used as an aid to synthesis as a first step in determining an approximation transfer function with real singularities, where a phase characteristic is specified. As in the procedure for magnitude, a straight line approximation is superimposed on the specified curve. This segmented characteristic is subject to two restrictions as follows:

1. At each corner frequency the slope must change by 45° per decade.
2. For each corner frequency ω_U there must be a corresponding corner frequency ω_L. These two frequencies must be separated by two decades, and at the two frequencies the changes in slope must be of opposite sign.

The latter restriction makes this synthesis procedure more complicated and more difficult to apply than in the case of magnitude.

6.13 Phase for complex singularities

The final factor whose phase characteristic remains to be considered is that for complex singularities. For a pair of complex singularities, say poles, the expres-

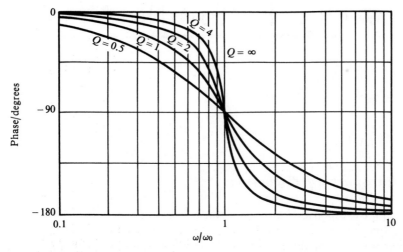

Figure 6.14 *Family of semilog phase characteristics for a two-pole transfer function.*

sion for phase has been given by (4.49), i.e.

$$\phi = -\tan^{-1} \frac{\omega/\omega_0}{Q[1 - (\omega/\omega_0)^2]} \qquad (6.17)$$

On a logarithmic frequency scale, the low frequency asymptote has a value of zero and the high frequency asymptote has a value of $-180°$. At $\omega = \omega_0$ the phase shift is $90°$. The shape of the curve, however, is a function of Q, since for very large values of Q the curve remains relatively flat until close to $\omega = \omega_0$. This is illustrated in Fig. 6.14.

Computer Exercise 6.10

Run Option B7 of ENTIS to display the phase response for the pair of complex poles, as given by (6.17), on a semilog plot. Observe the antisymmetry of the curves which all pass through the value $-90°$ at $\omega = \omega_0$. Observe also how as Q becomes large, the characteristic approaches the low frequency asymptote below ω_0 with an abrupt transition to the high-frequency asymptote at frequencies above ω_0.

7 FILTER DESIGN

7.1 Introductory discussion

The required response of a frequency selective network can be specified in either the frequency or the time domain. The former is more common and in this chapter we consider the general problem of designing a filter in the frequency domain. We will adopt the usual practice of basing the design on the lowpass filter and taking this as the prototype from which others such as highpass, bandpass and bandstop can be derived by means of transformations as described subsequently in Chapter 8.

In the frequency domain, the main specification is usually in terms of the magnitude-versus-frequency characteristic; the ideal lowpass filter magnitude characteristic is one which remains constant from d.c. up to the cut-off frequency and then abruptly falls to zero. This is often referred to as the 'brick wall' function and is shown in Fig. 7.1.

With regard to the phase characteristic, this is not important in some applications. For example, in design of audio signal filters, since the ear is insensitive to small phase changes, the specification is normally in terms of the magnitude

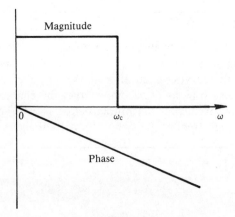

Figure 7.1 *Ideal 'brick wall' lowpass filter characteristic with linear phase.*

only. In other applications where the shape of the waveform in the time domain is important, both magnitude and phase must be considered. For example, in digital circuitry where the signal consists of a train of pulses, phase shift in the passband can introduce distortion due to the different frequencies being subjected to differing amounts of delay. Such distortion could theoretically be avoided by having zero phase shift over the passband, but this is not possible in practice since, as indicated by the Bode relationship, there is a minimum phase lag associated with any specified magnitude characteristic. Therefore, the ideal phase characteristic is usually considered to be one for which all the frequencies over the passband are subject to the same delay.

Consider a signal $v_i(t) = \sin(\omega t + \alpha)$ that is subject to a delay T. The output signal is

$$v_o(t) = \sin[\omega(t - T) + \alpha]$$

which can be written

$$v_o = \sin(\omega t + \alpha - \omega T)$$

Thus the delay introduces a phase shift $\phi = -\omega T$. If the delay T is constant at all frequencies then the phase lag is a linear function of frequency, as shown in Fig. 7.1, and this is generally taken to be the ideal phase characteristic.

There are several approaches to the problem of simultaneously satisfying the requirements for both magnitude and phase. One approach is to try several designs, each on the basis of the magnitude only but using different criteria, and then to examine the resulting phase characteristics in order to choose a satisfactory compromise. Another somewhat similar approach involves optimization of the phase characteristic only and examining the resulting magnitude characteristic. Finally, it is possible to improve the linearity of the phase characteristic without affecting the magnitude characteristic by the addition of an allpass network. However, the method of design of an allpass network to provide equalization of a specific phase characteristic is beyond the scope of this book.

We first consider the design of a filter by optimization of the magnitude characteristic. Returning to the 'brick wall' function of Fig. 7.1, it is clear that such a characteristic could never be achieved in practice and therefore must be approximated. In the previous chapter a design procedure was outlined for determining a transfer function with real singularities to provide an approximation to a specified magnitude characteristic. However, the restriction that the singularities lie on the real axis limits the application of the technique to those cases where there are no abrupt changes in the prescribed characteristic. To demonstrate this, consider a transfer function, $F(s)$, having n coincident poles on the negative real axis, at say $-1/T$, i.e.

$$F(s) = \frac{1}{(Ts + 1)^n} \tag{7.1}$$

The semilog straight line approximations to the magnitude characteristic for

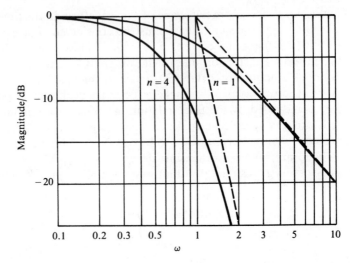

Figure 7.2 *Magnitude characteristics for filters with real coincident poles. The transfer function is given by (7.1).*

$n = 1$ and $n = 4$ are shown in Fig. 7.2. The high frequency asymptote has a slope $-20n$ dB/decade and as $n \to \infty$ the two-segment approximation tends to that of the 'brick wall' characteristic. However, it is important to observe that as n increases, the deviation increases between the actual characteristic and the asymptotes as shown in Fig. 7.2.

Computer Exercise 7.1

Use Option C of ENTIS to display the magnitude characteristic of the transfer function of (7.1) for various values of n. Observe the straight line approximations and the actual characteristics.

It can be concluded from Fig. 7.2 and the results of the above exercise, that the use of a transfer function with only real poles cannot provide an abrupt transition between passband and stopband. Increasing the number of poles does not result in an improved characteristic in the region of the cut-off frequency. Such an improvement can be obtained only by the use of complex poles. This is demonstrated by considering the family of second-order characteristics which were shown in Fig. 6.9 and are repeated in Fig. 7.3. The curve for the case of coincident real poles ($Q = 1/2$) which is 6 dB down at $\omega = \omega_0$ is seen to have a less abrupt transition at $\omega = \omega_0$ than the curves for which the poles are complex ($Q > 0.5$). The choice of a value for Q to provide an optimum second-order filter

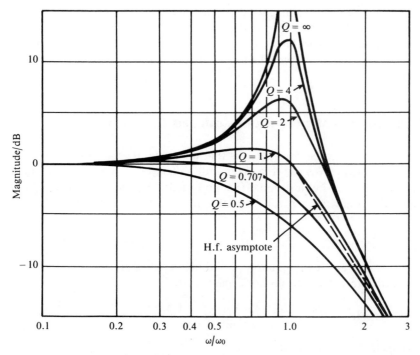

Figure 7.3 *Family of semilog magnitude characteristics for a two-pole transfer function.*

characteristic could be achieved simply by inspection of the characteristics, or by consideration of the peaking circle as discussed in Chapter 4. The latter approach leads to a value $Q = 1/\sqrt{2}$ for which the characteristic is 3 dB down at $\omega = \omega_0$. For higher order filters, however, there is no simple method for determining the coefficients or singularity locations to give the best approximation to the ideal characteristic. A possible approach would be to cascade a number r of identical second-order sections with, say, $Q = 1/\sqrt{2}$. This would yield a characteristic which was $3r$ dB down at $\omega = \omega_0$. This is an improvement on the characteristic for $2r$ real coincident poles which would be $6r$ dB down at $\omega = \omega_0$. However, a better characteristic can be achieved by using pole-pairs with different values of Q as will be shown.

Modern methods of filter derivation are usually based on an approach in which the magnitude function is optimized and then an associated system function is determined. This approach therefore requires knowledge of the conditions that must be satisfied by a magnitude function for an associated rational system function to exist. We also need to develop a method of determining an associated transfer function from a given magnitude function. These relationships will therefore now be investigated. In accordance with usual practice, we will take the magnitude squared, rather than the magnitude, since this eliminates the square root and leads to a function which is rational in ω. When expressed in logarithmic units the magnitude and magnitude squared yield the same value. For example when using dBs we can take either $20 \log |F(\mathrm{j}\omega)|$ or $10 \log |F(\mathrm{j}\omega)|^2$.

7.2 Properties of magnitude-squared function

The first property to be considered is that a rational transfer function with real coefficients always gives rise to a magnitude-squared function which is a rational *even* function in ω, i.e. a rational function of ω^2. A proof of this is as follows: consider the following general form of a rational transfer function $F(s)$

$$F(s) = \frac{a_0 + a_1 s + a_2 s^2 + \ldots + a_m s^m}{1 + b_1 s + b_2 s^2 + \ldots + b_n s^n} \tag{7.2}$$

The numerator and denominator of the above transfer function can each be partitioned into their even and odd parts as follows:

$$F(s) = \frac{(a_0 + a_2 s^2 + a_4 s^4 + \ldots) + s(a_1 + a_3 s^2 + a_5 s^4 + \ldots)}{(1 + b_2 s^2 + b_4 s^4 + \ldots) + s(b_1 + b_3 s^2 + b_5 s^4 + \ldots)} \tag{7.3}$$

The frequency response function is

$$F(\mathrm{j}\omega) = \frac{(a_0 - a_2 \omega^2 + a_4 \omega^4 - \ldots) + \mathrm{j}\omega(a_1 - a_3 \omega^2 + a_5 \omega^4 - \ldots)}{(1 - b_2 \omega^2 + b_4 \omega^4 - \ldots) + \mathrm{j}\omega(b_1 - b_3 \omega^2 + b_5 \omega^4 - \ldots)} \tag{7.4}$$

and the magnitude-squared function is

$$|F(\mathrm{j}\omega)|^2 = \frac{(a_0 - a_2 \omega^2 + a_4 \omega^4 + \ldots)^2 + \omega^2(a_1 - a_3 \omega^2 + a_5 \omega^4 - \ldots)^2}{(1 - b_2 \omega^2 + b_4 \omega^4 - \ldots)^2 + \omega^2(b_1 - b_3 \omega^2 + b_5 \omega^4 - \ldots)^2} \tag{7.5}$$

It is seen from (7.5) that the magnitude-squared function is an even function in ω whose order is twice that of the associated transfer function. The fact that the magnitude-squared function is even implies that the curve of magnitude versus frequency on a linear frequency scale is symmetrical about $\omega = 0$. This property can be readily deduced from the graphical relationship between frequency response and singularity locations in the s-plane; since the p–z plot is symmetrical about the real axis, it follows that evaluation of the magnitude by moving a point P along the real frequency axis and measuring the distances to the singularities will produce the same result in both positive and negative directions.

It was shown in Section 5.4 that for realizability, the order of the numerator of $F(s)$ must be less than or equal to the order of the denominator. It follows from the above that this condition must be satisfied also by the magnitude-squared function. It now remains to determine what other conditions must be satisfied for a rational even function in ω to have an associated realizable transfer function. This can be answered by considering how an associated transfer function can be determined from a given magnitude-squared function specified as an even rational function in ω.

7.3 Determination of *F*(s) from $|F(j\omega)|^2$

The required process is a reversal of the procedure of replacing s by $j\omega$ and then determining the magnitude squared. However, the reverse procedure is not generally as straightforward as the procedure itself, as illustrated by the following example. Let

$$F(s) = \frac{1}{s^2 + 7s + 10} \tag{7.6}$$

hence

$$F(j\omega) = \frac{1}{(10 - \omega^2) + 7j\omega} \tag{7.7}$$

and

$$|F(j\omega)|^2 = \frac{1}{\omega^4 + 29\omega^2 + 100} \tag{7.8}$$

Consider now the problem of determining an associated transfer function from a magnitude-squared function specified as a rational even function in ω. For example, starting with $|F(j\omega)|^2$ as specified by (7.8), how do we arrive at the expression for $F(s)$ as given by (7.6)? The difficulty arises in obtaining $F(j\omega)$, as given by (7.7) from $|F(j\omega)|^2$. To overcome this problem we first observe that, in general, a magnitude-squared function can be expressed as

$$|F(j\omega)|^2 = F(j\omega)F^*(j\omega) \tag{7.9}$$

where * denotes complex conjugate. Since $F(s)$ is real for s real it follows that $F^*(j\omega) = F(-j\omega)$.

Therefore (7.9) can be written

$$|F(j\omega)|^2 = F(j\omega)F(-j\omega) \tag{7.10}$$

Replacing $j\omega$ by s in each side of (7.10) we obtain

$$|F(j\omega)|^2_{j\omega = s} = F(s)F(-s) \tag{7.11}$$

(7.11) can be expressed more conveniently by denoting the specified magnitude function as $G(\omega^2)$ and noting that the operation of replacing $j\omega$ by s in an even function of ω is equivalent to replacement of ω^2 by $-s^2$. (7.11) then becomes

$$G(-s^2) = F(s)F(-s) \tag{7.12}$$

It can be seen from (7.12) that the function $G(-s^2)$ has all the singularities of

$F(s)$ together with those of $F(-s)$. The singularities of $F(-s)$ are the negatives of those of $F(s)$, that is, the p–z pattern of $F(-s)$ is the reflection in the j-axis of the s-plane, of the p–z pattern of $F(s)$. If it is assumed that $F(s)$ is a minimum phase function, the singularities of $F(s)$ can be determined by partitioning $G(-s^2)$ into its left-half and right-half plane singularities and assigning the left-half plane ones to $F(s)$.

EXAMPLE 7.1

To demonstrate the above procedure we return to the example of (7.6) to (7.8). Suppose the specified magnitude-squared function is

$$G(\omega^2) = \frac{1}{\omega^4 + 29\omega^2 + 100} \tag{7.13}$$

Applying the above procedure we obtain

$$F(s)F(-s) = G(-s^2) = \frac{1}{s^4 - 29s^2 + 100} \tag{7.14}$$

(7.14) can be expressed in factored form as

$$F(s)F(-s) = \frac{1}{(s+2)(s-2)(s+5)(s-5)} \tag{7.15}$$

Deleting the right-half plane poles gives

$$F(s) = \frac{1}{(s+2)(s+5)} = \frac{1}{s^2 + 7s + 10} \tag{7.16}$$

Figure 7.4 shows the s-plane diagrams for $G(-s^2)$ and $F(s)$.

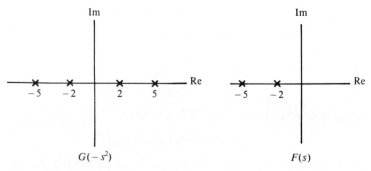

Figure 7.4 s-*plane diagrams for Example 7.1.*

EXAMPLE 7.2

For the case where $F(s)$ has complex singularities, suppose the specified magnitude-squared function is

$$G(\omega^2) = \frac{1}{4\omega^4 - 2\omega^2 + 1} \tag{7.17}$$

We have

$$G(-s^2) = \frac{1}{4s^4 + 2s^2 + 1} \tag{7.18}$$

The singularities of $G(-s^2)$ are determined by observing that the denominator polynomial is a quadratic in s^2 and that the poles of $G(-s^2)$ can therefore be expressed by

$$s^2 = \frac{-1 \pm j\sqrt{3}}{4} \tag{7.19}$$

Taking the square root gives the poles as

$$s = \pm 0.3536 \pm j0.6124 \tag{7.20}$$

and therefore $G(-s^2)$ can be written

$$G(-s^2) = F(s)F(-s) = \frac{H^2}{(s + a + jb)(s + a - jb)(s - a + jb)(s - a - jb)} \tag{7.21}$$

where $a = 0.3536$, $b = 0.6124$ and the value of H, by comparison of (7.18) and (7.21), is 0.5. (7.21) can be partitioned, assigning the left-half plane poles to $F(s)$, to give

$$F(s) = \frac{1}{2s^2 + 1.414s + 1} \tag{7.22}$$

It can be readily verified that the above transfer function leads to the magnitude-squared function of (7.17).

The examples given so far have been restricted to second-order transfer functions. For higher orders, the determination of the singularities where the magnitude-squared function is expressed as the ratio of polynomials generally necessitates numerical methods. However, the Butterworth filter will subsequently provide an example of a case where a closed form solution can be obtained for any order.

7.4 Nonminimum phase

If the required transfer function $F(s)$ is not restricted to be minimum phase then ambiguity can arise in the partitioning of $G(-s^2)$ into $F(s)$ and $F(-s)$. In the case of the poles it is, of course, necessary to assign the left-half ones to $F(s)$ to achieve stability. For the zeros, however, either left-half or right-half ones can

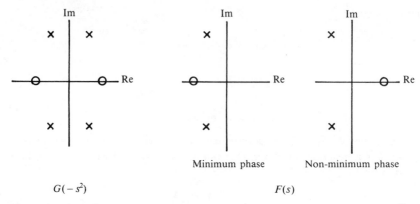

Figure 7.5 *Ambiguity in assigning zeros to* F(s) *from a given* G($-s^2$).

be assigned to $F(s)$, the only restriction being that nonreal zeros be assigned in conjugate pairs. Figure 7.5 illustrates this ambiguity. Further control over the phase characteristic without affecting the magnitude characteristic is possible by assigning an additional set of singularities of any allpass function as described in Section 5.5.2.

7.5 Realizability conditions

The remaining conditions which must be satisfied by a specified magnitude-squared function $G(\omega^2)$ to have a realizable associated transfer function can now be readily determined. The conditions that $G(\omega^2)$ is a rational even function with real coefficients guarantee that the singularities of $G(-s^2)$ form a pattern which is symmetrical about both axes in the s-plane. However, circumstances can still arise where realizable partitioning of $G(-s^2)$ is not possible; for example, if $G(-s^2)$ has a pair of conjugate zeros on the j-axis then these cannot be separated for assignment in equal numbers to $F(s)$ and $F(-s)$. If there is an *even* number of pairs of coincident (multiple) conjugate zeros then no such problem exists. It can be stated therefore that $G(-s^2)$ must have no conjugate singularities of odd multiplicity on the j-axis.

It is useful to consider the significance of the nonrealizable case where $G(-s^2)$ has a pair of zeros on the j-axis. This corresponds to $G(\omega^2)$ being equal to zero for two real distinct values of ω, and implies that the magnitude-squared function becomes negative over a range of real values of ω. Since such a specification would not normally arise, the restriction concerning the multiplicity of the singularities of $G(-s^2)$ on the j-axis does not have any practical significance.

In conclusion therefore, the conditions for a specified magnitude-squared function to be realizable are as follows:

1. It must be an even function in ω.
2. The order of the numerator must be less than or equal to that of the denominator.
3. It must not become negative for any real value of ω.

7.6 All-pole filters

As previously stated, the 'brick wall' lowpass characteristic can never be achieved in practice, and in many applications it is sufficient for the following conditions to be met:

1. In the passband from d.c. to some upper frequency, say ω_1, the gain must approximate a constant with prescribed limits.
2. In the stopband from some frequency, say ω_2, to infinity (with $\omega_2 > \omega_1$), the attenuation must exceed a prescribed value.
3. At high frequencies the magnitude should fall off as rapidly as possible.

It was shown in Section 5.4 that for a transfer function with m zeros and n poles the slope of the semilog magnitude characteristic tends to $-20(n - m)$ dB/decade at high frequencies (i.e. $-20q$ dB/decade where q is the number of zeros at infinity). Therefore in the interest of maximizing the rate of fall-off at high frequencies for a given number of poles, it is desirable to have an all-pole transfer function; that is, one in which all the zeros are at infinity. The introduction of finite zeros, on the real frequency axis beyond the passband, can give a more abrupt transition from the passband to the stopband but at the expense of reduced attenuation at high frequencies.

A number of well-known filter types are based on an all-pole transfer function in the lowpass form and we consider this case first. The general form of the magnitude-squared function is then as follows:

$$G(\omega^2) = \frac{1}{c_0 + c_1\omega^2 + c_2\omega^4 + \ldots + c_n\omega^{2n}} \tag{7.23}$$

7.7 Maximal approximation

The next step in the procedure of filter design is to determine the optimum values of the coefficients in (7.23) to give best approximation to the required characteristic. The general problem of determining the values of a set of coefficients of a function to give best approximation to a specified characteristic is known as the *approximation problem*. We need to minimize the error between the required and the approximating functions over a band of frequencies, and the solution in any particular case depends upon the criterion used to define the 'best' approximation. For example, we could define this as the one which minimizes the maximum deviation between the two characteristics. Alternatively, we could minimize the total squared error between the two and this would yield a different solution. One of the best known criteria, and usually the easiest to apply, is that known as the *maximal* or *Taylor approximation* and this is now described.

Consider a specified function of, say ω, f_1 and an approximating function f_2. Let the error ε be defined as

$$\varepsilon = f_1 - f_2 \tag{7.24}$$

The basis of optimization in the Taylor or maximal sense is that the approximation is concentrated about a particular focus point, say $\omega = \omega_1$, which is chosen to be at or near the most important region of the approximation band. The first condition to be satisfied is that the error is to be zero at the frequency ω_1. Having made the error zero at the focus point, we then require that the error should remain as close as possible to zero over the whole range of the approximation band. The Taylor approximation attempts to achieve this by making the error curve as flat as possible in the region of the focus point. Provided that the error curve has no discontinuities, the condition for the error curve to be flat is that all the derivatives of ε with respect to ω are zero at $\omega = \omega_1$. In practice, we can make only the first p derivatives zero, where p depends upon the order of the approximating function. If these conditions are satisfied, the approximation is said to satisfy the maximal or Taylor criterion.

Thus, at $\omega = \omega_1$ we require

$$\varepsilon = 0 \qquad \frac{d\varepsilon}{d\omega} = 0 \qquad \frac{d^2\varepsilon}{d\omega^2} = 0 \qquad \dots \qquad \frac{d^P\varepsilon}{d\omega^p} = 0 \tag{7.25}$$

The conditions expressed by (7.25) imply that at $\omega = \omega_1$ the two functions f_1 and f_2 are equal and their rth derivatives are equal for all values of r in the range 1 to p. It follows that the functions $1/f_1$ and $1/f_2$ also are equal and their rth derivatives are equal. In other words, the same result can be obtained by defining error as $1/f_1 - 1/f_2$ and making the error maximally flat. This leads to mathematical simplification in some cases.

7.8 Butterworth or maximally flat filter

7.8.1 Magnitude-squared function

The above criterion can be applied to the problem of determining an all-pole lowpass magnitude-squared function by making the magnitude-squared function given by (7.23) approximate a constant in the maximal sense about $\omega = 0$. If we take the required function as unity and define error as $1/f_1 - 1/f_2$ we obtain from (7.24)

$$\varepsilon = 1 - 1/G(\omega^2) = 1 - (c_0 + c_1\omega^2 + c_2\omega^4 + \dots + c_n\omega^{2n}) \tag{7.26}$$

Making $\varepsilon = 0$ at $\omega = 0$ gives

$$c_0 = 1 \tag{7.27}$$

Differentiating (7.26) gives

$$\frac{d\varepsilon}{d\omega} = 2c_1\omega + 4c_2\omega^3 + \dots \qquad (7.28)$$

It is seen that the first derivative is zero at $\omega = 0$, independent of the values of coefficients c.

Differentiating again gives

$$\frac{d^2\varepsilon}{d\omega^2} = 2c_1 + 12c_2\omega^2 + \dots \qquad (7.29)$$

Equating the right-hand side of (7.29) to zero at $\omega = 0$ gives $c_1 = 0$.

Continuing in this way the following may be seen:

1. For p odd, the pth derivative is always zero at $\omega = 0$, independent of the values of c.
2. For p even, the condition for the derivative to be zero is $c_q = 0$ where $q = p/2$.

We continue making the coefficients zero from c_1 up to c_{n-1}. We cannot make the last coefficient c_n equal to zero of course, as this would yield a trivial solution $G(\omega_2) = 1$ which gives a perfectly flat response but with no stopband. The value of c_n determines the position of the high frequency asymptote and hence the cut-off frequency of the filter. It is convenient at this stage to let $c_n = 1$, which makes the corner frequency ω_c at the intersection of the low frequency and high frequency asymptotes equal to unity. This value can be readily changed by means of a procedure known as frequency scaling or frequency transformation which is described subsequently in Chapter 8.

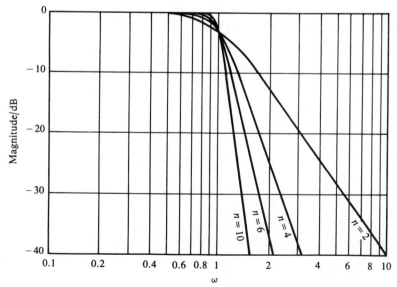

Figure 7.6 *Magnitude characteristics of Butterworth lowpass filters.*

Therefore the conditions for a maximally flat approximation are

$$c_0 = 1 \qquad c_1 = c_2 = \ldots = c_{n-1} = 0 \qquad c_n = 1 \tag{7.30}$$

and (7.23) becomes

$$G(\omega^2) = \frac{1}{1 + \omega^{2n}} \tag{7.31}$$

The family of characteristics for different values of n is shown using logarithmic scales in Fig. 7.6. The characteristics and the magnitude-squared function of (7.31) define the filter known as the Butterworth filter. Since the function is derived by approximating a constant, the filter is known also as maximally flat. The use of the name 'Butterworth' is normally applied to the case of the maximally flat all-pole lowpass filter and its highpass and bandpass equivalents. The term 'maximally flat' is more general and can be applied to other cases such as a filter with zeros on the real frequency axis.

Computer Exercise 7.2

Use Option D2 of ENTIS to verify the characteristics of Fig. 7.6. Observe in particular that the magnitude is 3 dB down at $\omega = 1$ for any order. Observe that the second-order case is identical to that derived by the alternative procedure based on the peaking circle construction in Section 4.7.4.

7.8.2 Butterworth transfer function

We can determine the transfer function of the Butterworth filter using the method described in Section 7.3. This is best done by treating the cases of n even and n odd separately.

n even
From (7.31) we have

$$G(-s^2) = \frac{1}{1 + s^{2n}} \tag{7.32}$$

We next require to determine the poles of $G(-s^2)$ which are the roots of

$$s^{2n} = -1 \tag{7.33}$$

To determine the $2n$ roots of this equation we first observe that the constant, -1, on the right-hand side of (7.33) can be written as $e^{j(2r+1)\pi}$ where r is any integer. (7.33) becomes

$$s^{2n} = e^{j(2r+1)\pi} \tag{7.34}$$

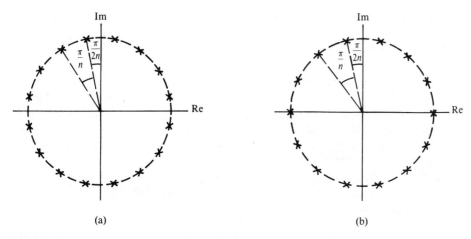

Figure 7.7 *Poles of* G$(-s^2)$ *for Butterworth filter: (a)* n $= 8$, *(b)* n $= 7$.

Therefore

$$s = e^{j(2r+1)\pi/2n} \tag{7.35}$$

The *2n* roots are determined by taking $r = 0, 1, ..., 2n\text{-}1$. All the roots have a magnitude of unity and therefore lie on the unit circle. The angles are $\pi/(2n)$, $3\pi/(2n)$, $5\pi/(2n)$, etc. That is, the poles of $G(-s^2)$ are spaced uniformly round the unit circle with an angular separation of π/n. The poles of the transfer function $F(s)$ are the *n* left-half plane poles and, starting with the pole-pair nearest to the negative real axis, can be written $-e^{\pm j\pi/2n}$, $-e^{\pm j3\pi/2n}$, etc. The pole positions of $G(-s^2)$ are illustrated in Fig. 7.7a for $n = 8$.

n odd
From (7.31) we have

$$G(-s^2) = \frac{1}{1-s^{2n}} \tag{7.36}$$

The poles of $G(-s^2)$ are the roots of

$$s^{2n} = 1 \tag{7.37}$$

In this case we observe that the constant, 1, on the right-hand side of (7.37) can be written $e^{j2r\pi}$ where r is any integer. (7.37) becomes

$$s^{2n} = e^{j2r\pi} \tag{7.38}$$

Therefore

$$s = e^{jr\pi/n} \tag{7.39}$$

As before, the *2n* roots are determined by taking $r = 0, 1, ..., 2n\text{-}1$. Again, all have a magnitude of unity and therefore lie on the unit circle. The angles are $0, \pi/n, 2\pi/n, 3\pi/n$, etc. That is, the poles of $G(-s^2)$ are uniformly spaced with an angular separation of π/n. The poles of $F(s)$, obtained by taking the left-half plane poles of $G(-s^2)$, can be written -1, $-e^{\pm j\pi/n}$, $-e^{\pm j2\pi/n}$, etc. The pole positions are illustrated in Fig. 7.7b for $n = 7$.

In general therefore, for any value of n, the poles of the transfer function lie on the unit circle and are separated by angles of π/n. For n odd, there is a pole on the negative real axis at -1. For n even, all the poles are complex and the two poles with the lowest Q-value are at angles $\pm \pi/(2n)$ to the negative real axis.

We can derive a general formula for the poles, applicable for all values of n, by considering first the pole p_1 in the left-half plane closest to the positive j-axis. For n both odd and even the position vector of this pole is at an angle $\pi/(2n)$ to the j-axis as shown in Fig. 7.7 and hence the coordinates are given by

$$p_1 = -\sin \frac{\pi}{2n} + j \, \cos \frac{\pi}{2n} \tag{7.40}$$

Moving anticlockwise in angular steps of π/n round the unit circle, we can derive a general formula for the position of the rth pole as

$$p_r = -\sin \frac{(2r-1)\pi}{2n} + j \, \cos \frac{(2r-1)\pi}{2n} \tag{7.41}$$

We can determine the expression for the highest Q-value, Q_b, for the Butterworth filter. Recalling from Section 3.3 (3.19) that for a complex pole pair, Q is given by the distance from the origin divided by twice the magnitude of the real part, we have from (7.40)

$$Q_b = \frac{1}{2 \, \sin(\pi/2n)} \tag{7.42}$$

EXAMPLE 7.3

Determine the transfer function of the third-order Butterworth filter.

Solution
For $n = 3$, the angular separation is $\pi/3$ or $60°$. The poles are at -1 and $-\cos \pi/3 \pm j \sin \pi/3$, as shown in Fig. 7.8a. Hence the transfer function $F(s)$ is

$$F(s) = \frac{1}{(s+1)(s+1/2+j\sqrt{3}/2)(s+1/2-j\sqrt{3}/2)}$$

$$= \frac{1}{(s+1)(s^2+s+1)}$$

$$= \frac{1}{s^3 + 2s^2 + 2s + 1} \tag{7.43}$$

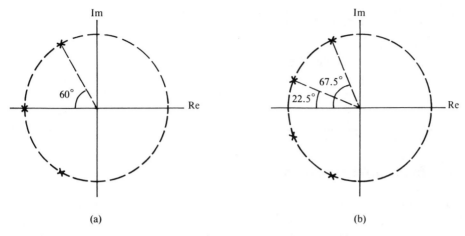

(a)   (b)

Figure 7.8 *Poles of* F(s) *for Butterworth filter: (a)* n = 3, *(b)* n = 4.

EXAMPLE 7.4

Determine the transfer function of the fourth-order Butterworth filter.

Solution

For $n = 4$, the angular separation is $\pi/4$ or $45°$. The poles are at
$-\cos \pi/8 \pm j\sin \pi/8$, and $-\cos 3\pi/8 \pm j\sin 3\pi/8$, as shown in Fig. 7.8b. Hence the transfer function F(s) is

$$F(s) = \frac{1}{(s + 0.9329 \pm j0.3827)(s + 0.3827 \pm j0.9329)}$$

$$= \frac{1}{(s^2 + 1.8478s + 1)(s^2 + 0.7654 + 1)}$$

$$= \frac{1}{s^4 + 2.613s^3 + 3.414s^2 + 2.6131s + 1} \qquad (7.44)$$

Computer Exercise 7.3

Input the pole locations derived above for the third-order case to Option D1 of ENTIS and verify that the magnitude characteristic corresponds to that obtained in Computer Exercise 7.1.

> **Computer Exercise 7.4**
>
> Option E6.1 of ENTIS calculates the poles of the Butterworth filter for any order in the range 2 to 9. Repeat Example 7.4 for higher values of n and verify the results using Option E6.1. For each case, input the pole locations to Option D1 and verify that the magnitude characteristic corresponds to the respective one obtained in Computer Exercise 7.1.

7.9 Equiripple approximation

A limitation of the use of Taylor or maximal approximation is that the resulting error curve is excellent very close to the point of maximal approximation, but becomes progressively worse further away. In engineering, it is common practice to specify a tolerable limit of error that is constant over the approximation band, and in this case it seems likely that a better approximation would be obtained by one in which the error was distributed more evenly over the band. For such a requirement, the optimum criterion would be that which minimized the maximum magnitude of error over the specified range. This is sometimes known as the *minimax criterion* and leads to the concept of approximation in the equiripple or Chebyshev sense. The latter name originates from the mathematician P. L. Chebyshev who originally addressed the problem in an application concerning the design of steam engines.

To understand the significance of the term 'equiripple' we consider first a trial-and-error approach to the problem of minimizing maximum error. Suppose that a first attempt to approximate some specified characteristic over a fixed band using, say, a curve-fitting method yields an error curve which oscillates about the required value of zero as shown in Fig. 7.9a. For such a characteristic, the error is always greatest at either one of the ends of the approximation band or at one of the turning points. We will refer to these points as the critical points and denote the absolute magnitudes of error at the critical points as $E_1, E_2, \ldots$ at frequencies $\omega_1, \omega_2, \ldots$ respectively. For the curve shown in Fig. 7.9a, the error is greatest at the peak which occurs at ω_2. Adjustment of the parameters to reduce this peak will improve the approximation but only as long as the absolute magnitudes at the other critical points all remain less than E_2. When the point is reached at which E_2 is equal to, say, the magnitude E_3 at the trough at ω_3, as shown in Fig. 7.9b, then further improvement is obtained only by simultaneously reducing E_2 and E_3. Suppose that we find a method of adjustment of parameters such that E_2 and E_3 can be simultaneously reduced while remaining equal. Again, improvement is obtained only while the absolute magnitudes at the other critical points remain less than E_2 and E_3. Once the point is reached at which E_2 and E_3 equal, say, the absolute magnitude E_4 of the trough at ω_4, then it is necessary to reduce E_2, E_3 and E_4 simultaneously.

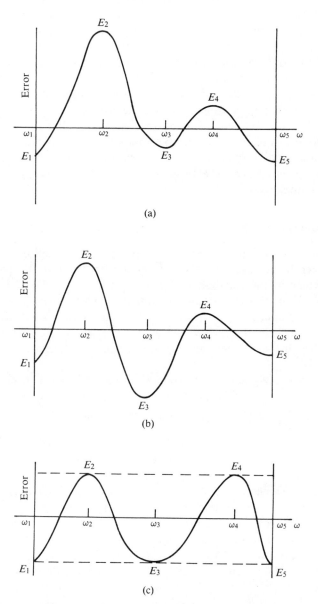

Figure 7.9 *Minimization of maximum error: (a) initial approximation, (b) approximation with* $E_2 = E_3$, *(c) equiripple approximation.*

Continuing in this way we finally reach the point at which the absolute magnitudes at all the critical points have the same value, as shown in Fig. 7.9c. Such a characteristic is known as *equiripple*. It might then be supposed intuitively that no further improvement can then be obtained; that is, minimization of maximum error results in an equiripple characteristic. The conditions for which this is the case have been investigated mathematically by Rhodes (1976). A necessary but insufficient condition is that the number of turning points of the error characteristic should be a maximum consistent with the order of the approximation. It can be shown that for the case of a rational approximation to a flat magnitude characteristic for a filter, the equiripple solution minimizes the maximum error. However, it should be noted that in some cases, for example in approximation to a constant group delay, the equiripple characteristic has no significance in providing a minimax solution.

7.9.1 Chebyshev filter

The equiripple criterion can be applied to the determination of the all-pole lowpass filter to achieve an equiripple characteristic over the passband. The result is known as the Chebyshev filter.

The derivation of the system function of a Chebyshev filter is based on Chebyshev polynomials. The reader is referred to Budak (1974) for a more detailed treatment of the theory of Chebyshev polynomials. We consider here the properties of the polynomials that are relevant to the characteristics of Chebyshev filters.

The Chebyshev polynomial of order n can be determined from the recursion formula

$$C_{n+1}(z) = 2zC_n(z) - C_{n-1}(z)$$

with

$$C_0 = 1 \qquad C_1 = z \tag{7.45}$$

Using (7.45) we can construct Table 7.1 which lists the polynomials in the range $n = 0$ to $n = 8$. The Chebyshev polynomial $C_n(z)$, where z is a real variable, has the property that over the range $-1 \leqslant z \leqslant 1$ the function has an equiripple characteristic between the limits -1 and 1. Figure 7.10 shows the characteristics of $C_n(z)$ versus z for $n = 2$ to $n = 5$.

Consider now the function $[C_n(z)]^2$. It can be readily deduced from Fig. 7.10 that over the range $-1 \leqslant z \leqslant 1$ the function will exhibit equiripple behaviour between the limits 0 and 1, and as $z \to \pm \infty$, $[C_n(z)]^2 \to \infty$. This behaviour is shown in Fig. 7.11 for $n = 5$.

A further relevant property which can be observed from Table 7.1 is that for n even, C_n is even and for n odd, C_n is odd. Therefore, for all n, $[C_n(z)]^2$ is an even function. Hence we can form the following function $G(\omega^2)$, given by (7.46) below, which is a rational even function and is positive for all ω. It is therefore

Table 7.1 *Chebyshev polynomials* $C_n(z)$

n	$C_n(z)$
0	1
1	z
2	$2z^2 - 1$
3	$4z^3 - 3z$
4	$8z^4 - 8z^2 + 1$
5	$16z^5 - 20z^3 + 5z$
6	$32z^6 - 48z^4 + 18z^2 - 1$
7	$64z^7 - 112z^5 + 56z^3 - 7z$
8	$128z^8 - 256z^6 + 160z^4 - 32z^2 + 1$

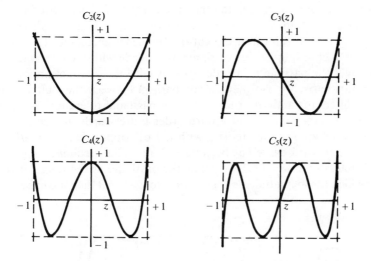

Figure 7.10 *Characteristics of Chebyshev polynomials* $C_n(z)$ *versus z in range* $n = 2$ *to* $n = 5$.

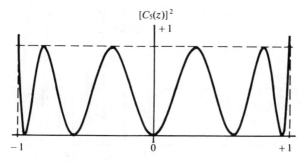

Figure 7.11 *Characteristics of* $[C_5(z)]^2$ *versus z.*

realizable as a magnitude-squared function:

$$G(\omega^2) = \frac{1}{1 + \varepsilon^2 [C_n(\omega)]^2} \qquad (7.46)$$

(7.46) defines the Chebyshev lowpass filter magnitude characteristic with a fixed cut-off frequency. The procedure for obtaining any desired cut-off frequency is described in Chapter 8. It follows from the properties of $C_n(z)$, as discussed above, that the magnitude response of the filter has the following properties: for ω in the range 0 to 1, it has equiripple behaviour between the limits 1 and $1/(1 + \varepsilon^2)$. In the range $\omega = 1$ to $\omega = \infty$, it falls monotonically to zero.

Variation of ε generates a family of characteristics. Fig. 7.12 shows a comparison of two third-order characteristics with ripples of 0.1 dB and 1 dB respectively. If we define the passband as the range over which the characteristic has equiripple behaviour, then, for the magnitude-squared function of (7.46), the cut-off frequency is unity. It can be seen from Fig. 7.12 that as the ripple is increased, the rate of fall-off at the cut-off frequency increases. Thus optimum design involves choosing a value of ripple to coincide with the tolerable limits of deviation over the passband, in order to maximize the attenuation in the stopband. On this basis, we can make a comparison between the Butterworth and Chebyshev filters for a given order and given passband tolerance. For example, Fig. 7.13 shows a comparison of a third-order Butterworth characteristic and a third-order Chebyshev characteristic with a 1 dB ripple. For comparison purposes the Butterworth curve has been moved along the frequency axis to make the curves intersect at $\omega = 1$. If we define the passband as the range of frequencies over which the magnitude does not fall below -1 dB then it can be seen that

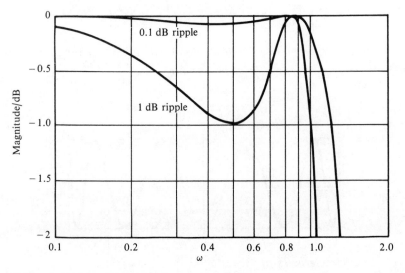

Figure 7.12 *Magnitude characteristics of third-order Chebyshev filters.*

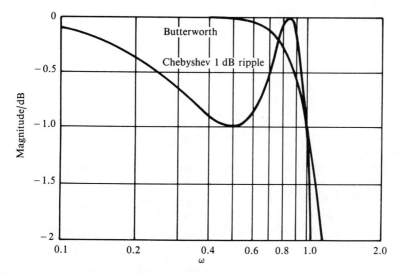

Figure 7.13 *Comparison of Butterworth and Chebyshev third-order lowpass magnitude characteristics.*

the Chebyshev characteristic has a greater rate of fall-off than the Butterworth at the end of the passband.

Computer Exercise 7.5

Use Option E1 of ENTIS to compare the magnitude characteristics of the Butterworth and the denormalized Chebyshev filters for various orders. Observe how the rate of fall-off at the end of the passband of the Chebyshev filter is related to the passband ripple. (Note that the significance of the terms 'normalized' and 'denormalized' with reference to Chebyshev filters is explained below.)

The derivation of a closed-form expression for the transfer function of the Chebyshev filter is somewhat involved. The reader is referred to Van Valkenburg (1960) for the proof, where it is shown that the poles p_r ($r = 1$ to n) can be expressed as follows:

$$p_r = \alpha_r + j\beta_r \tag{7.47}$$

where

$$\alpha_r = -\sin\left[\frac{\pi}{2n}(2r-1)\right]\sinh \eta$$

$$\beta_r = \cos\left[\frac{\pi}{2n}(2r-1)\right]\cosh \eta$$

and

$$\eta = \frac{1}{n} \sinh^{-1} \frac{1}{\varepsilon}$$

From (7.47) it follows that

$$\left(\frac{\alpha_r}{\sinh \eta}\right)^2 + \left(\frac{\beta_r}{\cosh \eta}\right)^2 = 1 \tag{7.48}$$

Hence the poles are on an ellipse whose minor and major axes lie on the real and imaginary axes respectively. The intercepts of the ellipse on the real and imaginary axes are $\pm \sinh \eta$ and $\pm \cosh \eta$ respectively.

It can be shown (Van Valkenburg, 1960) that the magnitude at the frequency $\omega_a = \cosh \eta$ where the ellipse intercepts the positive j-axis is given by

$$F(j\omega_a)| = \frac{1}{(2 + \varepsilon^2)^{1/2}} \tag{7.49}$$

For $\varepsilon^2 \ll 2$ this magnitude approximates to 0.707, i.e. the 3 dB frequency.

A comparison of (7.41) and (7.47) indicates that the poles of the Chebyshev filter can be obtained by multiplying the real and imaginary parts of the poles of the Butterworth by $\sinh \eta$ and $\cosh \eta$ respectively. A more useful comparison, however, can be made if we first modify the cut-off frequency of the Chebyshev. In Section 7.8 a brief reference was made to the procedure known as frequency scaling, which can be used to derive a system function of a filter with any specified cut-off frequency from a prototype with a cut-off frequency of, say, unity. Frequency scaling is covered in detail in Chapter 8 under the more general topic of frequency transformations. For the present it is sufficient to state that if we replace s by s/γ in a prototype system function $F_1(s)$ to obtain the transformed system function $F_2(s) = F_1(s/\gamma)$, then the magnitude of the prototype at any frequency ω_p is the same as the magnitude of the transformed filter at frequency $\gamma\omega_p$. On a logarithmic frequency scale, the magnitude characteristic of the transformed filter has the identical shape to that of the prototype but it is shifted along the frequency axis. The singularities of the transformed filter are obtained by multiplication of each singularity of the prototype by γ.

We can apply frequency scaling to the Chebyshev filter to make the ellipse on which the poles lie intercept the j-axis at $\omega = 1$ by using a scaling factor $\gamma = \mathrm{sech} \, \eta$. We obtain a filter whose 3 dB frequency occurs, for $\varepsilon \ll 1$, at $\omega = 1$ instead of at $\omega = \cosh \eta$. In this form, the filter is referred to as the normalized Chebyshev case. The normalized poles p_r ($r = 1$ to n) can be expressed as follows:

$$p_r' = \alpha_r' + j\beta_r' \tag{7.50}$$

where

$$\alpha_r' = -\sin\left[\frac{\pi}{2n}(2r-1)\right]\tanh\eta$$

$$\beta_r' = \cos\left[\frac{\pi}{2n}(2r-1)\right]$$

From a comparison of (7.41) and (7.50) it is seen that the normalized Chebyshev poles can be obtained from those of the Butterworth by multiplying the real part of the latter by $\tanh\eta$ and leaving the j-part unchanged.

Observing that for $\varepsilon = 0$, $\tanh\eta = 1$ and for $\varepsilon > 0$, $\tanh\eta < 1$, we conclude that the Butterworth filter can be considered as a special case of the normalized Chebyshev with $\varepsilon = 0$. As the ripple ε is increased from zero, the poles move parallel to the real axis towards the j-axis, thereby increasing the Q-values of the poles. This is illustrated in Fig. 7.14 for $n = 5$.

The pole-pair with the highest Q-value is given by taking $r = 1$ in (7.50). Using the result of Section 3.3 (3.19), the highest Q-value, Q_c, is given by

$$Q_c = \frac{1}{2\sin\theta}\left(1 + \frac{\cos^2\theta}{\sinh^2\eta}\right)^{1/2} \tag{7.51}$$

where

$$\theta = \frac{\pi}{2n}$$

From (7.42) and (7.51), Q_c can be written in terms of the highest Q-value, Q_b, for the Butterworth filter as

$$Q_c = Q_b\left(1 + \frac{\cos^2\theta}{\sinh^2\eta}\right)^{1/2} \tag{7.52}$$

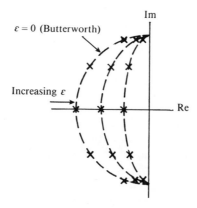

Figure 7.14 *Poles of normalized Chebyshev fifth-order filter.*

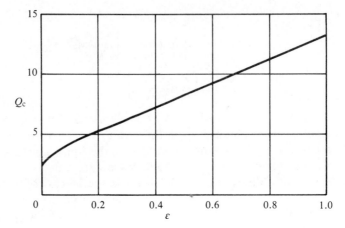

Figure 7.15 *Characteristic of maximum value of* Q_c *versus* ε *for Chebyshev poles (n = 6).*

The associated Q-value for the Chebyshev filter can be very much greater than that of the Butterworth filter, particularly for large ripple factors, and this must be taken into account in the practical design of high-order filters. Figure 7.15 shows the curve of Q_c versus ε for $n = 6$.

Computer Exercise 7.6

Determine the pole location of the denormalized and normalized Chebyshev filters for various orders and ripple factors. Verify the results using Option E6.1 of ENTIS. Use Option D1 to verify the magnitude characteristics.

7.10 Phase characteristics

We now inspect and compare the phase characteristics of the Butterworth and Chebyshev filters. Fig. 7.16 shows the family of phase characteristics for $n = 5$. It is seen that over the passband the Butterworth filter has a more linear characteristic than the Chebyshev filter, and also as the ripple is increased the deviation from the ideal increases. It is thus concluded that the superior magnitude characteristics of the Chebyshev filter are obtained at the expense of a deterioration of phase.

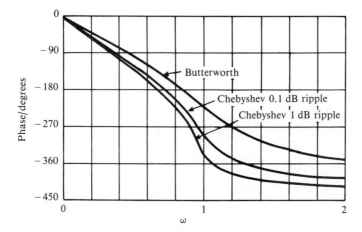

Figure 7.16 *Comparison of phase characteristics of Butterworth and Chebyshev filters (n = 5).*

Computer Exercise 7.7

Use Option E23 of ENTIS to compare the phase characteristics of the Butterworth and Chebyshev filters for various orders. Use Option E3 to investigate the delay characteristics.

7.11 Bessel filters

So far the filters considered have been derived on the basis of optimization of the magnitude characteristic. We next consider briefly a filter that is derived by optimization of the phase response. The criterion adopted is one of making the delay of an all-pole filter maximally flat at $\omega = 0$. The reader is referred to Budak (1974) or Van Valkenburg (1987) for the derivation that leads to a transfer function which, when normalized to make both the delay and the d.c. gain unity, is given by

$$F(s) = \frac{B_n(0)}{B_n(s)} \tag{7.53}$$

where $B_n(s)$ is a Bessel polynomial given by the recurrence relationship

$$B_r(s) = (2r - 1)B_{r-1}(s) + s^2 B_{r-2}(s) \tag{7.54}$$

with

$$B_0(s) = 1$$
$$B_1(s) = s + 1$$

Table 7.2 *Bessel polynomials* B$_n$*(s)*

n	$B_n(s)$
0	1
1	$s + 1$
2	$s^2 + 3s + 3$
3	$s^3 + 6s^2 + 15s + 15$
4	$s^4 + 10s^3 + 45s^2 + 105s + 105$
5	$s^5 + 15s^4 + 105s^3 + 420s^2 + 945s + 945$
6	$s^6 + 21s^5 + 210s^4 + 1260s^3 + 4725s^2 + 10395s + 10395$

Hence we can construct Table 7.2 which lists the coefficients of the Bessel polynomials for $n = 2$ to 6. The filter whose transfer function is defined by (7.53) is known as the Bessel or Thomson filter.

Unlike the Butterworth and Chebyshev filters, there is no simple closed-form expression for the pole locations of the Bessel filter, but these can be determined using numerical methods for factorization of $B_n(s)$. The pole locations are available using Option E6 of ENTIS.

Comparisons between the Butterworth and Bessel sixth-order filters are shown in Figs. 7.17 and 7.18 for the magnitude and phase respectively. Here, the Bessel filter has been scaled to make the angular 3 dB frequency equal to unity. It is seen that the improved phase linearity of the Bessel filter is obtained at the

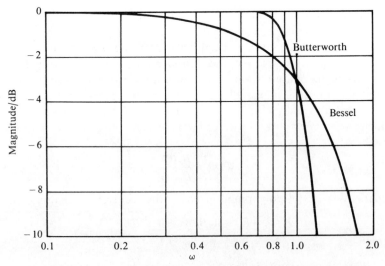

Figure 7.17 *Comparison of Butterworth and Bessel lowpass magnitude characteristics (*n = 6*).*

expense of a more gradual transition from passband to stopband. Figure 7.19 shows a comparison of the *s*-plane diagrams of the third-order Bessel, Butterworth and Chebyshev filters. It is seen that the *Q*-values of the Bessel poles are lower than those of the Butterworth poles.

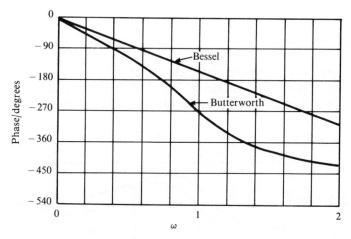

Figure 7.18 *Comparison of phase characteristics of Butterworth and Bessel filters (*n = 6).*

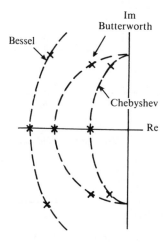

Figure 7.19 *Comparison of* s-*plane diagram of Bessel, Butterworth and Chebyshev filters (*n = 3).*

Computer Exercise 7.8

Use Option E2 of ENTIS to compare the phase characteristics of the Butterworth and Bessel filters for various orders. Use Option E3 to investigate the delay characteristics.

7.12 Step response

A comparison of the step response curves of the Bessel, Butterworth and Chebyshev filters for $n = 4$ is given in Fig. 7.20. The curves demonstrate how improved phase linearity results in a faster rise time and reduced settling time.

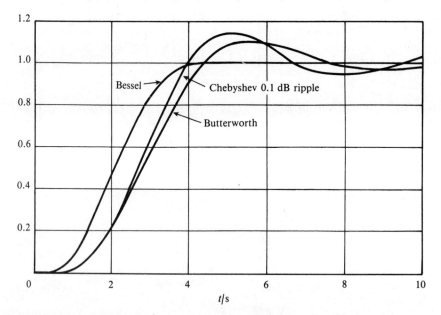

Figure 7.20 *Comparison of step responses of Bessel, Butterworth and Chebyshev filters (n = 4).*

Computer Exercise 7.9

Use Option E4 of ENTIS to compare the step responses of the Bessel, Butterworth and Chebyshev filters.

7.13 Elliptic or Cauer filters

The Bessel, Butterworth and Chebyshev filters all belong to the class for which the lowpass function is based on an all-pole transfer function; that is, the zeros are all at infinity. However, the introduction of finite zeros on the real frequency axis can provide the benefits of a sharper transition from passband to stopband as well as infinite attenuation at certain frequencies. The improvements are generally obtained at the expense of a reduction in attenuation at high frequencies, an increase in the Q-values of the poles, and an increase in circuit complexity.

As in the case of the all-pole filter, the optimization of a filter with finite zeros can be based on various criteria. For example, it is possible to specify the locations of the zeros and then either (a) make the approximation maximally flat at $\omega = 0$ (Budak, 1974) or (b) make the magnitude exhibit equiripple behaviour over the passband (Temes and LaPatra, 1977). However, the best-known type is that in which the singularity locations are chosen to make the magnitude characteristic equiripple in both the passband and the stopband. This type of filter is known as the elliptic filter, or less commonly the Cauer filter. The elliptic filter provides the minimum-order solution for a specified passband ripple, stopband attenuation and distance between passband and stopband. An example of an elliptic magnitude characteristic together with the s-plane diagram is shown in Fig. 7.21.

The derivations of the transfer functions of elliptic filters require rather complex mathematics involving the use of Jacobian elliptic functions; the reader

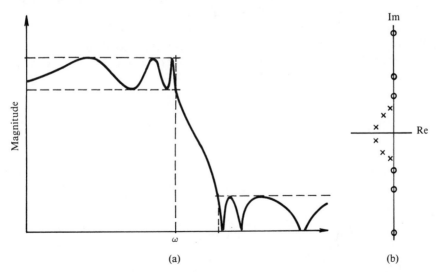

Figure 7.21 *Example of sixth-order elliptic filter: (a) magnitude response, (b) s-plane.*

is referred to Van Valkenburg (1987) for a more detailed treatment of the elliptic filter. Because several parameters are required to define an elliptic filter the documentation requires extensive tables.

7.14 Summary of filter characteristics

We have considered several filter types starting with the best known, namely the Butterworth filter. This has a magnitude characteristic that is maximally flat about $\omega = 0$ and exhibits monotonic behaviour. The 3 dB frequency coincides with the corner frequency of the asymptote approximation for any order.

The Chebyshev family of filters have magnitude characteristics that exhibit equiripple behaviour over the passband. Choice of the appropriate value of ripple provides, for a given passband deviation, a faster rate of fall-off at the end of the passband than that of the Butterworth characteristic. The improvement in magnitude characteristic for the Chebyshev filter, compared with the Butterworth, is obtained at the expense of higher Q-factors for the poles, a less linear phase characteristic and a more oscillatory transient response.

The Bessel filter has a phase characteristic that approximates to a linear one in the maximal sense. Consequently, in comparison with the Butterworth filter, the phase characteristic is more linear, the Q-values of the poles are lower and the transient response is less oscillatory. These improvements are obtained at the expense of a deterioration in the magnitude characteristic.

The above filters belong to the class in which the zeros of the lowpass are all at infinity. The elliptic filter, however, has finite zeros on the real frequency axis and exhibits equiripple behaviour in both the passband and the stopband. This results in a much sharper transition from passband to stopband compared to an all-pole filter. This improvement is obtained at the expense of higher Q-values for the poles, reduced attenuation at high frequencies and a more complex circuit for realization.

8 IMPEDANCE AND FREQUENCY TRANSFORMATIONS

The filter derivations in the previous chapter were applied only to the lowpass cases, and it was stated that other types could be obtained by means of transformations. In this chapter we consider the various transformations that are applicable in filter synthesis, and these can be divided into the categories of impedance and frequency transformations.

An impedance transformation is one in which the impedances of a network are altered in some prescribed way, leaving the transfer function and hence the frequency response unchanged. A frequency transformation can be applied to a network or a theoretical system function, and is one which leads to a new network or system function respectively, whose frequency response is related to the prototype in some prescribed way.

For both impedance and frequency transformations, the simplest forms are those of scaling which can be explained as follows. Suppose a prototype filter is designed on the basis of making a particular impedance, say the input resistance, be equal to one ohm. Suppose also that the frequency at some defined point in the response, for example the cut-off frequency, is taken to be one radian per second. Such a filter is said to be normalized and the user can determine the values for any particular practical requirements of input resistance and cut-off frequency by what will be shown to be a very simple procedure of scaling. The use of a normalized prototype has the advantage of simplification in design and greatly reduces the amount of data required in filter design tables. It can also eliminate the unwieldy factors of 2π and powers of ten that occur in the practical values of L, C and R. It should be noted that a normalized design may involve very large values of capacitance, often of the order of farads, but these will usually be reduced by many orders of magnitude when scaled for practical specified values of impedance level and cut-off frequency.

8.1 Impedance scaling

A voltage or current transfer function is dimensionless and therefore can be written as a function of ratios of impedances. For example, the inverted-L

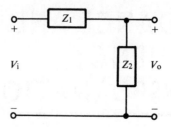

Figure 8.1 *Inverted-L section.*

section of Fig. 8.1 has a voltage transfer function which can be written

$$\frac{V_o}{V_i} = \frac{Z_2}{Z_1 + Z_2} = \frac{1}{1 + Z_2/Z_1} \tag{8.1}$$

It follows therefore that the transfer function is unaltered if each impedance is multiplied by the same factor k. For example, if a normalized filter has an input resistance of $1\,\Omega$ then a filter with the same transfer function but with an input impedance of, say $600\,\Omega$, can be determined by increasing each resistor and inductor value by a factor of 600 and reducing each capacitor value by a factor of 600. In this way the impedance level is scaled by a factor of 600.

EXAMPLE 8.1

Figure 8.2a shows a lowpass filter with a resistor value of $1\,\Omega$. Apply impedance scaling to obtain an equivalent filter with a resistor value of $50\,\Omega$.

SOLUTION

The inductor value becomes 4.50×50 mH $= 225$ mH. The capacitor value becomes $(220/50)$ nF $= 4.4$ nF. Hence the scaled filter is as shown in Fig. 8.2b.

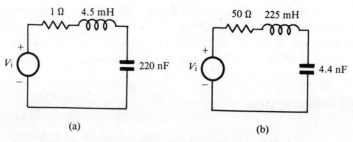

(a)   (b)

Figure 8.2 *Impedance scaling: (a) prototype filter, (b) scaled filter.*

8.2 Further impedance transformations

The procedure of multiplying each impedance by the same factor to leave the transfer function unchanged is theoretically valid even if the multiplier is a function of s, although in practice only a limited number of cases lead to realizable impedances. Examples that are realizable occur when the network is an RL or RC type. For example, consider an RL network and choose the multiplying function to be $1/s$. A resistor R_1 will need to be replaced by a generalized impedance R_1/s which is achieved by means of a capacitor $C = 1/R_1$. An inductor L, which has an impedance Ls, will need to be replaced by an element whose impedance is L; i.e. a resistor $R_2 = L$. In this way an RL network can be transformed into an RC network, and vice versa, without change of transfer function. Impedance scaling can then be applied if necessary to obtain the required impedance level.

EXAMPLE 8.2

Figure 8.3a shows an RL lowpass filter. Apply an impedance transformation to determine an equivalent RC filter in which the resistor value is 500 Ω.

SOLUTION

If we divide each impedance by s, the inductor is transformed to a resistor $R = 2.5 \times 10^{-3}$ Ω. The 100 Ω resistor transforms to an impedance $Z = 100/s$ which is that of a capacitor $C = 1/100$ F. To obtain a resistor value of 500 Ω we apply impedance scaling by multiplying each impedance by $500/(2.5 \times 10^{-3}) = 2 \times 10^5$. This produces a value of 50 nF for the capacitor. Fig. 8.3b shows the transformed filter.

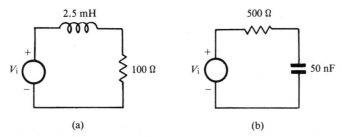

(a)   (b)

Figure 8.3 *Impedance transformation,* LR *to* RC: *(a) prototype* RL *filter, (b) transformed filter.*

8.3 Frequency scaling

Although the procedure for frequency scaling is perhaps fairly obvious, we will use a formal method for its derivation. While this may seem somewhat

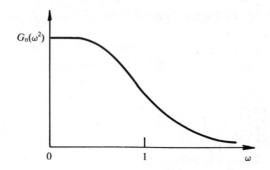

Figure 8.4 *Normalized lowpass magnitude-squared function.*

unnecessary for such a simple relationship, it is useful in forming a basis for other transformations and demonstrates the necessity of ensuring realizability for any proposed transformation.

Suppose we have a normalized magnitude-squared function $G_n(\omega^2)$ with a cut-off frequency of 1 rad/s^{-1} as shown by the characteristic of Fig. 8.4. A linear frequency scale has been used to show the characteristic at $\omega = 0$. Suppose that we wish to derive a corresponding magnitude-squared function $G_s(\omega^2)$ with a different cut-off frequency. The simplest mathematical transformation in which a curve of a function $f(x)$ can be shifted a distance a along the x-axis is by replacing x by $(x - a)$. For the application to frequency scaling, the variable is ω and therefore the shift is accomplished by replacing ω by $X_0(\omega)$ where $X_0(\omega) = (\omega - \omega_a)$ and ω_a is the required change in cut-off frequency. However, such a transformation would lead to an unrealizable magnitude-squared function. The reason for this can be demonstrated by taking a simple example. Suppose we have

$$G_n(\omega^2) = \frac{1}{1 + \omega^2} \tag{8.2}$$

Replacement of ω by $X_0(\omega)$ in (8.2) gives

$$G_s(\omega^2) = \frac{1}{1 - 2\omega_a\omega + \omega^2 + \omega_a^2} \tag{8.3}$$

It is seen that this transformation leads to a magnitude-squared function with an odd part, thus violating the conditions for realizability.

It is also instructive to observe the theoretical characteristic that would be obtained. To do this we need to consider the curve of $G_n(\omega^2)$ for negative as well as positive values of ω as shown in Fig. 8.5. A shift along the ω-axis without change of shape would result in the characteristic shown. It is also clear from the graphical relationship between frequency response and singularities in the s-plane that the above transformation would correspond to a shift of all the singularities by a distance ω_a in a direction parallel to the real frequency axis. This

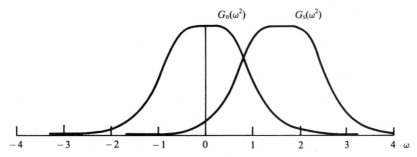

Figure 8.5 *Application of transformation $X_0(\omega)$ to $G_n(\omega^2)$ leading to unrealizable function.*

leads to a pattern which is not symmetrical about the real axis and is therefore not physically realizable.

We can therefore state the problem as follows. We require to determine the simplest function $X_1(\omega)$ which, when substituted for ω in $G_n(\omega^2)$ leads to an even rational function $G_s(\omega^2)$ which, as shown in Fig. 8.6, is of a similar nature to the prototype (in this case lowpass), but with a different cut-off frequency ω_c.

Thus we have

$$G_s(\omega^2) = G_n\{[X_1(\omega)]^2\} \tag{8.4}$$

If $G_s(\omega^2)$ is to be a rational even function then $[X_1(\omega)]^2$ must itself be a rational even function. We determine a set of further conditions that must be satisfied by $X_1(\omega)$ as follows:

1. At $\omega = 0$ the magnitudes of the two functions must be equal. Therefore

$$G_s(0) = G_n(0) \tag{8.5}$$

But from (8.4)

$$G_s(0) = G_n\{[X_1(0)]^2\} \tag{8.6}$$

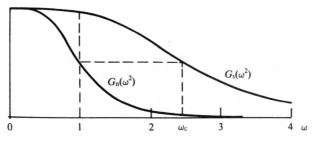

Figure 8.6 *Required characteristic for scaled function $G_s(\omega^2)$.*

Hence from (8.5) and (8.6)

$$X_1(0) = 0 \qquad (8.7)$$

2. At $\omega = \infty$ the magnitudes of the two functions must be equal, i.e.

$$G_s(\infty^2) = G_n(\infty^2) \qquad (8.8)$$

But from (8.4)

$$G_s(\infty) = G_n\{[X_1(\infty)]^2\} \qquad (8.9)$$

Hence from (8.8) and (8.9)

$$X_1(\infty) = \pm \infty \qquad (8.10)$$

3. The magnitudes of the two functions at their respective cut-off frequencies must be equal, i.e.

$$G_s(\omega_c^2) = G_n(1) \qquad (8.11)$$

But from (8.4)

$$G_s(\omega_c^2) = G_n\{[X_1(\omega_c)]^2\} \qquad (8.12)$$

Hence from (8.11) and (8.12)

$$X_1(\omega_c) = \pm 1 \qquad (8.13)$$

To determine the simplest rational function that satisfies the conditions expressed by (8.7), (8.10) and (8.13), consider $X_1(\omega)$ expressed in factored form, i.e. in terms of its singularities and a scale factor. (Note that although, so far, we have referred to singularities only in the s-plane, a rational function in any variable can be expressed in terms of its poles and zeros. Here, the poles and zeros are understood to mean the values of ω for which $X_1(\omega)$ becomes infinity and zero respectively.)

(8.7) and (8.10) state respectively that $X_1(\omega)$ has a zero at the origin, i.e. a factor ω in the numerator, and a pole at infinity. These conditions can be simultaneously satisfied by making $X_1(\omega) = k\omega$ where k is an arbitrary scale factor. (8.13) can be used to determine the scale factor and we obtain

$$X_1(\omega) = \frac{\omega}{\omega_c} \qquad (8.14)$$

It is clear that $X_1(\omega)$ satisfies the condition that the magnitude-squared function will remain an even function after transformation. Thus we have

$$G_s(\omega^2) = G_n\left(\frac{\omega^2}{\omega_c^2}\right) \qquad (8.15)$$

We can examine the exact nature of the transformation by considering the general relationship between corresponding points on the two curves. Let the magnitude of the prototype at frequency ω_n be equal to the magnitude of the transformed function at frequency ω_s. Hence, using (8.15) we have

$$G_n(\omega_n^2) = G_n\left(\frac{\omega_s^2}{\omega_c^2}\right) \tag{8.16}$$

and therefore

$$\frac{\omega_s}{\omega_n} = \omega_c \tag{8.17}$$

(8.17) states that the ratio of the frequencies for any pair of corresponding points on the two characteristics is constant. Therefore on a logarithmic frequency scale, the corresponding frequencies are a fixed distance apart, i.e. the two curves have identical shapes when plotted on a logarithmic frequency scale.

The above transformation is not restricted to a normalized lowpass characteristic and can be applied to any frequency-selective function to obtain a shift along the logarithmic frequency scale without change of shape.

The variable ω/ω_c is known as a normalized frequency variable. By plotting magnitude against normalized frequency, a single curve can be used to display a characteristic independent of cut-off frequency.

8.3.1 Scaling in s-plane

The replacement of ω by ω/ω_c in a frequency response function $F(j\omega)$ leads to the scaled function $F(j\omega/\omega_c)$. The transfer function of the scaled filter is found by replacing $j\omega$ by s and is therefore given by $F(s/\omega_c)$. Hence in the s-plane the scaling corresponds to replacing s by s/ω_c. If $F(s)$ is expressed in factored form, then a factor $(s - s_r)$ becomes $(s/\omega_c - s_r) = (s - \omega_c s_r)/\omega_c$ in the scaled function. Thus a singularity s_r in the prototype function leads to a singularity $\omega_c s_r$ in the scaled filter. Hence the scaled filter in the s-plane corresponds to multiplication of all the singularities by a factor ω_c. For a pair of complex-conjugate singularities, the scaling leaves the Q value unchanged but multiplies the ω_0 value by ω_c.

8.3.2 Scaled Butterworth filter

We can apply scaling to the Butterworth filter from which we obtain the magnitude-squared function as

$$|F(j\omega/\omega_c)|^2 = \frac{1}{1 + (\omega/\omega_c)^{2n}} \tag{8.18}$$

where ω_c is the 3 dB frequency.

Applying the scaling in the s-plane, it is seen that the poles of the scaled Butterworth filter lie on a circle of radius ω_c.

8.3.3 Immittances

It is possible to apply scaling directly to a network without knowledge of the system function. This is achieved by replacing each impedance $Z(s)$ by $Z(s/\omega_c)$.

Thus each inductor L is replaced by an inductor L/ω_c, each capacitor C is replaced by a capacitor C/ω_c and resistors are unchanged. This procedure is illustrated in Fig. 8.7.

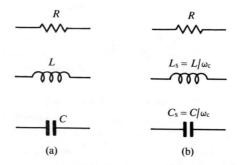

(a)   (b)

Figure 8.7 *Frequency scaling of a network with a normalized angular cut-off frequency: (a) normalized values, (b) scaled values.*

EXAMPLE 8.3

Figure 8.8 shows the circuit of a normalized lowpass filter with source and load resistances of $1\ \Omega$ and a cut-off frequency $1\ \text{rad s}^{-1}$. Scale the filter to determine the components to provide source and load impedances of $600\ \Omega$ and a cut-off frequency of $1\ \text{kHz}$.

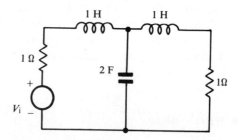

Figure 8.8 *Normalized lowpass filter.*

SOLUTION

Applying impedance scaling we obtain the following intermediate values:

$$R_1 = 600\ \Omega \qquad L_1 = 600\ \text{H} \qquad C_1 = \frac{1}{300}\ \text{F}$$

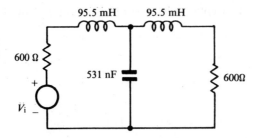

Figure 8.9 *Scaled lowpass filter.*

Applying frequency scaling we obtain the following final values as shown in Fig. 8.9:

$$R_2 = 600 \ \Omega \qquad L_2 = \frac{600}{2\pi \times 10^3} = 95.5 \ \text{mH} \qquad C_2 = \frac{1}{300 \times 2\pi \times 10^3} = 531 \ \text{nF}$$

8.4 Lowpass-to-highpass transformation

We now develop a transformation for the construction of highpass functions and networks from lowpass prototypes. As in the previous transformation we take the magnitude-squared function $G_n(\omega^2)$ as the starting point.

We can state the problem as follows. We require to determine the simplest function $X_2(\omega)$ which, when substituted for ω in $G_n(\omega^2)$, will lead to an even rational highpass function $G_h(\omega^2)$ as shown in Fig. 8.10. It will suffice to consider the case where the frequency at which the curves intersect is unity, i.e. a lowpass filter normalized to a cut-off frequency of unity will transform to a highpass filter normalized to a cut-off frequency of unity. The highpass filter can then subsequently be scaled to yield the required cut-off frequency. Thus we have

$$G_h(\omega^2) = G_n\{ [X_2(\omega)]^2 \} \tag{8.19}$$

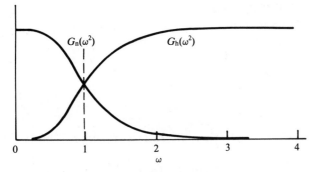

Figure 8.10 *Required characteristic for highpass function $G_h(\omega^2)$.*

We determine a set of conditions that must be satisfied by $X_2(\omega)$ as follows:

1. The magnitude of the highpass at $\omega = \infty$ must be equal to the magnitude of the lowpass at $\omega = 0$, i.e.

$$G_h(\infty) = G_n(0) \tag{8.20}$$

But from (8.19)

$$G_h(\infty) = G_n\{[X_2(\infty)]^2\} \tag{8.21}$$

Hence from (8.20) and (8.21)

$$X_2(\infty) = 0 \tag{8.22}$$

2. The magnitude of the highpass at $\omega = 0$ must be equal to the magnitude of the lowpass at $\omega = \infty$, i.e.

$$G_h(0) = G_n(\infty) \tag{8.23}$$

But from (8.19)

$$G_h(0) = G_n\{[X_2(0)]^2\} \tag{8.24}$$

Hence from (8.23) and (8.24)

$$X_2(0) = \pm\infty \tag{8.25}$$

3. The magnitudes of the highpass and lowpass must be equal at $\omega = 1$, i.e.

$$G_h(1) = G_n(1) \tag{8.26}$$

But from (8.19)

$$G_h(1) = G_n\{[X_2(1)]^2\} \tag{8.27}$$

Hence

$$X_2(1) = \pm 1 \tag{8.28}$$

We next determine the simplest rational function which satisfies the conditions expressed by (8.22), (8.25) and (8.28).

(8.22) and (8.25) state respectively that $X_2(\omega)$ has a zero at infinity and a pole at the origin. These conditions can be simultaneously satisfied by making $X_2(\omega) = k/\omega$ where k is an arbitrary scale factor. (8.28) can be used to determine the scale factor and we obtain

$$X_2(\omega) = \pm\frac{1}{\omega} \tag{8.29}$$

It is seen from (8.29) that $[X_2(\omega)]^2$ is an even function. Thus we have

$$G_h(\omega^2) = G_n\left(\frac{1}{\omega^2}\right) \tag{8.30}$$

We can examine the exact nature of the transformation by considering the general relationship between corresponding points on the two curves. Let the magnitude of the prototype at frequency ω_n be equal to the magnitude of the transformed function at frequency ω_h. Hence, using (8.30) we have

$$G_n(\omega_n^2) = G_n\left(\frac{1}{\omega_h^2}\right) \tag{8.31}$$

and therefore

$$\omega_n\omega_h = 1 \tag{8.32}$$

(8.32) states that on a logarithmic frequency scale ω_n and ω_h are equidistant from $\omega = 1$. For example if $\omega_n = 0.5$ then $\omega_h = 2$ and each frequency is one octave from $\omega = 1$. Therefore $G_h(\omega^2)$ is the reflection of $G_n(\omega^2)$ about $\omega = 1$ on a logarithmic frequency scale.

The above transformation is not restricted to a lowpass characteristic and can be applied to any frequency-selective function to obtain a reflection about $\omega = 1$ on the logarithmic frequency scale without change of shape.

8.4.1 Transformation in *s*-plane

The replacement of ω by $\pm 1/\omega$ in a lowpass frequency response function $F(j\omega)$ leads to the function $F(\pm j/\omega)$. For realizability it is necessary to take the negative sign which leads to the frequency response function $F(1/j\omega)$. The highpass transfer function is found by replacing $j\omega$ by s and is therefore given by $F(1/s)$. Hence in the *s*-plane the transformation corresponds to replacing s by $1/s$.

Consider a lowpass transfer function $F_n(s)$ with a pole p_n. To examine how the denominator factor $(s - p_n)$ transforms we can write

$$F_n(s) = \frac{F(s)}{s - p_n} \tag{8.33}$$

where $F(s)$ contains the factors which express the other singularities.

Applying the above transformation, we obtain the highpass transfer function $F_h(s)$ given by

$$F_h(s) = \frac{F(1/s)}{1/s - p_n}$$

$$= \frac{sF(1/s)}{p_n(1/p_n - s)} \tag{8.34}$$

Therefore, a pole at p_n in the lowpass function gives rise to a pole $p_h = 1/p_n$ and a zero at the origin. In the same way a zero at z_n in the lowpass function gives rise to a zero $z_h = 1/z_n$ and a pole at the origin. Where a lowpass function has n poles and m finite zeros then cancellation of singularities at the origin will produce $(n - m)$ zeros at the origin. Therefore, the number of zeros at the origin

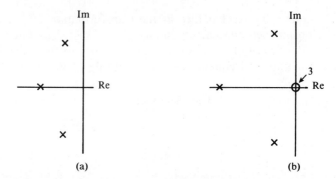

Figure 8.11 *Lowpass-to-highpass transformation in the* s-*plane for a three-pole lowpass filter.*

for the highpass function is equal to the number of zeros at infinity for the lowpass function. Figure 8.11 shows the transformation in the *s*-plane for a three-pole lowpass filter.

If the pole of the lowpass function is written in modulus argument form, i.e.

$$p_n = |p_n| e^{j\theta_1} \tag{8.35}$$

then we have

$$p_h = \frac{1}{|p_n|} e^{-j\theta_1} \tag{8.36}$$

It follows from (8.36) that a pair of complex poles of the lowpass function produces a pair of complex poles in the highpass function which have the same angles and hence the same Q value, i.e. only the magnitude is changed. But for complex poles the magnitude is equal to ω_0. Therefore, denoting $\omega_{0_{lp}}$ and $\omega_{0_{hp}}$ as the values of ω_0 for the lowpass and highpass poles respectively, we have that

$$\omega_{0_{lp}} = \frac{1}{\omega_{0_{hp}}} \tag{8.37}$$

8.4.2 Butterworth highpass singularities

We can now determine the singularities of the Butterworth *n*th order highpass filter with a cut-off frequency ω_c.

We start with the normalized Butterworth lowpass filter with the poles on the unit circle. Let us first apply the normalized lowpass-to-highpass transformation. It can be readily seen from (8.36) with $|p_n| = 1$, that the poles of the normalized highpass filter are identical to the poles of the normalized lowpass filter. In addition, the highpass has *n* zeros at the origin. Applying scaling to derive the transfer function of a highpass filter with a cut-off frequency ω_c, we find that the poles of the scaled Butterworth highpass filter are identical to those of the lowpass filter, equally spaced round a circle of radius ω_c, and the n zeros are all at the origin.

EXAMPLE 8.4

Determine the singularities of the Chebyshev third-order highpass filter with a passband ripple of 1 dB and a cut-off frequency (to 1 dB) of 10 kHz.

SOLUTION

We start with the denormalized third-order lowpass Chebyshev with 1 dB ripple. Using Option E6.1 of ENTIS, we find that the poles are as follows:

Complex pole-pair: $\omega_0 = 0.9971$; $Q = 2.0177$
Real pole at -0.4942

From the above theory and (8.36) and (8.37) the denormalized highpass has three zeros at the origin and poles as follows:

Complex pole-pair: $\omega_0 = 1/0.9971 = 1.0029$; $Q = 2.01777$
Real pole at $-1/0.4942 = -2.0235$

To determine the locations of the complex poles we note that the pole angle $\psi = \cos^{-1} 1/(2Q) = 75.70°$. Therefore the complex pole pair is

$$p_1, p_2 = 1.0029(\cos \psi \pm j \sin \psi) = -0.2485 \pm j0.9716$$

We finally scale the poles by a factor $2\pi \times 10^4$ to obtain the following values:

Complex poles: $(-1.5615 \pm j6.0149) \times 10^4$
Real pole: -1.2714×10^5

Computer Exercise 8.1

Determine the poles of various Chebyshev highpass filters and check the results using Option E6.2 of ENTIS.

8.4.3 Immittances

It is possible to apply the lowpass-to-highpass transformation directly to a network without knowledge of the system function. This is achieved by replacing each impedance $Z(s)$ by $Z(1/s)$. Thus each inductor L_n, which has an impedance $L_n s$ is replaced by an impedance L_n/s which is that of a capacitor $C_h = 1/L_n$. Similarly, a capacitor C_n is replaced by an inductor $L_h = 1/C_n$. Resistors are unchanged. It should be observed that the magnitudes of the impedances of the replacing and replaced components are equal at the frequency $\omega = 1$. Figure 8.12

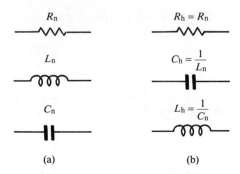

Figure 8.12 *(a) Lowpass to (b) highpass transformation of network elements.*

illustrates how the immittances are transformed by the lowpass-to-highpass transformation.

EXAMPLE 8.5

Transform the circuit of the normalized lowpass filter of Fig. 8.8 to determine the components to provide a highpass filter with source and load impedances of 50 Ω and a cut-off frequency of 20 kHz.

SOLUTION

Applying a lowpass-to-highpass transformation about $\omega = 1$, we replace the inductor L by a capacitor C_1 and the capacitor C by an inductor L_1 as follows:

$$C_1 = 1\text{ F} \qquad L_1 = 0.5\text{ H}$$

By applying frequency scaling to change the cut-off frequency to 20 kHz, the following intermediate values for the inductor and capacitor are obtained:

$$C_2 = \frac{1}{4\pi \times 10^4}\text{ F} \qquad L_2 = \frac{1}{8\pi \times 10^4}\text{ H}$$

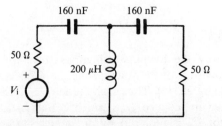

Figure 8.13 *Highpass filter obtained by transformation of lowpass prototype of Fig. 8.8.*

Finally, we apply impedance scaling to obtain the following values as shown in the circuit of Fig. 8.13:

$$R_3 = 50 \ \Omega \qquad C_4 = \frac{1}{50 \times 4\pi \times 10^4} = 160 \ \text{nF} \qquad L = \frac{50}{8\pi \times 10^4} = 200 \ \mu\text{H}$$

8.4.4 *RC* lowpass to *CR* highpass transformation

The direct replacement of capacitors by inductors in the lowpass-to-highpass transformation is usually undesirable in purely *RC* networks, particularly in the case of active *RC* networks that have been designed specifically to exclude inductors. We can derive an *RC* lowpass to *CR* highpass transformation by combining the *RC*-to-*RL* frequency transformation with an *RL*-to-*CR* impedance transformation. That is, as an intermediate theoretical step, we replace each capacitor C_n in the lowpass by an inductor $L_h = 1/C_n$. Each resistor is unchanged. We then impedance transform by theoretically dividing each impedance by s. The notional inductor L_h is replaced by a resistor R_h whose value is equal to L_n, hence $R_h = 1/C_n$. The resistor R_n is replaced by a capacitor $C_h = 1/R_n$. Thus the overall transformation consists of replacing each capacitor C_n with a resistor $R_h = 1/C_n$ and each resistor R_n with a capacitor $C_h = 1/R_n$. This is illustrated in Fig. 8.14. An example of this transformation is given in Chapter 11.

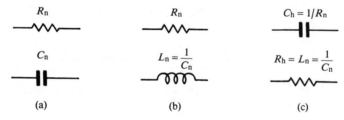

Figure 8.14 RC *lowpass to* CR *highpass transformation.*

8.5 Lowpass-to-bandpass transformation

We now develop a transformation for the construction of bandpass functions and networks from lowpass prototypes. As in the previous transformations, we take the magnitude-squared function $G_n(\omega^2)$ as the starting point.

We can state the problem as follows. We require to determine the simplest function $X_3(\omega)$ which, when substituted for ω in $G_n(\omega^2)$ leads to an even rational bandpass function $G_b(\omega^2)$, i.e.

$$G_b(\omega^2) = G_n\{[X_3(\omega)]^2\} \tag{8.38}$$

A solution to this problem is suggested by consideration of the lowpass magnitude-squared function $G_n(\omega^2)$ on a linear frequency scale, as shown in

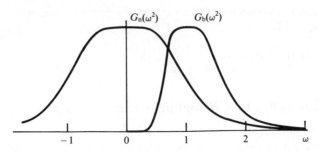

Figure 8.15 *Magnitude-squared characteristics for lowpass to bandpass transformation.*

Fig. 8.15, where it is seen that over negative and positive frequencies the characteristic has the nature of a bandpass characteristic but with a centre frequency at $\omega = 0$. Therefore we require to shift the characteristic to increase the centre frequency as shown by $G_b(\omega^2)$ in Fig. 8.15. We can recall that a shift of this nature was theoretically produced by the transformation $X_0(\omega)$, which was attempted as a means of frequency scaling. However, this was found to be unrealizable and in any case did not produce the required characteristic at low frequencies, as can be seen by comparing $G_s(\omega^2)$ in Fig. 8.5 with $G_b(\omega^2)$ in Fig. 8.15. We will now determine a realizable transformation to produce the required characteristic. It will suffice to assume a normalized centre frequency for the bandpass characteristic since frequency scaling can be subsequently applied.

We determine a set of conditions that must be satisfied by $X_3(\omega)$ as follows:

1. The magnitude of the bandpass at $\omega = 1$ must be equal to the magnitude of the lowpass at $\omega = 0$, i.e.

$$G_b(1) = G_n(0) \tag{8.39}$$

But from (8.38)

$$G_b(1) = G_n\{[X_3(1)]^2\} \tag{8.40}$$

Hence from (8.39) and (8.40)

$$X_3(1) = 0 \tag{8.41}$$

2. The magnitude of the bandpass at $\omega = 0$ must be equal to the magnitude of the lowpass at $\omega = \pm \infty$, i.e.

$$G_b(0) = G_n(\infty) \tag{8.42}$$

But from (8.38)

$$G_b(0) = G_n\{[X_3(0)]^2\} \tag{8.43}$$

Hence from (8.42) and (8.43)

$$X_3(0) = \pm \infty \qquad (8.44)$$

3. The magnitude of the bandpass at $\omega = \infty$ must be equal to the magnitude of the lowpass at $\omega = \infty$, i.e.

$$G_b(\infty) = G_n(\infty) \qquad (8.45)$$

But from (8.38)

$$G_b(\infty) = G_n\{[X_3(\infty)]^2\} \qquad (8.46)$$

Hence from (8.45) and (8.46)

$$X_3(\infty) = \pm \infty \qquad (8.47)$$

We next determine the simplest rational function that satisfies the conditions expressed by (8.41) and (8.44) and (8.47).

The above conditions state respectively that in the ω-plane, $X_3(\omega)$ has a zero at 1, a pole at the origin and a pole at infinity. That is, a numerator factor $(\omega - 1)$, a denominator factor ω, and a further arbitrary finite zero to provide the pole at infinity.

We need also to consider the condition that $[X_3(\omega)]^2$ be an even function. Note that this does not necessarily imply that $X_3(\omega)$ be even; the function $X_2(\omega) = 1/\omega$, for example, is an odd function but satisfies the condition. The condition that $[X_3(\omega)]^2$ be even can be expressed simply: the pole–zero pattern of $X_3(\omega)$ must be symmetrical about the j-axis. For example, a factor $(\omega + \omega_a)$ in, say, the numerator or denominator, must be accompanied by a factor $(\omega - \omega_a)$ in the numerator or denominator respectively.

Therefore to make $[X_3(\omega)]^2$ an even function, the factor $(\omega - 1)$ must be accompanied by a factor $(\omega + 1)$. That is, the arbitrary zero required to produce a pole at infinity must be in the mirror-image position of the other real zero. Thus we have

$$X_3(\omega) = \frac{(\omega - 1)(\omega + 1)}{B\omega}$$

$$= \frac{\omega^2 - 1}{B\omega}$$

$$= \frac{1}{B}\left(\omega - \frac{1}{\omega}\right) \qquad (8.48)$$

where B is an arbitrary multiplier. The constant B has been included in the denominator rather than the numerator in anticipation of the results of the following analysis, which investigates the significance of the multiplying factor.

To examine the exact nature of the transformation, consider the general relationship between corresponding points on the two curves. Let the magnitude of the prototype at frequency ω_n be equal to the magnitude of the transformed function at frequency ω_b, i.e.

$$G_n(\omega_n^2) = G_n\{\,[X_3(\omega_b)]^2\} \tag{8.49}$$

Substituting in (8.49) for $X_3(\omega_b)$ from (8.48), and equating the arguments of the function on either side we obtain

$$\omega_b^2 \pm B\omega_n\omega_b - 1 = 0 \tag{8.50}$$

(8.50) has four solutions for ω_b since the two quadratics obtained by taking the positive and negative signs respectively each have two solutions. These four solutions are illustrated in Fig. 8.16. If we denote the two positive solutions as ω_L and ω_U where $\omega_L < \omega_U$ then

$$\left.\begin{aligned}
\omega_L &= \frac{(B^2\omega_n^2 + 4)^{1/2} - B\omega_n}{2} \\[2mm]
\omega_U &= \frac{(B^2\omega_n^2 + 4)^{1/2} + B\omega_n}{2}
\end{aligned}\right\} \tag{8.51}$$

From (8.51) we find that

$$\omega_L\omega_U = 1 \tag{8.52}$$

and

$$\omega_U - \omega_L = B\omega_n \tag{8.53}$$

(8.52) states that on a logarithmic frequency scale ω_L and ω_U are equidistant from $\omega = 1$. For example, if $\omega_L = 0.5$ then $\omega_U = 2$ and hence each frequency is one octave from $\omega = 1$. Therefore the bandpass characteristic is symmetrical about $\omega = 1$ on a logarithmic frequency scale.

To determine the bandwidth of the bandpass characteristic, we need to know the frequencies to which the lowpass cut-off frequency $\omega = 1$ transforms. We let $\omega_n = 1$. In (8.53) the left-hand side $(\omega_U - \omega_L)$ then represents the bandwidth of

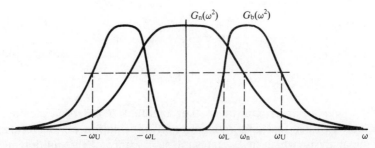

Figure 8.16 *Determination of frequencies on bandpass function which correspond to the frequency ω_n on the lowpass.*

the bandpass filter and is equal to B. Thus the multiplying factor B in the denominator of $X_3(\omega)$ is the bandwidth B of the normalized bandpass filter obtained from the normalized lowpass filter.

Note that the operation of frequency scaling a bandpass filter by a factor, say, ω_m to obtain a centre frequency ω_m scales the bandwidth by ω_m, i.e. the bandwidth B_m of the scaled filter is given by

$$B_m = \omega_m B \qquad (8.54)$$

Thus to ensure the correct bandwidth for the scaled filter we apply the transformation initially to a normalized lowpass and with B given by

$$B = \frac{B_m}{\omega_m} \qquad (8.55)$$

8.5.1 Transformation in s-plane

The replacement of ω by $X_3(\omega)$ in a frequency response function $F(j\omega)$ leads to the function $F(jX_3(\omega))$. We have

$$jX_3(\omega) = \frac{\pm j}{B}\left(\omega - \frac{1}{\omega}\right)$$

$$= \frac{\pm 1}{B}\left(j\omega + \frac{1}{j\omega}\right) \qquad (8.56)$$

For realizability it is necessary to take the positive sign in the right-hand side of (8.56). Hence in the s-plane the transformation corresponds to replacing s by $P_3(s)$ where

$$P_3(s) = \frac{1}{B}\left[s + \frac{1}{s}\right] \qquad (8.57)$$

To examine the relationship between the singularities of the lowpass and bandpass functions, consider a lowpass transfer function $F_n(s)$ with a single pole p_n. To examine how the denominator factor $(s - p_n)$ transforms we express $F_n(s)$ as

$$F_n(s) = \frac{F(s)}{s - p_n} \qquad (8.58)$$

where $F(s)$ contains the factors expressing the other singularities.

Applying the transformation defined by (8.57), we obtain the bandpass transfer function $F_b(s)$ given by

$$F_b(s) = \frac{F'(s)}{P_3(s) - p_n}$$

$$= \frac{sBF'(s)}{s^2 - Bp_n s + 1} \qquad (8.59)$$

where $F'(s) = F(P_3(s))$.

Therefore, a pole at p_n in the lowpass function gives rise to two poles p_{b_1} and p_{b_2} and a zero at the origin. In the same way, a zero in the lowpass function gives rise to two zeros and a pole at the origin. Where a lowpass function has n poles and m finite zeros then cancellation of singularities at the origin will produce $(n - m)$ zeros at the origin for the bandpass function.

To determine the number of zeros at infinity for the bandpass function, we observe that the bandpass function has $(n - m)$ zeros at the origin, a further $2m$ finite zeros and $2n$ poles. Therefore the number of zeros at infinity is

$$\{2n - [2m + (n - m)]\} = (n - m)$$

Therefore, we conclude that each zero at infinity of the lowpass function transforms to a zero at the origin and a zero at infinity in the bandpass function.

From (8.59) it is seen that the bandpass poles are complex if p_n is complex. If p_n is real the bandpass poles are complex only if $|p_n| < 2/B$, i.e. if the bandwidth is sufficiently small. From (8.59), the poles are given by

$$\left. \begin{aligned} p_{b_1} &= \lambda + (\lambda^2 - 1)^{1/2} \\ p_{b_2} &= \lambda - (\lambda^2 - 1)^{1/2} \end{aligned} \right\} \tag{8.60a}$$

where

$$\lambda = Bp_n/2$$

It should be observed from (8.60a) that if p_n is complex then p_{b_1} and p_{b_2} are complex but are not conjugate. However, the lowpass function will have the complex conjugate of p_n which gives rise to another pair of poles that are the conjugates of p_{b_1} and p_{b_2} respectively.

From (8.60a) we have also the following relationship:

$$p_{b_1}p_{b_2} = 1$$

i.e.

$$p_{b_1} = 1/p_{b_2} \tag{8.60b}$$

Let ω_{0_1} and Q_1 denote the Q and ω_0 values respectively for the pole-pair p_{b_1} and its complex conjugate. Let ω_{0_2} and Q_2 denote the Q and ω_0 values respectively for the pole–pair p_{b_2} and its complex conjugate. From (8.60b) we have

$$\left. \begin{aligned} \omega_{0_1} &= \frac{1}{\omega_{0_2}} \\ Q_1 &= Q_2 \end{aligned} \right\} \tag{8.60c}$$

The above relationships are illustrated in Fig. 8.17. The solution of (8.60) to determine the singularities of a bandpass filter with specified cut-off frequency and bandwidth is demonstrated in the following example.

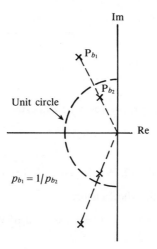

Figure 8.17 *Bandpass poles obtained by transformation of a complex pole-pair of a lowpass function.*

EXAMPLE 8.6

Determine the singularities of a fourth-order Butterworth bandpass filter whose 3 dB frequencies are 2 kHz and 8 kHz respectively.

SOLUTION

The centre angular frequency ω_m is given by

$$\omega_m = 2\pi \times (2 \times 8)^{1/2} \times 10^3 \tag{8.61}$$

and the bandwidth B_m is

$$B_m = 2\pi \times (8 - 2) \times 10^3 \tag{8.62}$$

Hence, from (8.55), (8.61) and (8.62)

$$B = 1.5 \tag{8.63}$$

We start with the prototype second-order normalized lowpass Butterworth filter. From (7.41) or Option E6.1 of ENTIS the poles p_{n_1} and p_{n_2} are given by

$$p_{n_1} = -0.7071 + j0.7071 \tag{8.64}$$

$$p_{n_2} = -0.7071 - j0.7071 \tag{8.65}$$

To determine the normalized bandpass poles from (8.60) we need transform p_{n_1} only, in (8.64). That is, transformation of p_{n_2} is not necessary since it would yield the complex conjugates of the poles obtained from p_{n_1}.

We have that

$$\lambda = Bp_{n_1}/2 = -0.5303 + j0.5303 \tag{8.66}$$

We need to evaluate $\gamma^{1/2}$ where

$$\gamma = \lambda^2 - 1 = -1 - j0.5625 \tag{8.67}$$

We express γ in modulus argument form to evaluate $\gamma^{1/2}$, i.e.

$$\gamma = Ae^{j\phi}$$

where

$$A = (0.5625^2 + 1)^{1/2} = 1.1473$$

and, observing that ϕ is in the third quadrant

$$\phi = \tan^{-1}(0.5625) + \pi = 3.6539 \tag{8.68}$$

We have that

$$\gamma^{1/2} = A^{1/2}e^{j\phi/2} = A^{1/2}(\cos \phi/2 + j \sin \phi/2)$$

$$= -0.2714 + j1.0361 \tag{8.69}$$

Hence from (8.60), (8.66) and (8.69) we have

$$\left. \begin{array}{l} p_{b_1} = -0.8018 + j1.5665 \\ p_{b_2} = -0.2589 - j0.5059 \end{array} \right\} \tag{8.70}$$

Application of the above transformation to the pole p_{n_2} would yield the conjugates of p_{b_1} and p_{b_2}. By introducing the conjugate poles and scaling by a factor ω_m as given by (8.61), we obtain the following pole-pairs:

$$\text{Pole-pair 1: } -2.015 \times 10^4 \pm j3.937 \times 10^4$$

$$\text{Pole-pair 2: } -6.507 \times 10^3 \pm j1.271 \times 10^4$$

8.5.2 Approximate formula for bandpass poles

An approximate formula which eliminates the necessity to solve quadratic equations with complex coefficients is now derived for $B_m \ll \omega_m$, i.e. $B \ll 1$.

We consider (8.60) and observe that $|p_n|$, the magnitude of a pole of the normalized lowpass prototype, is generally not very much greater than unity (for the Butterworth filter $|p_n| = 1$ and for filters such as the Bessel and Chebyshev the poles are not far from the unit circle). Thus for $B \ll 1$, the term λ^2 can be neglected in comparison with 1, and (8.60) can be approximated as

$$\left. \begin{array}{l} p_{b_1} = \dfrac{Bp_n}{2} + j \\ \\ p_{b_2} = \dfrac{Bp_n}{2} - j \end{array} \right\} \tag{8.71}$$

(8.71) states that the approximation for the poles p_{b_1} and p_{b_2} can be obtained by scaling the lowpass poles by a factor $B/2$ and then shifting by $\pm j$. The scaled lowpass poles constitute a bandpass filter with a centre frequency $\omega = 0$ and a bandwidth from the negative to the positive cut-off frequency of B. These poles are then moved to make the normalized centre frequency $\omega = 1$ by the shift $\pm j$. Note the similarity between this and the distribution obtained by the theoretical transformation $X_0(\omega)$, which was examined as a means of scaling but found to be unrealizable. However, the approximate bandpass transformation differs from $X_0(\omega)$, in that the former also introduces the complex conjugate poles in the third quadrant centred about $-j$, thus ensuring realizability, and also introduces $(n - m)$ zeros at the origin to make the slope of the low frequency asymptote equal to that of the high frequency one.

If we now scale the poles p_{b_1} and p_{b_2} of (8.71) by a factor ω_m we obtain the scaled bandpass poles p_{bs_1} and p_{bs_2} as

$$\left. \begin{aligned} p_{bs_1} &= \frac{\omega_m B p_n}{2} + j\omega_m \\[2mm] p_{bs_2} &= \frac{\omega_m B p_n}{2} - j\omega_m \end{aligned} \right\} \tag{8.72}$$

Thus to obtain the scaled bandpass poles using the approximate method, we scale each pole of the normalized lowpass prototype by a factor $B_m/2$ for a bandwidth of B_m and then displace each scaled pole by $\pm j\omega_m$. We then include the zeros at the origin. Figure 8.18 shows the application in the s-plane of the

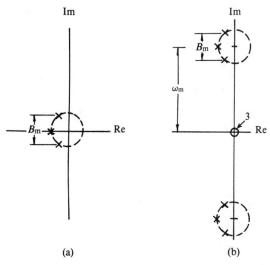

(a)   (b)

Figure 8.18 *Approximate lowpass-to-bandpass transformation in s-plane.*

approximate transformation to an appropriately scaled third-order lowpass filter.

It might appear that the approximate transformation has limited value since the exact locations of the poles can be readily determined using, for example, Option E6.3 of ENTIS. However, the method gives a useful graphical representation in the *s*-plane which can lead to a better understanding of the nature of the transformation.

EXAMPLE 8.7

Determine the singularities of a fourth-order normalized Butterworth bandpass filter with $B = 0.02$ using the approximate formula, and compare the values obtained with those from the exact formula.

SOLUTION

The pole-pair of the lowpass prototype is

$$p_n = -0.7071 \pm j0.7071$$

We scale by $B/2 = 0.01$ and shift by $\pm j$ to obtain the following pole-pairs:

Pole-pair 1: $-7.071 \times 10^{-3} \pm j1.007$

Pole-pair 2: $-7.071 \times 10^{-3} \pm j0.9929$

Using the method of Example 8.6, or from Option E6.3 of ENTIS, we find that the exact locations are

Pole-pair 1: $-7.120 \times 10^{-3} \pm j1.007$

Pole-pair 2: $-7.020 \times 10^{-3} \pm j0.9929$

Computer Exercise 8.2

Use the approximate formula to derive the poles of various bandpass filters and compare the results with the exact values from Option E6.3 of ENTIS.

8.5.3 Immittances

It is possible to apply the lowpass-to-bandpass transformation directly to a network without knowledge of the system function. This is achieved by replacing each impedance $Z(s)$ by $Z(P_3(s))$ or each admittance $Y(s)$ by $Y(P_3(s))$ where

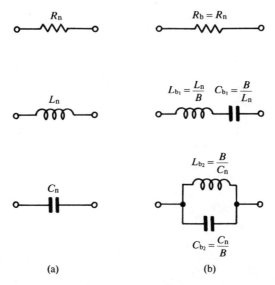

R_n

$R_b = R_n$

L_n

$L_{b_1} = \dfrac{L_n}{B}$ $C_{b_1} = \dfrac{B}{L_n}$

C_n

$L_{b_2} = \dfrac{B}{C_n}$

$C_{b_2} = \dfrac{C_n}{B}$

(a)   (b)

Figure 8.19 *(a) Lowpass to (b) bandpass transformation of network elements.*

$P_3(s)$ is given by (8.57). This procedure is shown in Fig. 8.19. Thus each inductor L_n, which has an impedance $L_n s$, is replaced by an impedance $L_n P_3(s) = L_n s/B + L_n/(Bs)$ which is a series combination of an inductor $L_{b_1} = L_n/B$ and a capacitor $C_{b_1} = B/L_n$. Similarly, a capacitor C_n which has an admittance $C_n s$ is replaced by an admittance $C_n P_3(s) = C_n s/B + C_n/(Bs)$ which is a parallel combination of a capacitor $C_{b_2} = C_n/B$ and an inductor $L_{b_2} = B/C_n$. Resistors are unchanged.

EXAMPLE 8.8

Transform the circuit of Fig. 8.8 to provide a bandpass filter with source and load impedances of 50 Ω, a centre frequency of 20 kHz and a bandwidth of 500 Hz.

SOLUTION

By applying a lowpass-to-bandpass transformation as described above, we obtain the circuit of Fig. 8.20.

We obtain the component values by means of the following steps:

1. Apply the normalized lowpass-to-bandpass transformation with $B = 0.025$.
2. Frequency scale by a factor $\omega_m = 4\pi \times 10^4$.
3. Impedance scale by a factor of 50.

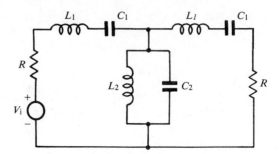

Figure 8.20 *Bandpass filter obtained by transformation of lowpass prototype of Fig. 8.8.*

The values obtained after each step are as follows:

	L_1		C_1		L_2		C_2		R
1	40	H	25	mF	12.5	mH	80	F	1 Ω
2	318.3	μH	199	nF	99	nH	637	μF	1 Ω
3	15.9	mH	3.98	nF	4.97	μH	12.7	μF	50 Ω

8.6 Lowpass-to-bandstop transformation

We now develop a transformation for the construction of bandstop functions and networks from lowpass prototypes. This can be achieved by appropriate combination of the transformations previously derived.

Consider a highpass magnitude-squared function plotted on a linear frequency scale as shown in Fig. 8.21. It can be seen that the characteristic can be regarded

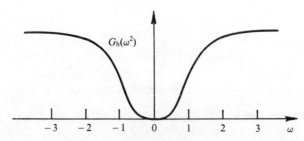

Figure 8.21 *Highpass magnitude-squared characteristic on a linear frequency scale.*

as a bandstop characteristic with centre frequency $\omega = 0$. If we transform the characteristic to move the centre frequency to $\omega = 1$, we obtain a bandstop response. Thus the transformation $X_3(\omega)$, which was derived to construct a bandpass function from a lowpass function, can be applied to a highpass characteristic to construct a bandstop characteristic.

If we start with a normalized prototype lowpass function, we can successfully apply the transformations $X_2(\omega)$ and $X_3(\omega)$ to obtain a bandstop. These procedures can be combined into a single lowpass-to-bandstop transformation $X_4(\omega)$. If we first replace ω by $1/\omega$ to obtain a normalized highpass function and then replace ω by $H(\omega - 1/\omega)$, this is equivalent to replacing ω by $X_4(\omega)$ where

$$X_4(\omega) = \frac{B\omega}{\omega^2 - 1} \qquad (8.73)$$

It follows from the previously derived properties of the transformation $X_3(\omega)$ that the bandstop characteristic is symmetrical about $\omega = 1$ on a logarithmic frequency scale, and the width of the stopband is B.

8.6.1 Transformation in s-plane

In the s-plane, the lowpass-to-highpass function $1/s$ can be combined with the lowpass-to-bandpass transformation $P_3(s)$, resulting in the lowpass-to-bandstop function $P_4(s)$, given by

$$P_4(s) = \frac{Bs}{s^2 + 1} \qquad (8.74)$$

To examine the singularities of the bandstop function, consider a highpass transfer function $F_h(s)$ with a single pole and a zero at the origin and given by

$$F_h(s) = \frac{s}{s - p_h} \qquad (8.75)$$

By applying the transformation $P_3(s)$ defined by (8.57), we obtain the bandstop transfer function $F_{bs}(s)$ given by

$$F_{bs}(s) = \frac{P_3(s)}{P_3(s) - p_h}$$

$$= \frac{s^2 + 1}{s^2 - Bp_h s + 1} \qquad (8.76)$$

Therefore, a pole at p_h in the highpass function gives rise to two poles p_{bs_1} and p_{bs_2}, and the zero at the origin gives two conjugate zeros on the real frequency axis at $\pm j$. Factorization of the quadratic denominator of the right-hand side of (8.76), which in general will have complex coefficients, yields the locations of the poles of the bandstop function.

EXAMPLE 8.9

Determine the singularities of a fourth-order bandstop filter with the following specification: equiripple passband; passband ripple, 1 dB; centre frequency, 50 kHz; stopband width to − 1 dB, 5 kHz.

SOLUTION

We use the second-order Chebyshev filter with a 1 dB passband ripple as prototype. From Option E6.1 of ENTIS, we obtain the following values of Q and ω_0 for the lowpass prototype with a normalized − 1 dB angular frequency: $Q = 0.9565$; $\omega_{0_{lp}} = 1.0500$.

We proceed as in Example 8.4, applying a lowpass-to-highpass transformation, and we obtain two zeros at the origin and the following pole-pair:

$$p_1, \ p_2 = 0.4978 \pm j0.8119$$

We next apply the transformation $P_3(s)$ and obtain two pairs of zeros at $\pm j$ and, using the method of Example 8.6 with $B = 0.1$, we obtain the following pole-pairs:

$$p_1, \ p_2 = -0.0239 \pm j0.9599$$

$$p_3, \ p_4 = -0.0259 \pm j1.0411$$

Finally, we scale the singularities by a factor $2\pi \times 50 \times 10^3$ to obtain the following:

$$\text{2 pairs of zeros at } \pm j3.1416E5$$

pole-pairs:

$$p_1, \ p_2 = -7.503E3 \pm j3.016E5$$

$$p_3, \ p_4 = -8.137E3 \pm j3.271E5$$

8.6.2 Approximate transformation

For the case where the width of the stopband is very much less than the centre frequency, the normalized bandstop singularities can be obtained by application of the approximate transformation. That is, the highpass singularities are scaled by a factor $B/2$. The singularities are then shifted by $\pm j$. Scaling can then be applied to obtain the required centre frequency. Note that B is the ratio of the width of the stopband to the stopband centre frequency.

Alternatively, we can scale the highpass singularities by a factor $B_m/2$, where B_m is the required stopband width, and then shift by $\pm j\omega_m$ where ω_m is the required centre frequency of the stopband.

Figure 8.22 shows how the singularities of a bandstop filter are obtained by means of the approximate transformation.

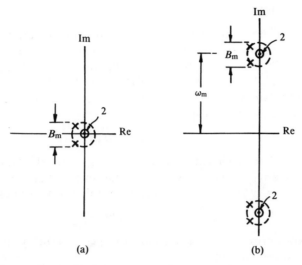

Figure 8.22 *Approximate highpass-to-bandstop transformation in* s-*plane.*

EXAMPLE 8.10

Apply the approximate transformation to Example 8.9.

SOLUTION

We first scale the highpass poles by a factor $B/2 = 0.05$ and obtain the following pole-pair:

$$p_1, p_2 = -0.02489 \pm j0.04060$$

We next shift by $\pm j$ and scale by $2\pi \times 50 \times 10^3$ and obtain the following pole-pairs:

$$p_1, p_2 = -7.819E3 \pm j3.014E5$$

$$p_3, p_4 = -7.819E3 \pm j3.269E5$$

The zeros are as determined in Example 8.9.

Computer Exercise 8.3

Determine the singularities of various bandstop filters and check the results using Option E6.4 of ENTIS.

8.6.3 Immittances

It is possible to apply the lowpass-to-bandstop transformation directly to a network without knowledge of the system function. This is achieved by replacing each impedance $Z(s)$ by $Z(P_4(s))$ or each admittance $Y(s)$ by $Y(P_4(s))$ where $P_4(s)$ is given by (8.74). This procedure is shown in Fig. 8.23. Thus each inductor L_n, which has an impedance $L_n s$, is replaced by an impedance $L_n P_4(s)$. In admittance form this can be expressed as

$$Y = s/(BL_n) + 1/(BL_n s)$$

which is a parallel arrangement of a capacitor $C_{bs_1} = 1/(BL_n)$ and an inductor $L_{bs_1} = BL_n$. Similarly, a capacitor C_n, which has an admittance $C_n s$, is replaced by an admittance $C_n P_4(s)$. In impedance form this can be expressed as

$$Z = s/(BC_n) + 1/(BC_n s)$$

which is a series arrangement of an inductor $L_{bs_2} = 1/(BC_n)$ and a capacitor $C_{bs_2} = BC_n$. Resistors are unchanged.

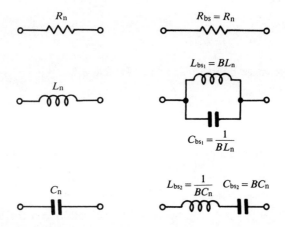

Figure 8.23 *Lowpass-to-bandstop transformation of network elements.*

EXAMPLE 8.11

Transform the circuit of Fig. 8.8 to determine the components to provide a bandstop filter with source and load impedances of 50 Ω, a centre frequency of 20 kHz and a stopband width of 500 Hz.

SOLUTION

By applying a lowpass to bandstop transformation as described above, we obtain the circuit of Fig. 8.24.

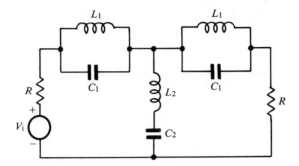

Figure 8.24 *Bandstop filter obtained by transformation of lowpass prototype of Fig. 8.8.*

We obtain the component values by means of the following steps:

1. Apply the normalized lowpass-to-bandstop transformation with $B = 0.025$.
2. Frequency scale by a factor $4\pi \times 10^4$.
3. Impedance scale by a factor of 50.

The values obtained after each step are as follows:

	L_1		C_1		L_2		C_2		R	
1	25	mH	40	F	20	H	50	mF	1	Ω
2	198.9	nH	318.3	μF	159.1	μH	397.9	nF	1	Ω
3	9.947	μH	6.367	μF	7.958	mH	19.89	μF	50	Ω

9 SYNTHESIS OF PASSIVE NETWORKS

9.1 Introduction

The theory on synthesis so far has been concerned with the determination of a system function to provide a specified response. The next step in the synthesis procedure is that of determining the physical network. As discussed earlier, the network may either consist of purely passive elements or contain active devices. We first consider the problem of determining a passive network to provide a specified system function. It must be emphasized that the general topic of passive network synthesis is a very extensive one, and only an introduction and a brief treatment of selected aspects will be given. The reader is referred elsewhere for more detailed treatments. In particular, we develop techniques which lead to the realization of the types of filter which, in the lowpass form, have all zeros at infinity.

9.2 Ladder networks

The synthesis procedures to be described are based on the unbalanced ladder network shown in Fig. 9.1. This network is widely used in filter applications and has many desirable properties. These include the following:

1. The input and output have a common terminal.
2. The zeros can be determined by inspection.
3. Analysis is relatively straightforward.
4. Direct synthesis methods are available for a wide range of practical cases.

These properties will be considered further in the following sections.

9.2.1 Analysis

We consider first an analysis technique for ladder networks. General matrix techniques based on, for example, loop or nodal analysis, can be applied. However, these methods are usually inefficient, particularly when used in computer-aided analysis, since they do not take advantage of the specific topology of the circuit.

162

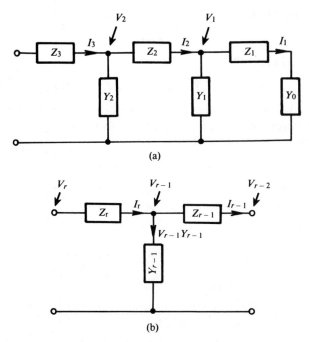

Figure 9.1 *Ladder network analysis: (a) general arrangement, (b) recurrence relationship.*

A simple, efficient method of determining the system function of a ladder is one in which analysis is started at the output port and, by successive application of Ohm's law and summations of voltages and currents, it is possible to work back to the input port to obtain the relationship between input and output.

To illustrate this technique we consider the case of determining the voltage transfer function. We assume that the first element is a series element, since a shunt element across the input voltage source would change only the input impedance, but would not affect the voltage transfer function. For convenience we write each series element in impedance form and each shunt element in admittance form as shown in Fig. 9.1a.

Denoting the voltage across admittance Y_r as V_r, and the current through Z_r as I_r, as shown, we have, from Fig. 9.1b, the following recurrence relationships:

$$I_r = I_{r-1} + V_{r-1}Y_{r-1} \tag{9.1a}$$

and

$$V_r = V_{r-1} + Z_rI_r \tag{9.1b}$$

We start by writing

$$I_1 = V_0Y_0 \tag{9.2}$$

From (9.1b) and (9.2)

$$V_1 = V_0(1 + Z_1 Y_0) \qquad (9.3)$$

From (9.1a), (9.2) and (9.3)

$$I_2 = I_1 + V_1 Y_1 = V_0 Y_0 + V_0 Y_1 (1 + Z_1 Y_0) \qquad (9.4)$$

Continuing in this way, we can evaluate expressions for V_2, I_3, V_3, I_4, etc., until we obtain an expression for the input voltage in terms of output voltage. This will be demonstrated in the following example.

EXAMPLE 9.1

Determine the transfer function of the normalized lowpass filter of Fig. 9.2.

SOLUTION

We have

$$I_1 = V_0$$
$$V_1 = V_0(1 + s)$$
$$I_2 = V_0(1 + 2s + 2s^2)$$
$$V_2 = V_0[1 + s + (1 + s)(1 + 2s + 2s^2)]$$
$$= V_0(2 + 4s + 4s^2 + 2s^3)$$

Hence

$$\frac{V_0}{V_2} = \frac{1}{2(1 + 2s + 2s^2 + s^3)} \qquad (9.5)$$

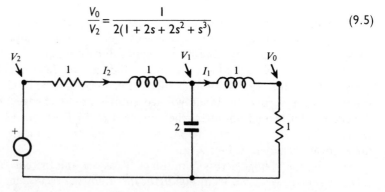

Figure 9.2 *Normalized lowpass filter.*

9.2.2 Transmission zeros

The determination of the system poles requires the determination of the system function followed by factorization of the denominator polynomial. The zeros, however, including those at infinity, can be determined directly, simply by inspection of the circuit elements. Hence, the order or number of poles, which equals the total number of zeros, can be determined by inspection. The zeros occur for each value of s for which a series element has infinite impedance, and for each value of s for which a shunt impedance becomes zero. Thus the zeros of the transfer function of Fig. 9.1 are the poles of $Z_1, Z_2, \ldots$ and the poles of $Y_0, Y_1, \ldots$.

A zero at the origin is caused by a capacitor which is a series element or an inductor which is a shunt element. A zero at infinity is caused by an inductor which is a series element or a capacitor which is a shunt element. Inspection of the circuit of Fig. 9.2 confirms that there are three zeros at infinity and hence the circuit has three poles.

Other examples of series element immittances that introduce zeros are as follows:

A parallel LC combination, which has a resonant frequency $\omega = 1/\sqrt(LC)$, introduces zeros on the real frequency axis at $\pm j/\sqrt(LC)$.

A parallel RC combination introduces a zero at $-1/(RC)$.

Examples of shunt element immittances that introduce zeros are as follows:

A series LC combination, which has a resonant frequency $\omega = 1/\sqrt(LC)$, introduces zeros on the real frequency axis at $\pm j/\sqrt(LC)$.

A series RC combination introduces a zero at $-1/(RC)$.

EXAMPLE 9.2

Determine by inspection the locations of the zeros and the order of the transfer function of the network of Fig. 9.3.

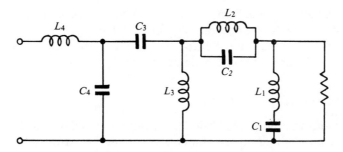

Figure 9.3 *Eighth-order ladder network of Example 9.2.*

SOLUTION

The elements L_4 and C_4 each introduce a zero at infinity. The elements C_3 and L_3 each introduce a zero at the origin. The shunt combination L_2 and C_2 in the series arm introduces zeros at $\pm j/\sqrt{(L_2 C_2)}$. The series combination L_1 and C_1 in the shunt arm introduces zeros at $\pm j/\sqrt{(L_1 C_1)}$. Hence there are eight zeros and consequently eight poles.

A situation can arise where a zero shunt impedance does not produce a transmission zero. For example, in the ladder network of Fig. 9.4 the inductor L_2 does not introduce a zero at the origin. This is because at $\omega = 0$ the two impedances L_1 and L_2 which form a potential divider are both zero. Similarly, there are cases where an infinite series impedance does not introduce a zero because the impedance to the right is infinite, and therefore the signal is subjected to a potential divider formed by two infinite impedances. These, however, are special cases, and the absence of the zero can be regarded as the result of pole–zero cancellation.

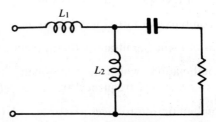

Figure 9.4 *Example where a shunt inductor does not produce a zero at the origin.*

9.3 Synthesis of driving-point immittances

Although the ultimate aim here is to synthesize a network with a specified transfer function, it will be shown that this can be reduced to the problem of determining a network with a specified driving-point immittance. We therefore consider first the problem of driving-point immittance synthesis.

9.3.1 Realizability conditions

The conditions that must be satisfied by a rational function which is realizable as the driving-point immittance of a passive network are stronger than those for a transfer function, and can be expressed in the form known as the positive real conditions.

A function $F(s)$ is positive real if it satisfies the following conditions:

1. $F(s)$ is real for all real values of s.
2. The real part of $F(s)$ is greater than or equal to zero when the real part of s is greater than or equal to zero.

It is readily seen that condition 1 must be satisfied by any function that is obtained by the arithmetic operations of addition, subtraction, multiplication and division on the basic impedance functions R, Ls and $1/Cs$. Van Valkenburg (1960) gives a proof of condition 2, based on the property that the power absorbed by a passive network cannot be negative. It is clear also from the above definition that if $F(s)$ is positive real then $1/F(s)$ is positive real.

It can be shown that a positive real function has the following properties:

1. There are no singularities in the right-half plane.
2. There can be no more than one singularity at the origin and no more than one singularity at infinity.
3. Any singularities on the real frequency axis must be simple.

The general problem of synthesis of a passive network to provide any specified driving-point immittance which satisfies the positive real conditions is a complex one. Some simplification of the problem is obtained from the theorem of S. Darlington (1939) which states that a solution always exists using a network that consists of only reactive elements and terminates with a single resistor. The original theorem was based on a realization which included mutual inductance for the general cases, although it was later shown that a solution always exists without mutual inductance. The exclusion of mutual inductance may necessitate an increase in the number of elements.

One approach to the problem of determining a network from a specified driving-point immittance function which satisfies the above conditions is based on a partial fraction expansion of the function, and leads to combinations of parallel and series elements. These forms are known as *Foster realizations.*

An alternative approach is based on a different form of expansion and leads to a ladder network. These forms are known as *Cauer realizations.* Here, only the Cauer method is described. Budak (1974) gives a description of the Foster form of synthesis.

Because of the specific topology of a ladder network with alternating series and shunt branches, the driving-point immittances can be expressed in a particular form. Referring to the ladder network shown in Fig. 9.5, it is seen that the input impedance is given by Z_1 in series with the impedance to the right of Z_1.

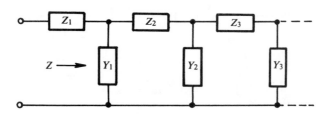

Figure 9.5 *Input impedance of ladder network which starts with a series element.*

The latter is equal to the inverse of the admittance to the right of Z_1 and this admittance is given by Y_1 in parallel with the admittance to the right of Y_1. Similarly, the admittance to the right of Y_1 is equal to the inverse of the impedance to the right of Y_1 and this impedance is equal to Z_2 in series with the impedance to the right of Z_2. Continuing in this way it is seen that the input impedance of the ladder is given by

$$Z = Z_1 + \cfrac{1}{Y_1 + \cfrac{1}{Z_2 + \cfrac{1}{Y_2 + \dots}}} \tag{9.6}$$

For a ladder network which starts with a shunt element as shown in Fig. 9.6 the driving-point immittance can be expressed as an admittance Y given by

$$Y = Y_1 + \cfrac{1}{Z_1 + \cfrac{1}{Y_2 + \cfrac{1}{Z_2 + \dots}}} \tag{9.7}$$

The right-hand sides of (9.6) and (9.7) are both in a form known as a continued fraction.

Any rational function can be expressed as a continued fraction expansion by successive division and inversion. For example, consider the function $F(s)$ given by

$$F(s) = \frac{s^3 + s^2 + 2s + 1}{s^2 + s + 1} \tag{9.8}$$

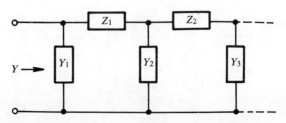

Figure 9.6 *Input admittance of a ladder network which starts with a shunt element.*

If we divide the numerator by the denominator starting with the highest power we obtain

$$F(s) = s + \frac{s+1}{s^2+s+1} \qquad (9.9)$$

Inverting the fraction we have

$$F(s) = s + \frac{1}{\dfrac{s^2+s+1}{s+1}} \qquad (9.10)$$

Dividing again we obtain

$$F(s) = s + \cfrac{1}{s + \cfrac{1}{s+1}} \qquad (9.11)$$

Thus, to synthesize a ladder network to provide a specified driving-point immittance function, we first expand the function as either an impedance or an admittance in continued fraction form and then identify the terms that correspond to circuit elements. For example, to synthesize the impedance $Z = F(s)$ where $F(s)$ is given by (9.8), we refer to the continued fraction expansion of (9.11) and obtain the ladder network of Fig. 9.7.

Clearly, for an expansion to correspond to a realizable ladder network, all the coefficients of the expansion must be positive. A necessary condition for this is that the specified function must be positive real. However, this condition is insufficient, since not all immittance functions can be realized by means of the ladder network structure.

A given rational function does not have a unique continued fraction expansion, since each division can be carried out starting with the lowest or highest powers of s. That is, the numerator and denominator polynomials can be arranged in ascending or descending powers of s. Where each division is started with the highest powers, the procedure is known as the *Cauer I method*. Where each division is started with the lowest powers, the procedure is known as the *Cauer II method*. Mixed forms of methods I and II are possible as well as mixed forms of Foster and Cauer. Here only the pure forms of Cauer I and II are

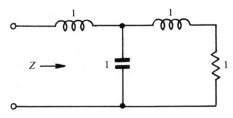

Figure 9.7 *Realization of input impedance of (9.8).*

described. All methods are applicable to an immittance expressed either as an impedance or as an admittance. However, not all the expansions lead to a realizable ladder structure. This is considered further in the following section.

9.3.2 *LC* driving-point immittances

As previously stated, the problem of synthesis of a network to realize a specified transfer function can be reduced to that of synthesis of a given driving-point immittance. As will be shown, in many cases the required immittance is realizable using only *LC* elements. We therefore next consider the problem of synthesis of *LC* driving-point immittances.

We first examine the conditions that must be satisfied by a rational function in order to be realizable as an *LC* driving-point immittance.

Figure 9.8 shows three simple arrangements of *LC* immittances and the corresponding *s*-plane diagrams. It is seen that in each case the singularities are on the real frequency axis. Moreover, the poles and zeros are simple and alternate. It can be shown that all *LC* immittances satisfy these conditions. That the poles and zeros alternate implies that there is always a singularity at the origin and a singularity at infinity. Each conjugate pair of singularities introduces a factor which can be expressed in the form $(s^2 + a^2)$, where a is a real constant. Since there is also a singularity at the origin, it follows that a driving-point *LC* immittance is always an odd function.

To demonstrate the Cauer method for synthesis of *LC* immittances, we first apply the technique to some particular examples. Consider the impedance function $Z(s)$ given by

$$Z(s) = \frac{s(s^2 + 2)}{(s^2 + 1)(s^2 + 3)}$$

$$= \frac{s^3 + 2s}{s^4 + 4s^2 + 3} \tag{9.12}$$

It is seen from the factored form that $Z(s)$ satisfies the condition to be realizable as an *LC* impedance. However, if we form a continued fraction by starting the division with the highest powers of s we obtain

$$Z(s) = \frac{1}{s} - \frac{2s + 3/s}{s^4 + 4s^2 + 3} \tag{9.13}$$

The negative sign indicates that this does not correspond to a realizable ladder network. An explanation for this can be obtained by examining the behaviour of $Z(s)$ at zero frequency, i.e. from (9.12) we have $Z(0) = 0$. However, the expansion of (9.13) indicates that the ladder starts with a series capacitor and this would give $Z(0) = \infty$.

Consider next the expansion of $Z(s)$ obtained by starting the division with the lowest powers of *s*. We can write

$$Z(s) = \frac{2s + s^3}{3 + 4s^2 + s^4}$$

$$= \frac{2s}{3} - \frac{5s^3/3 + 2s^5/3}{3 + 4s^2 + s^4} \tag{9.14}$$

Again, the negative sign indicates that this does not correspond to a realizable ladder network. An explanation for this can be obtained by examining the

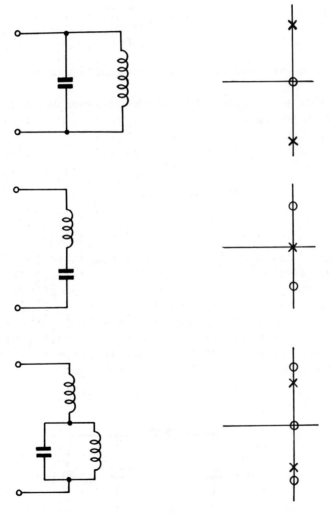

Figure 9.8 *Input impedances of* LC *networks and the corresponding* s-*plane diagrams.*

behaviour of $Z(s)$ at infinite frequency, i.e. from (9.12) we have $Z(\infty) = 0$. However, the expansion of (9.14) indicates that the ladder starts with a series inductor and this would give $Z(\infty) = \infty$.

Next consider the expansion of the immittance function of (9.12) expressed in admittance form. If we perform a continued fraction starting each division with the highest powers of s we have

$$Y(s) = \frac{s^4 + 4s^2 + 3}{s^3 + 2s}$$

$$= s + \cfrac{1}{s/2 + \cfrac{1}{4s + \cfrac{6}{s}}} \tag{9.15}$$

This corresponds to a realizable ladder which starts with a shunt capacitor as shown in Fig. 9.9.

Now consider the expansion of the above admittance starting each division with the lowest powers of s. We have

$$Y(s) = \frac{3 + 4s^2 + s^4}{2s + s^3}$$

$$= 3/(2s) + \cfrac{1}{4/(5s) + \cfrac{1}{25/(2s) + \cfrac{1}{1/(5s)}}} \tag{9.16}$$

This corresponds to a realizable ladder network which starts with a shunt inductor as shown in Fig. 9.10.

We have demonstrated in the above example that two of the four possible Cauer expansions resulted in realizable ladders. Moreover, it was possible to predict which expansions were unrealizable by consideration of the first element and the behaviour of the function at $s = 0$ and $s = \infty$. However, there are some cases where an expansion leads to the correct type of element but does not correspond to a realizable ladder. We demonstrate this by the following example

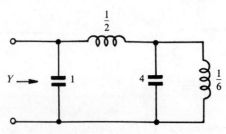

Figure 9.9 *Synthesis of input admittance of (9.15).*

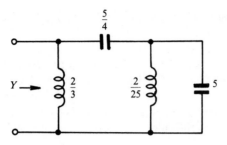

Figure 9.10 *Synthesis of input admittance of (9.16)*

where $Z(s)$ is given by

$$Z(s) = \frac{s(s^2 + 2)}{s^2 + 1} = \frac{s^3 + 2s}{s^2 + 1} \qquad (9.17)$$

Performing the expansion by starting division of the highest powers of s we obtain

$$Z(s) = s + \cfrac{1}{s + \cfrac{1}{s}} \qquad (9.18)$$

This leads to the realizable ladder network of Fig. 9.11 which starts with a series inductor.

Next consider the expansion obtained by starting each division at the lowest powers of s. We obtain

$$Z(s) = \frac{2s + s^3}{1 + s^2}$$

$$= 2s - \frac{s^3}{1 + s^2} \qquad (9.19)$$

As in the previous expansion, the first element is a series inductor which is consistent with the behaviour of $Z(s)$ at $s = 0$ and $s = \infty$. In fact the overall structure, consisting of series inductors and shunt capacitors, is the same as that of

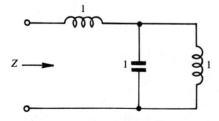

Figure 9.11 *Synthesis of input impedance of (9.18).*

the previous expansion which led to a realizable ladder. Here, however, negative values are obtained.

The question that arises therefore is whether it is possible to predict which expansions, if any, will lead to realizable ladder networks. The answer is that both the Cauer I and Cauer II methods give a realizable continued fraction provided that in each respective case the immittance function is arranged in the correct form (i.e. impedance and admittance) before expansion. Van Valkenburg (1960) gives a proof of the rules for correct choice which are described below.

Cauer I

For division starting with the highest powers of s, we expand the function (admittance or impedance) which has a pole at infinity, i.e. the order of the numerator is greater than that of the denominator. (Note that an LC immittance function always has a singularity at infinity.) This leads to an expansion starting with a term of the form ks where k is a constant.

It follows that the Cauer I method will always lead to a ladder with series inductors and shunt capacitors.

Cauer II

For division starting with the lowest powers of s we expand the function (admittance or impedance) which has a pole at the origin. (Note that an LC immittance function always has a singularity at the origin.) This leads to an expansion starting with a term of the form k/s where k is a constant.

It follows that the Cauer II method will always lead to a ladder with series capacitors and shunt inductors.

Returning to the expansion of (9.17) it is seen that $Z(s)$ has a pole at infinity and therefore leads to a realizable Cauer I expansion. However, since $Z(s)$ does not have a pole at the origin, a Cauer II expansion of $Z(s)$ is not realizable, as demonstrated by (9.19). To obtain the Cauer II ladder we expand $Y(s)$, which has a pole at the origin, and obtain

$$Y(s) = \frac{1 + s^2}{2s + s^3}$$

$$= 1/(2s) + \cfrac{1}{4/s + \cfrac{1}{1/(2s)}} \tag{9.20}$$

9.4 Transfer function synthesis

We next consider the problem of synthesis of a ladder network to provide a specified transfer function. This ladder comprises a purely LC network with resistive termination and it is appropriate to first review some properties of the transfer functions of LC networks.

It can be shown that the poles of such networks are simple and are on the real frequency axis. There can be no poles at the origin since such a pole would imply infinite gain at d.c., which is clearly not possible. Hence the poles occur in conjugate pairs and therefore the order of the transfer function is always even.

The zeros are on the real frequency axis and/or at infinity. The zeros do not have to interlace the poles, but any zeros at the origin must be of even multiplicity. The above restrictions lead to the important property that the transfer function of an *LC* network is always an even function.

A single resistor, namely the source or load resistor, is sufficient to move the poles into the left-half plane. The above restriction on the location of the zeros still applies, except that the multiplicity of zeros at the origin is no longer restricted to be even. Also, the number of poles is no longer restricted to be even.

Thus the conditions for a specified transfer function $T(s)$ to be realizable by a resistive terminated *LC* network can be expressed as follows: let

$$T(s) = \frac{N(s)}{D(s)} \qquad (9.21)$$

The $N(s)$ must have all its zeros on the real frequency axis and $D(s)$ must have all its zeros in the left-half plane.

9.4.1 Routh–Hurwitz conditions

If $D(s)$ is expressed as a polynomial rather than in factored form then it is possible to determine whether all its zeros are in the left-half plane by means of a set of tests on the coefficients. Depending upon the form in which the conditions are arranged, the rules are known most commonly as either the *Routh* or the *Hurwitz criteria*. A polynomial which satisfies the criteria is known as a *Hurwitz polynomial*.

For a first-order or second-order polynomial, the only condition necessary to satisfy the Hurwitz criterion is that the coefficients all be positive. Higher order polynomials can be expressed as the product of first-order and/or second-order polynomials. It is clear, therefore, that the coefficients of a Hurwitz polynomial, for any order, must all be positive. This is a necessary condition, but it is insufficient for third and higher order polynomials. Consider, for example, the polynomial $P(s)$ given by

$$P(s) = 6s^3 + s^2 + s + 1 \qquad (9.22)$$

Although all the coefficients are positive, $P(s)$ is not a Hurwitz polynomial as can be demonstrated by writing it in the following factored form:

$$P(s) = (2s + 1)(3s^2 - s + 1) \qquad (9.23)$$

The further condition that must be satisfied by a general third-order polynomial $a_3 s^3 + a_2 s^2 + a_1 s + a_0$ can be shown to be

$$a_1 a_2 > a_0 a_3 \qquad (9.24)$$

The general conditions for an nth-order polynomial become progressively more complex with increasing n; Dorf (1974) gives the full set of conditions.

There is a further way in which the conditions satisfied by a Hurwitz polynomial can be expressed, and this form is of particular importance in network synthesis. Let a Hurwitz polynomial be partitioned into its even and odd parts $E(s)$ and $O(s)$ respectively, i.e.

$$P(s) = E(s) + O(s) \tag{9.25}$$

It can be shown that the zeros of the polynomials $E(s)$ and $O(s)$ are all simple and located on the real frequency axis. Moreover, the zeros of $E(s)$ interlace the zeros of $O(s)$. It follows therefore that the function $F(s) = E(s)/O(s)$ is realizable as an *LC* driving-point immittance function. We make use of this property in the synthesis procedure developed in the following section.

EXAMPLE 9.3

Show that $E(s)$ and $O(s)$ of the polynomial $P(s) = s^3 + as^2 + bs + 1$ satisfy the above conditions if $P(s)$ is Hurwitz.

SOLUTION

We have

$$\left. \begin{array}{l} O(s) = s^3 + bs = s(s^2 + b) \\ E(s) = as^2 + 1 \end{array} \right\} \tag{9.26}$$

Thus $O(s)$ has a zero at the origin and zeros at $\pm jb^{1/2}$. $E(s)$ has zeros at $\pm j/a^{1/2}$. Therefore the condition that the zeros of $E(s)$ interlace those of $O(s)$ is

$$1/a^{1/2} < b^{1/2}$$

i.e.

$$ab > 1 \tag{9.27}$$

This is identical to the condition expressed by (9.24) for $P(s)$ to be Hurwitz.

9.4.2 *LC* ladder with resistive terminations

The most general form of the network to be considered is shown in Fig. 9.12 where the energy source is a voltage generator with an output resistance R_1 and is coupled to a resistive load R_2 by an *LC* ladder network. Such an arrangement is known as a double-terminated network and has a wide range of applications in communication systems.

The synthesis procedure is simplified, however, if only a single resistor is used, as would be the case in certain circumstances. For example, if the source resist-

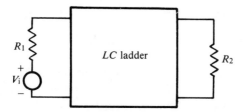

Figure 9.12 *General form of* LC *ladder with resistive terminations.*

ance is negligible compared to the input impedance of the terminated *LC* network then the energy source can be considered as an ideal voltage generator. In another application, where the network is used as an interstage coupling between active devices, the load impedance may be sufficiently large to be considered as an open circuit.

9.5 Resistive termination at the source

We first consider the case where the load resistance is an open circuit as shown in Fig. 9.13. The value of the source resistance has been normalized to 1 Ω; this does not lead to any loss of generality since the impedance level can subsequently be scaled to any convenient value.

We first analyze the network to compare the transfer function with that of the specified function. Let V_a be the input voltage to the *LC* network as shown, and let $T_1(s)$ be the transfer function of the *LC* network from port 1 to port 2. We have

$$\frac{V_o}{V_a} = T_1(s) \tag{9.28}$$

If Z_1 is the input impedance of the *LC* network at port 1, the transfer function from the input source to port 1 is given by

$$\frac{V_a}{V_i} = \frac{Z_1}{1 + Z_1} \tag{9.29}$$

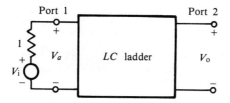

Figure 9.13 LC *ladder with source resistance.*

From (9.28) and (9.29) we have

$$\frac{V_o}{V_i} = \frac{Z_1 T_1(s)}{1 + Z_1} \tag{9.30}$$

where, as previously stated in consideration of the properties of *LC* networks, Z_1 is an odd function and $T_1(s)$ is even.

Let the specified transfer function $T(s)$ be written as

$$T(s) = \frac{N(s)}{D(s)} \tag{9.31}$$

where $D(s)$ is a Hurwitz polynomial which can be partitioned into its even and odd parts as $D(s) = E(s) + O(s)$, and $N(s)$ is either odd or even depending upon the number of zeros at the origin.

We have

$$T(s) = \frac{N(s)}{E(s) + O(s)} \tag{9.32}$$

We require to rearrange (9.32) into a similar form to that of (9.30). This is done in one of two ways, depending upon whether $N(s)$ is odd or even.

N(s) even

To obtain an expression whose numerator is odd, we divide the numerator and denominator of (9.32) by $O(s)$ and obtain

$$T(s) = \frac{N(s)/O(s)}{1 + E(s)/O(s)} \tag{9.33}$$

Since $D(s)$ is Hurwitz it follows that $E(s)/O(s)$ is realizable as an *LC* driving-point immittance function. Thus if we synthesize $Z_1 = E(s)/O(s)$ as the driving-point impedance of a Cauer ladder network, the poles of the terminated network will be those of $T(s)$. If the zeros of $T(s)$ are all at infinity then a Cauer I expansion ensures that the zeros of the network are also at infinity. Similarly, if the zeros of $T(s)$ are all at the origin then a Cauer II expansion is appropriate.

N(s) odd

To obtain an expression whose numerator is odd, we divide the numerator and denominator of (9.32) by $E(s)$ and obtain

$$T(s) = \frac{N(s)/E(s)}{1 + O(s)/E(s)} \tag{9.34}$$

In this case we synthesize $Z_1 = O(s)/E(s)$ as the driving-point impedance of a Cauer ladder network, and then proceed in the same way as for $N(s)$ even.

EXAMPLE 9.4

Synthesize, by means of the structure of Fig. 9.13, the third-order Butterworth filter transfer function $T(s)$ given by

$$T(s) = \frac{H}{s^3 + 2s^2 + 2s + 1} \tag{9.35}$$

where the scale factor H has the necessary value for realizability.

SOLUTION

We have

$$N(s) = H \qquad E(s) = 2s^2 + 1 \qquad O(s) = s^3 + 2s$$

Since $N(s)$ is even, we require

$$Z_1 = \frac{E(s)}{O(s)} = \frac{2s^2 + 1}{s^3 + 2s} \tag{9.36}$$

We next synthesize Z_1 in the form of a Cauer I ladder network. Since Z_1 has a zero at infinity we must rewrite it as an admittance Y_1 before expanding it as a continued fraction, i.e.

$$\begin{aligned} Y_1 &= \frac{s^3 + 2s}{2s^2 + 1} \\ &= s/2 + \cfrac{1}{4s/3 + \cfrac{1}{3s/2}} \end{aligned} \tag{9.37}$$

This leads to the network shown in Fig. 9.14. It is readily seen by inspection of the series and shunt elements that the zeros of this network are all at infinity. It is clear also from inspection of the network that the d.c. gain is unity. But from (9.35) the value of the d.c. magnitude of $T(s)$ is H. Hence the value of H for the resulting realization is unity.

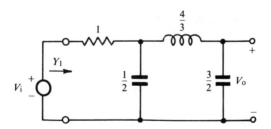

Figure 9.14 *Synthesis of the transfer function of (9.35).*

9.6 Resistive termination at the load

We next consider the case where the source resistance can be considered negligible as shown in Fig. 9.15. The value of the load resistance has been normalized to $1 \, \Omega$.

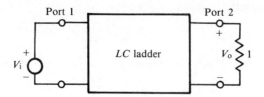

Figure 9.15 LC *ladder with resistive load.*

To analyze this network, let the network to the left of port 2 (i.e. excluding the load resistor) be replaced by its Thevenin equivalent as shown in Fig. 9.16. The voltage source in the Thevenin equivalent is the open-circuit voltage at port 2, and is therefore equal to $V_i T_1(s)$, where $T_1(s)$ is the open-circuit voltage transfer function of the LC network from port 1 to port 2. The source impedance Z_2 in the Thevenin equivalent circuit is the driving-point impedance at port 2 with the voltage source V_1 replaced by a short circuit.

The current I through the 1 Ω load resistor is given by

$$I = \frac{V_i T_1(s)}{1 + Z_2} \tag{9.38}$$

Hence the voltage transfer function is given by

$$\frac{V_o}{V_i} = \frac{T_1(s)}{1 + Z_2} \tag{9.39}$$

where $T_1(s)$ is an even function.

Let the specified transfer function $T(s)$ be written as

$$T(s) = \frac{N(s)}{D(s)} \tag{9.40}$$

where $D(s)$ is a Hurwitz polynomial which can be partitioned into its even and odd parts as $D(s) = E(s) + O(s)$ and the parity of $N(s)$ is determined by the number of zeros at the origin. We have

$$T(s) = \frac{N(s)}{E(s) + O(s)} \tag{9.41}$$

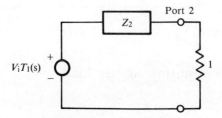

Figure 9.16 *Thevenin equivalent of network of Fig. 9.15.*

As before we rearrange (9.41) into a similar form to that of (9.39) as described below.

N(s) even

To obtain an expression whose numerator is even, we divide the numerator and denominator of (9.41) by $E(s)$ and obtain

$$T(s) = \frac{N(s)/E(s)}{1 + O(s)/E(s)} \tag{9.42}$$

Since $D(s)$ is Hurwitz it follows that $O(s)/E(s)$ is realizable as an LC driving-point immittance function. We have that $Z_2 = O(s)/E(s)$. We synthesize Z_2 as the driving-point impedance of a Cauer ladder network. The poles of the terminated network will be those of $T(s)$. If the zeros of $T(s)$ are all at infinity then a Cauer I expansion ensures that the zeros of the network are also at infinity. Similarly, if the zeros of $T(s)$ are all at the origin then a Cauer II expansion is appropriate.

N(s) odd

To obtain an expression whose numerator is even, we divide numerator and denominator of (9.41) by $O(s)$ and obtain

$$T(s) = \frac{N(s)/O(s)}{1 + E(s)/O(s)} \tag{9.43}$$

We have that $Z_2 = E(s)/O(s)$. We synthesize Z_2 as the driving point impedance of a Cauer ladder network, and then proceed in the same way as for $N(s)$ even.

EXAMPLE 9.5

Synthesize, by means of the structure of Fig. 9.15, the third-order Butterworth filter transfer function $T(s)$ given by (9.35).

SOLUTION

As in Example 9.4, we have

$$N(s) = H \qquad E(s) = 2s^2 + 1 \qquad O(s) = s^3 + 2s$$

Since $N(s)$ is even, we require

$$Z_2 = \frac{O(s)}{E(s)} = \frac{s^3 + 2s}{2s^2 + 1} \tag{9.44}$$

We next synthesize Z_2 in the form of a Cauer I ladder network. Since Z_2 has a

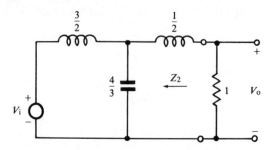

Figure 9.17 *Synthesis of the transfer function of (9.45).*

pole at infinity it is in the correct form for expansion as a continued fraction, i.e.

$$Z_2 = \frac{s^3 + 2s}{2s^2 + 1}$$

$$= s/2 + \cfrac{1}{4s/3 + \cfrac{1}{3s/2}} \tag{9.45}$$

This leads to the network shown in Fig. 9.17. As in the previous case it is readily seen that the zeros of this network are all at infinity and the value of H for the resulting realization is unity.

9.7 Double-terminated *LC* ladder

We next consider the more general case of resistive termination of the *LC* ladder at both the source and the load, as shown in Fig. 9.18. Here the previous methods are no longer applicable and a different method, originally proposed by S. Darlington (1939) is used. The method is based on the consideration of power transfer from the source to the load in the steady-state frequency domain.

Let $Z_1(s)$ be the input impedance at port 1 of the *LC* network terminated with R_L as shown in Fig. 9.18, i.e. the current I_1 and the voltage V_1 at port 1 are

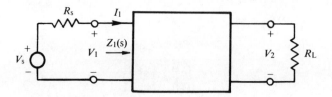

Figure 9.18 *Double-terminated LC ladder.*

related by

$$I_1 = \frac{V_1}{Z_1(s)} \tag{9.46}$$

and V_1 is related to the source voltage V_s by

$$\frac{V_1}{V_s} = \frac{Z_1(s)}{R_s + Z_1(s)} \tag{9.47}$$

For a steady-state sinusoidal input, the average power P_1 absorbed at port 1 is given by

$$P_1 = |I_1|^2 R_1 = \left|\frac{V_1}{Z_1(j\omega)}\right|^2 R_1 \tag{9.48}$$

where R_1 is the real part of $Z_1(j\omega)$.

The average power P_2 dissipated in the load resistor is given by

$$P_2 = \frac{|V_2|^2}{R_L} \tag{9.49}$$

Since the LC network is lossless, we have that $P_1 = P_2$. Hence from (9.48) and (9.49)

$$\left|\frac{V_2}{V_1}\right|^2 = \frac{R_1 R_L}{|Z_1(j\omega)|^2} \tag{9.50}$$

From (9.47) we can write

$$\left|\frac{V_1}{V_s}\right| = \left|\frac{Z_1(j\omega)}{R_s + Z_1(j\omega)}\right| \tag{9.51}$$

Hence from (9.50) and (9.51), the transfer function $T(s) = V_2/V_s$ is given by

$$|T(j\omega)|^2 = \left|\frac{V_2}{V_s}\right|^2 = \frac{R_1 R_L}{|R_s + Z_1(j\omega)|^2} \tag{9.52}$$

We next determine the solution of (9.52) for Z_1 in terms of the specified transfer function $T(s)$ and the resistances R_L and R_s in order to reduce the problem to that of synthesis of a driving-point immittance.

Let $Z_1(j\omega)$ be written as

$$Z_1(j\omega) = R_1 + jX_1 \tag{9.53}$$

From (9.52) and (9.53)

$$\frac{1}{R_L}|T(j\omega)|^2 = \frac{R_1}{(R_1 + R_s)^2 + X_1^2}$$

$$= \frac{R_1}{R_1^2 + R_s^2 + 2R_1 R_s + X_1^2} \tag{9.54}$$

If we now multiply throughout (9.54) by $4R_s$ and then subtract each side from unity we obtain

$$1 - \frac{4R_s}{R_L}|T(j\omega)|^2 = \frac{(R_1 - R_s)^2 + X_1^2}{(R_1 + R_s)^2 + X_1^2}$$

$$= \left|\frac{Z_1(j\omega) - R_s}{Z_1(j\omega) + R_s}\right|^2 \tag{9.55}$$

It is clear that the right-hand side of (9.55) cannot be negative, and therefore by applying this condition to the left-hand side we obtain the following realizability condition:

$$|T(j\omega)|^2 \leqslant \frac{R_L}{4R_s} \tag{9.56}$$

Assuming that the condition expressed by (9.56) is satisfied, we can denote the left-hand side of (9.55) by $|S(j\omega)|^2$, i.e.

$$|S(j\omega)|^2 = 1 - \frac{4R_s}{R_L}|T(j\omega)|^2 \tag{9.57}$$

In microwave transmission line theory, the function $S(s)$ is known as the reflection coefficient or scattering coefficient.

From (9.55) and (9.57) we have

$$|S(j\omega)| = \left|\frac{Z_1(j\omega) - R_s}{Z_1(j\omega) + R_s}\right| \tag{9.58}$$

Hence

$$S(s) = \pm\frac{Z_1(s) - R_s}{Z_1(s) + R_s} \tag{9.59}$$

This gives two alternative solutions depending upon whether the positive or negative sign is selected in (9.59), i.e.

$$Z_1(s) = \frac{1 + S(s)}{1 - S(s)}R_s \tag{9.60}$$

or

$$Z_1(s) = \frac{1 - S(s)}{1 + S(s)}R_s \tag{9.61}$$

The impedance function of (9.61) is the inverse of the impedance function of (9.60). The two functions lead to networks A and B having the same topology, for which each impedance Z_A in A has a counterpart Z_B in B related by $Z_A Z_B = k$ where k is a constant. Such networks are said to be the dual of each other.

(9.59) thus reduces the synthesis problem to that of determining a driving-point immittance. The overall procedure starts with the magnitude-squared $|T(j\omega)|^2$ of the specified transfer function. We can then determine the magnitude-squared $|S(j\omega)|^2$ of the scattering coefficient from (9.57). $S(s)$ is then determined using the procedure described in Section 7.3 where we replace ω^2 by $-s^2$ in the magnitude-squared function and select the left-half plane singularities. We then determine $Z_1(s)$ from (9.60) or (9.61) and synthesize $Z_1(s)$ as a ladder by means of a continued fraction expansion.

To ensure realizability, the specified transfer function must be correctly scaled. Also, the ratio R_L/R_s may need to satisfy certain conditions, as will now be shown for the case of $T(s)$ with all zeros at infinity.

For the case of all zeros at infinity, the LC network does not introduce any attenuation at d.c. and therefore the magnitude $T_{dc} = |T(0)|$ is given by

$$T_{dc} = \frac{R_L}{R_L + R_s}$$

$$= \frac{1}{1 + \gamma} \tag{9.62}$$

where $\gamma = R_s/R_L$.

Hence the specified transfer function must be scaled to have the d.c. gain as given by (9.62). However, to satisfy the condition expressed by (9.56), the value of $|T(j\omega)|$ cannot exceed T_{max} where

$$T_{max} = 1/(2\gamma^{1/2}) \tag{9.63}$$

Consider the case where the source and load resistors are equal, i.e. $\gamma = 1$. From (9.62), the transfer function must be scaled to have a d.c. gain of 0.5. From (9.63) it is found that $T_{max} = 0.5$. Hence, only those filters for which the maximum gain occurs at d.c. can be realized with equal source and load resistors. These include the Butterworth, Bessel and odd-order Chebyshev filters. For even-order Chebyshev filters, there is a restriction on the range of possible values for γ which we can determine as follows: from (9.62) and (9.63)

$$\frac{T_{max}}{T_{dc}} = \frac{1}{2}(\gamma^{1/2} + 1/\gamma^{1/2}) \tag{9.64}$$

For a given value of the ratio of T_{max} to T_{dc} (9.64) is a quadratic in the variable $\gamma^{1/2}$ which can be solved to give the limiting values of γ for realizability. Denoting

$$\theta = \frac{T_{max}}{T_{dc}} \tag{9.65}$$

(9.64) can be solved to give

$$\gamma = [\theta + (\theta^2 - 1)^{1/2}]^2 \tag{9.66}$$

EXAMPLE 9.6

Determine the limiting values of γ for realization of a Chebyshev even-order filter with a 0.1 dB ripple.

SOLUTION

We have

$$20 \log \frac{T_{max}}{T_{dc}} = 0.1 \tag{9.67}$$

Hence

$$\theta = \frac{T_{max}}{T_{dc}} = 1.0116 \tag{9.68}$$

Substituting for θ in (9.66) we obtain the values 1.355 and 0.7378 for γ, i.e the ratio of source and load resistor values must be greater than or equal to 1.355, or less than or equal to 0.7378.

EXAMPLE 9.7

Synthesize a normalized third-order Butterworth lowpass filter using a double-terminated ladder.

SOLUTION

For the Butterworth filter, equal source and load resistors are possible. Hence we can choose $\gamma = 1$ and normalize both resistors to unity. Therefore $T_{dc} = 1/2$ and the specified magnitude-squared is

$$|T(j\omega)|^2 = \frac{1/4}{1 + \omega^6} \tag{9.69}$$

From (9.57) with $R_L = R_s$, and $|T(j\omega)|^2$ given by (9.69), we have

$$|S(j\omega)|^2 = 1 - \frac{1}{1 + \omega^6}$$

$$= \frac{\omega^6}{1 + \omega^6} \tag{9.70}$$

To determine $S(s)$ we replace $j\omega$ by s and obtain

$$S(s)S(-s) = \frac{-s^6}{1 - s^6} \tag{9.71}$$

The poles of the above function were determined in Section 7.8.2. Assigning

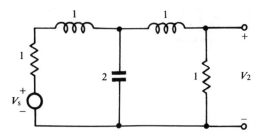

Figure 9.19 *Synthesis of third-order Butterworth filter using double-terminated* LC *ladder.*

the left-half-plane poles and three zeros at the origin to $S(s)$ we have

$$S(s) = \frac{\pm s^3}{s^3 + 2s^2 + 2s + 1} \tag{9.72}$$

Selecting, for example, the positive sign in (9.59), we next determine $Z_1(s)$ as follows:

$$Z_1(s) = \frac{1 + S(s)}{1 - S(s)}$$

$$= \frac{2s^3 + 2s^2 + 2s + 1}{2s^2 + 2s + 1} \tag{9.73}$$

Expressing $Z_1(s)$ in the form of a Cauer I continued fraction expansion

$$Z_1 = s + \cfrac{1}{2s + \cfrac{1}{s + 1}}$$

This leads to the network of Fig. 9.19.

Selection of the negative sign (9.59) would lead to the network shown in Fig. 9.20 which is the dual of the network of Fig. 9.19.

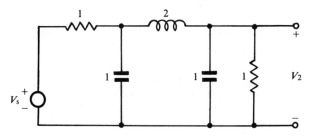

Figure 9.20 *Dual of network of Fig. 9.19.*

10 ALLPASS NETWORKS

10.1 Introduction

The allpass network was briefly introduced in Chapter 5 as an example of a non-minimum phase system. It is useful in filter synthesis where a specific phase characteristic, as well as a specified magnitude characteristic, is required. That is, the addition of an allpass network can be used to provide phase correction or equalization to a filter without altering the magnitude characteristic. In most applications where phase is important, the ideal requirement is one in which the phase-versus-frequency characteristic is linear over the passband. Methods for determining the optimum locations of the singularities of the allpass network to provide equalization for a given filter are not generally amenable to closed-form solutions. Curve-fitting methods or iterative procedures on a computer are usually used and these are beyond the scope of this book. Here we consider only the practical realization of a specified allpass transfer function.

In Chapter 5, a practical realization by means of a bridge circuit was described and analyses of first- and second-order realizations were given for unloaded output. In passive network applications, however, it is necessary to implement allpass characteristics in networks where source and load resistors are present, and these realizations are developed in this chapter.

10.2 Property of constant resistance

In passive network analysis, the allpass network has a particularly important property, namely that it can be realized by a constant-resistance network. A constant-resistance network is a two-port which, when loaded at, say, port 2 with the appropriate resistance R_0, known as the characteristic resistance, exhibits at port 1 an input impedance which is resistive and equal to R_0.

Figure 10.1 shows a cascaded arrangement of a number of constant-resistance sections, each with the same value of characteristic resistance R_0 and with a terminating load R_0. For this arrangement, each section is correctly loaded. Therefore the overall transfer function is the product of the transfer functions of the separate sections when correctly loaded. This permits a much simplified

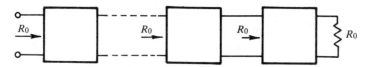

Figure 10.1 *Cascade of constant-resistance networks.*

synthesis procedure for high-order transfer functions, since the specified transfer function can be factorized into first-order and second-order allpass functions which can then each be realized by a separate section. Moreover, if the network is driven from a voltage source with an output resistance R_s, say, then this will simply introduce a scale factor $R_0/(R_0 + R_s)$ and will not otherwise affect the response.

10.3 General analysis

One serious limitation of the bridge or lattice network is that the input and output do not have a common ground terminal. This problem can be overcome by determining an equivalent unbalanced network such as a bridged T-section. We will first analyze the symmetrical lattice and establish the conditions for the properties of constant-resistance and allpass response. We will then show how equivalent unbalanced realizations are possible.

We consider only the symmetrical network since, as will be shown, this is sufficient to realize any allpass transfer function. Figure 10.2a shows the symmetrical lattice and Fig. 10.2b shows the same network drawn as a bridge circuit. It can be seen that the bridge is simply an unfolded form of the lattice.

We first determine the open-circuit parameters. Referring to Fig. 10.2b, it can be seen from the symmetry that the current through each impedance is $I_1/2$ and is equal to $V_1/(Z_A + Z_B)$. Hence

$$I_1 = \frac{2V_1}{Z_A + Z_B} \tag{10.1}$$

Hence the input impedance Z_1 is given by

$$Z_1 = \frac{Z_A + Z_B}{2} \tag{10.2}$$

To determine the voltage transfer function, we have

$$\left. \begin{aligned} V_{cb} &= \frac{Z_B}{Z_A + Z_B} \, V_1 \\[2mm] V_{db} &= \frac{Z_A}{Z_A + Z_B} \, V_1 \end{aligned} \right\} \tag{10.3}$$

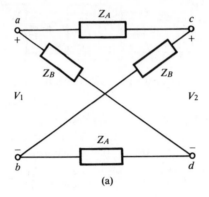

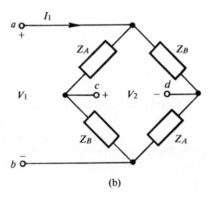

Figure 10.2 *Symmetrical lattice: (a) lattice form, (b) bridge form.*

But

$$V_2 = V_{cb} - V_{db} \tag{10.4}$$

From (10.3) and (10.4) we obtain the open-circuit transfer function T_{oc} as

$$T_{oc} = \frac{V_2}{V_1} = \frac{Z_B - Z_A}{Z_A + Z_B} \tag{10.5}$$

The analysis of the network when terminated with a load resistor is facilitated by the use of two-port z-parameters. In general, the z-parameters relate the currents and voltages by the equations

$$\left.\begin{array}{l} V_1 = Z_{11}I_1 + Z_{12}I_2 \\ V_2 = Z_{21}I_1 + Z_{22}I_2 \end{array}\right\} \tag{10.6}$$

where the current directions and voltage polarities are as shown in Fig. 10.3.
We can determine Z_{11} and Z_{21} in terms of the open-circuit input impedance

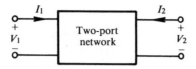

Figure 10.3 *Two-port network: current directions and voltage polarities.*

Z_1 and the open-circuit voltage transfer function T_{oc}. Putting $I_2 = 0$ in (10.6) we obtain

$$V_1 = Z_{11}I_1 \tag{10.7}$$

and

$$\frac{V_2}{V_1} = \frac{Z_{21}}{Z_{11}} \tag{10.8}$$

From (10.7), Z_{11} is the open-circuit input impedance, i.e.

$$Z_{11} = Z_1 \tag{10.9}$$

and from (10.8) and (10.9)

$$Z_{21} = Z_1 T_{oc} \tag{10.10}$$

For the symmetrical lattice we can therefore obtain expressions for Z_{11} and Z_{21} in terms of Z_A and Z_B from (10.2), (10.5), (10.9) and (10.10) as follows:

$$Z_{11} = \frac{Z_B + Z_A}{2} \tag{10.11a}$$

$$Z_{21} = \frac{Z_A - Z_B}{2} \tag{10.11b}$$

For a passive symmetrical network $Z_{12} = Z_{21}$ and $Z_{22} = Z_{11}$, hence (10.6) can be written

$$V_1 = Z_{11}I_1 + Z_{21}I_2 \tag{10.12a}$$

$$V_2 = Z_{21}I_1 + Z_{11}I_2 \tag{10.12b}$$

We now establish the condition for the property of constant resistance. For a load resistor R_0, we have

$$V_2 = -R_0 I_2 \tag{10.13}$$

where the negative sign arises because the convention is that the current flows into the upper terminal at each port. Substituting for V_2 from (10.13) in (10.12) we have

$$\left. \begin{array}{l} V_1 = Z_{11}I_1 + Z_{21}I_2 \\ 0 = Z_{21}I_1 + (Z_{11} + R_0)I_2 \end{array} \right\} \tag{10.14}$$

Solving for I_1 we obtain

$$I_1 = \frac{V_1(Z_{11} + R_0)}{Z_{11}(Z_{11} + R_0) - Z_{21}^2} \tag{10.15}$$

But if R_0 is the characteristic resistance then

$$V_1 = R_0 I_1 \tag{10.16}$$

From (10.15) and (10.16) we obtain

$$R_0^2 = Z_{11}^2 - Z_{21}^2 \tag{10.17}$$

For the symmetrical lattice, we substitute for Z_{11} and Z_{21} from (10.11a) and (10.11b) in (10.17) and obtain

$$R_0^2 = Z_A Z_B \tag{10.18}$$

(10.18) establishes the condition that the symmetrical lattice will have the property of constant resistance if the impedances Z_A and Z_B are reciprocal or dual impedances.

For an LC network, a further consequence of the property of constant resistance is that termination with R_0 is sufficient to ensure an allpass characteristic. This can be readily established by consideration of power in the steady-state frequency domain. Since the LC network is lossless, the input power P_1 is equal to the power P_2 dissipated in the load. But

$$P_1 = \frac{|V_1|^2}{R_0} \tag{10.19}$$

and

$$P_2 = \frac{|V_2|^2}{R_0} \tag{10.20}$$

Hence $|V_1| = |V_2|$ and therefore the response is allpass.

To determine the voltage transfer function of the terminated lattice we solve (10.14) for I_2 and obtain

$$I_2 = \frac{Z_{21}V_1}{Z_{21}^2 - Z_{11}^2 - Z_{11}R_0} \tag{10.21}$$

From (10.13), (10.17) and (10.21) we obtain

$$\frac{V_2}{V_1} = \frac{Z_{21}}{R_0 + Z_{11}} \tag{10.22}$$

Substituting for Z_{11} and Z_{21} from (10.11a), (10.11b) and (10.12), and for Z_B from (10.18), we determine the expression for the transfer function as

$$\frac{V_2}{V_1} = \frac{Z_B - R_0}{Z_B + R_0} = \frac{R_0 - Z_A}{R_0 - Z_A} \tag{10.23}$$

If the network is driven from a voltage source V_s with an output resistance R_s then clearly this introduces a scale factor $H = R_0/(R_0 + R_s)$.

We have

$$\frac{V_1}{V_s} = H \tag{10.24}$$

and (10.23) becomes

$$\frac{V_2}{V_s} = H \frac{Z_B - R_0}{Z_B + R_0} = H \frac{R_0 - Z_A}{R_0 + Z_A} \tag{10.25}$$

If the characteristic resistance is normalized to unity, then (10.18) and (10.25) respectively become

$$Z_A Z_B = 1 \tag{10.26}$$

and

$$\frac{V_2}{V_s} = H \frac{Z_B - 1}{Z_B + 1} = H \frac{1 - Z_A}{1 + Z_A} \tag{10.27}$$

10.4 First-order allpass network

Suppose we require to synthesize the first-order allpass transfer function $T(s)$ given by

$$T(s) = \frac{1}{2} \frac{1 - s}{1 + s} \tag{10.28}$$

The time constant has been normalized to unity and can subsequently be changed to any required value by frequency scaling. The scale factor of $1/2$ implies equal source and load resistances which can be normalized to unity.

Comparing (10.27) and (10.28) we obtain

$$Z_A = s \tag{10.29}$$

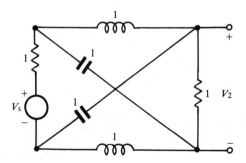

Figure 10.4 *Realization of first-order allpass transfer function of (10.28).*

and hence

$$Z_B = \frac{1}{s} \qquad (10.30)$$

Figure 10.4 on the preceeding page shows the corresponding network.

10.5 Second-order allpass network

Consider next the synthesis of the general second-order allpass transfer function $T(s)$ with the undamped resonant frequency ω_0 normalized to unity and with equal source and load resistances:

$$T(s) = \frac{1}{2} \frac{s^2 - s/Q + 1}{s^2 + s/Q + 1} \qquad (10.31)$$

To identify the expression of (10.31) with that of (10.27), we partition the numerator and denominator polynomials of $T(s)$ into even and odd parts and divide throughout by either the even or the odd part. Since the denominator is a Hurwitz polynomial, we know that the ratio of its odd and even parts is a driving-point LC immittance (see Section 9.4). Dividing, for example, by the even part, we obtain

$$T(s) = \frac{1 - \dfrac{s}{Q(s^2 + 1)}}{1 + \dfrac{s}{Q(s^2 + 1)}} \qquad (10.32)$$

Comparing (10.27) and (10.32) we obtain

$$Z_A = \frac{s}{Q(s^2 + 1)} \qquad (10.33)$$

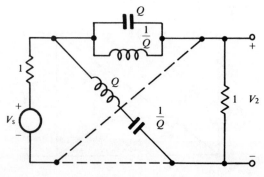

Figure 10.5 *Realization of second-order allpass transfer function of (10.31).*

Writing the above in admittance form, $Y_A = 1/Z_A$, and noting that from (10.26) $Y_A = Z_B$, we have

$$Y_A = \frac{Q}{s} + Qs \qquad (10.34a)$$

$$Z_B = \frac{Q}{s} + Qs \qquad (10.34b)$$

Fig. 10.5 shows the corresponding network.

10.6 Lattice decomposition

We next consider the problem of decomposition of a symmetrical network to find an equivalent symmetrical unbalanced network with a common ground terminal between input and output. This is facilitated by *Bartlett's bisection theorem*. The theorem is based on the procedure of dividing a symmetrical network into two mirror-image half-sections as shown in block diagram form in Fig. 10.6a. Fig. 10.6b and 10.6c shows a particular case of a bridged T-section divided into half-sections.

Consider the z-parameters of the whole section, which relate the currents and voltages according to (10.13). Suppose equal voltages with the same polarity are applied to each port, i.e. $V_1 = V_2 = V$. It is clear from the symmetry of the network and also from (10.12) that $I_1 = I_2$. Also, from symmetry, the current in

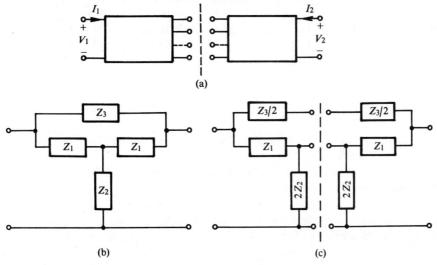

(a)

(b)   (c)

Figure 10.6 *Bisection of symmetrical network: (a) block diagram, (b) bridged T-section, (c) bisected bridged T-section.*

each link between the half-sections is zero. Therefore each link may be cut without any change in the currents and voltages. From (10.13a), with $I_1 = I_2$, we have that the driving-point impedance $Z_{\frac{1}{2}oc}$ at port 1 is given by

$$Z_{\frac{1}{2}oc} = Z_{11} + Z_{21} \tag{10.35}$$

Suppose next that equal voltages with opposite polarities are applied to each port, i.e. $V_1 = V_2 = V$. It is clear from the symmetry of the network and also from (10.12) that $I_1 = -I_2$. Also, from symmetry, the voltage at each link between the half-sections is zero. Therefore each link may be connected to ground without any change in the currents and voltages. From (10.12a), with $I_1 = -I_2$, we have that the driving-point impedance at port 1, $Z_{\frac{1}{2}sc}$, is given by

$$Z_{\frac{1}{2}sc} = Z_{11} - Z_{21} \tag{10.36}$$

(10.35) establishes that we can find $Z_{11} + Z_{21}$ for a symmetrical network by determining the driving-point impedance at port 1 with all the half-section links on open circuit. Similarly, (10.36) establishes that we can find $Z_{11} - Z_{21}$ for a symmetrical network by determining the driving-point impedance at port 1 with all the half-section links short-circuited to ground.

For a symmetrical lattice, we can obtain from (10.11a) and (10.11b) the following relationships:

$$Z_A = Z_{11} - Z_{21} \tag{10.37}$$

$$Z_B = Z_{11} + Z_{21} \tag{10.38}$$

Comparison of (10.35) to (10.38) indicates a simple method of decomposition of a symmetrical unbalanced network into an equivalent lattice. That is, we bisect the unbalanced network into two mirror-image half-sections. The impedance Z_A of the equivalent lattice is the input impedance of the first half-section with the links short-circuited. The impedance Z_B of the equivalent lattice is the input impedance of the first half-section with the links open-circuited.

10.6.1 T-section to lattice

To demonstrate the above procedure we determine the lattice equivalent of a symmetrical T-section.

The T-section shown in Fig. 10.7a bisects into the inverted-L half-sections with series impedance Z_1 and shunt impedance $2Z_2$ as shown in Fig. 10.7b. Hence Z_A, which is the input impedance with the link on short circuit, is equal to Z_1. Z_B, which is the input impedance with the link on open circuit, is given by Z_1 and $2Z_2$ in series as shown in Fig. 10.7c. These relationships can be written

$$Z_A = Z_1 \tag{10.39a}$$

$$Z_B = Z_1 + 2Z_2 \tag{10.39b}$$

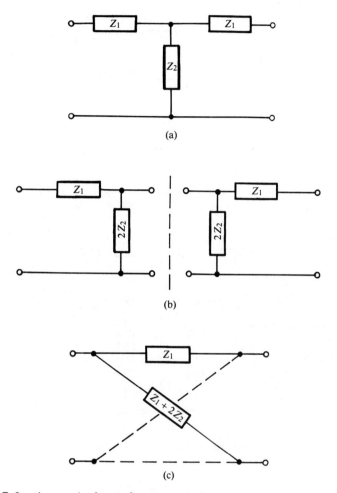

Figure 10.7 *Lattice equivalent of symmetrical T-section: (a) T-section, (b) bisected T-section, (c) equivalent lattice.*

10.6.2 Bridged T-section to lattice

As a further example we determine the lattice equivalent of a symmetrical bridged T-section.

The bridged T-section shown in Fig. 10.8a bisects into the half-sections shown in Fig. 10.8b. Hence Z_A is equal to Z_1 in parallel with $Z_3/2$. Z_B is given by Z_1 and $2Z_2$ in series as shown in Fig. 10.8c. These relationships can be written

$$Y_A = Y_1 + 2Y_3 \tag{10.40a}$$

$$Z_B = Z_1 + 2Z_2 \tag{10.40b}$$

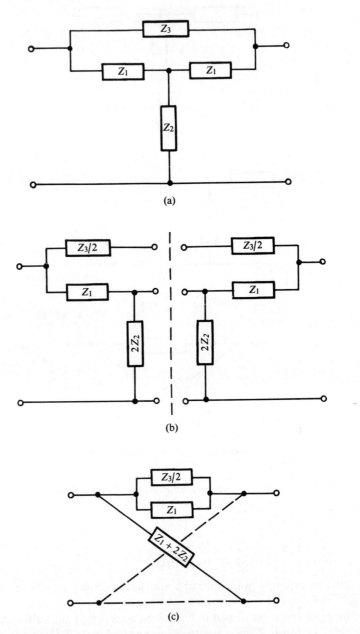

Figure 10.8 *Lattice equivalent of bridged T-section: (a) bridged T-section, (b) bisected bridged T-section, (c) equivalent lattice.*

10.6.3 Lattice to bridged T-section

It is clear from the above procedure that any realizable unbalanced symmetrical network has an equivalent realizable lattice. However, the reverse procedure of decomposing a symmetrical lattice into an equivalent unbalanced network is not always possible without the use of transformers. To demonstrate this, we next consider the decomposition of the second-order allpass lattice of Fig. 10.5 for which it has been shown that (10.34)

$$Y_A = \frac{Q}{s} + Qs \qquad (10.41a)$$

$$Z_B = \frac{Q}{s} + Qs \qquad (10.41b)$$

Comparing (10.40a) and (10.41a) we can assign Y_1 and Y_3 as follows:

$$Y_1 = \frac{Q}{s} \qquad (10.42a)$$

$$Y_3 = \frac{Qs}{2} \qquad (10.42b)$$

Comparing (10.40b) and (10.41b) and substituting for Y_1, from (10.42a) we obtain

$$Z_2 = \frac{1}{2}\left[\frac{Q}{s} + \left(Q - \frac{1}{Q}\right)s\right] \qquad (10.43)$$

Hence Z_2 is realizable as a series LC immittance for $Q > 1$. The complete bridged T-section network is shown in Fig. 10.9. For $Q = 1$, Z_2 becomes a capacitor only. For $Q < 1$, however, (10.43) requires negative inductance and is therefore not directly realizable.

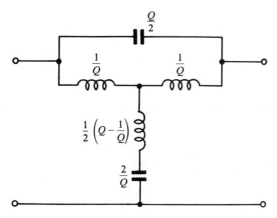

Figure 10.9 *Second-order allpass bridged T-section (Q ≥ 1).*

10.6.4 Equivalence between mutual inductance and negative inductance

One solution to the problem of negative impedance values is to perform a preliminary synthesis as above, leading to a negative inductance in one arm of a T-section, and then to determine a realizable equivalent T-section that has inductors in the other two arms which are mutually coupled. We now show how this can be achieved.

Consider the symmetrical T-section shown in Fig. 10.10a, which has an inductor L_a in each series arm, with mutual coupling $M = KL_c$ where K is the coefficient of coupling. The currents and voltages are as shown and the dots indicate corresponding ends of the coils where the voltages are in phase. Since one current flows into the dotted end and the other current flows out from the dotted end, the sign of the mutual inductance is negative. Hence the equations relating the voltages and currents are

$$\left. \begin{array}{l} V_1 = L_a s I_1 - KL_a s I_2 \\ V_2 = -KL_a s I_1 + L_a s I_2 \end{array} \right\} \tag{10.44}$$

Consider next the symmetrical T-section of Fig. 10.10b which has an inductor L_b in each series arm with no mutual coupling, and an inductor L_c in the shunt arm. With the currents and voltages as shown, the equations relating them are

$$\left. \begin{array}{l} V_1 = (L_b + L_c)s I_1 + L_c s I_2 \\ V_2 = L_c s I_1 + (L_b + L_c)s I_2 \end{array} \right\} \tag{10.45}$$

Comparing (10.44) and (10.45), we find that the circuits of Fig. 10.10a and 10.10b are equivalent if

$$\left. \begin{array}{l} L_b = (1 + K)L_a \\ L_c = -KL_a \end{array} \right\} \tag{10.46}$$

Therefore, the mutually coupled inductors, each with a self inductance L_a, are equivalent to two uncoupled inductors, each with a self inductance $(1 + K)L_a$, together with a negative inductor that has an inductance $-KL_a$ in the other branch, where K is the coefficient of coupling. This is illustrated in Fig. 10.10c.

10.6.5 Unbalanced realization of second-order allpass with $Q < 1$

We can apply the above result to the realization of an unbalanced second-order allpass network with $Q < 1$. (10.43) can be rewritten

$$Z_2 = \frac{1}{2} \left[\frac{Q}{s} - \left(\frac{1}{Q} - Q \right)s \right] \tag{10.47}$$

and the corresponding bridged T-section utilizing a negative inductor is shown

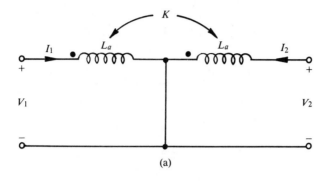

(a)

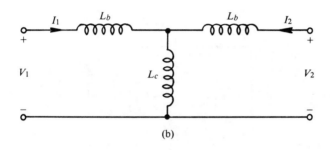

(b)

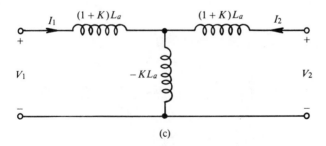

(c)

Figure 10.10 *Realization of negative inductance by means of mutually coupled coils: (a) mutually coupled coils, (b) coils without coupling, (c) T-section equivalent of (a) using uncoupled coils and negative inductance.*

in Fig. 10.11a. If we replace the inductors in the series arm with coupled inductors, each with a self inductance $1/[Q(1 + K)]$, where K is the coupling coefficient, this leaves the effective values of the inductors unchanged and introduces a negative inductance $-K/[Q(1 + K)]$ into the shunt arm. Equating the value of the negative inductance to the required value $(1/Q - Q)$ in 10.47, we obtain the

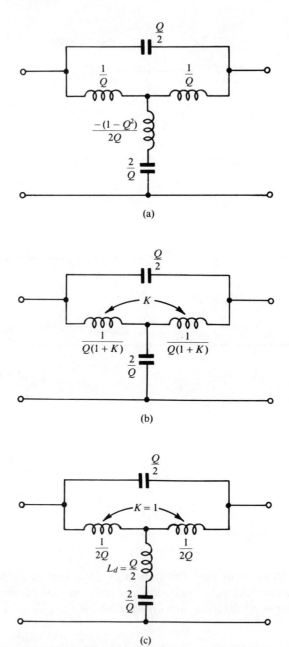

Figure 10.11 *Unbalanced realization of second-order allpass (Q < 1): (a) theoretical prototype using negative inductance, (b) equivalent bridged T-section using controlled coupling (K = (1 − Q²)/(1 + Q²)), (c) equivalent bridged T-section with unity coupling (K = 1).*

condition

$$K = \frac{1 - Q^2}{1 + Q^2} \qquad (10.48)$$

The resulting network is shown in Fig. 10.11b.

In practice, the construction of coils with a controlled coefficient of coupling may not be convenient, and it may be preferable to use a centre-tapped inductor with sufficiently tight coupling to permit K to be assumed to be unity. The requirements for the series branches can be met using inductors each with a self inductance $1/2Q$. This reflects a negative inductance $-1/2Q$, whose magnitude is greater than that required in the shunt arm and which therefore requires the introduction of an inductor L_d as shown in Fig. 10.11c. Equating the effective negative inductance value in the shunt arm to the required value, we have

$$L_d - \frac{1}{2Q} = -\frac{(1 - Q^2)}{2Q} \qquad (10.49)$$

Hence

$$L_d = \frac{Q}{2} \qquad (10.50)$$

10.6.6 Unbalanced realization of first-order allpass

Consider next the decomposition of the first-order allpass lattice of Fig. 10.4 into an unbalanced form. This cannot be achieved without the use of mutual induct-ance. We can base the synthesis on the T-section of Fig. 10.7. Comparing (10.29) and (10.39a) we obtain

$$Z_1 = s \qquad (10.51)$$

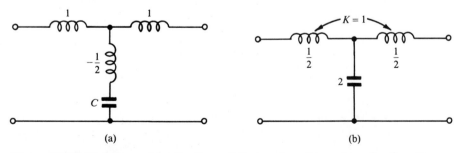

(a)   (b)

Figure 10.12 *Unbalanced realization of first-order allpass transfer function: (a) theoretical prototype using negative inductance, (b) equivalent network using mutual inductance.*

From (10.30), (10.39b) and (10.51) we have

$$Z_2 = \frac{1}{2s} - \frac{s}{2} \tag{10.52}$$

This is shown in Fig. 10.12a by utilizing an inductor $L = 1$ in each series arm and a negative inductor $L_n = -\frac{1}{2}$ in the shunt arm in series with a capacitor $C = 2$. The practical realization using an inductor $L = \frac{1}{2}$ in each series arm with unity coefficient of coupling is shown in Fig. 10.12b.

11 ACTIVE NETWORK SYNTHESIS

11.1 Introduction

Although any realizable rational transfer function with all its poles in the left-half plane can theoretically be implemented by means of a passive *LCR* network, the use of inductors can introduce practical problems. The disadvantages of inductors, namely the weight, cost, bulk and departure from the ideal characteristic, progressively increase as the filter cut-off frequency decreases. Consequently, *LCR* filters can become impractical for cut-off frequencies in the lower audio range and below. The exclusion of inductors, resulting in a purely *RC* network, imposes the condition that all the poles lie on the negative real axis, and this restriction prohibits the use of passive *RC* networks for most filter applications.

The restrictions imposed by the exclusion of inductors can be removed by the introduction of an active device. Although there are several possible active elements that can be used to realize inductorless filters, the most commonly used type is the voltage operational amplifier. The active *RC* synthesis methods described here utilize the voltage operational amplifier, which is basically a voltage amplifier with a high gain and a frequency response extending down to zero frequency. Operational amplifiers were originally vacuum-tube amplifiers used in analogue computing for system simulation and for the solution of differential equations. The techniques that were developed in analogue computing form the basis of most of the present-day methods of active *RC* network synthesis. Since the 1960s, operational amplifiers have been available in integrated circuit form, and in the late 1960s the 741 type was introduced. Since then, many improvements have been made but the 741 is still the most widely used general-purpose operational amplifier and is one of the lowest-cost integrated circuits available.

Theoretically, active *RC* networks can provide any transfer function realizable by a passive network. The decision as to whether a filter should be implemented either by an active *RC* network or by a passive *LCR* network is normally based on practical considerations. An active network can provide the following advantages.

205

1. Reduced bulk, weight and cost.
2. Realizability in integrated circuit form.
3. Availability of power gain.
4. High input impedance and low output impedance, thus permitting a very much simplified design procedure using a cascade of unloaded first-order and second-order sections.

On the other hand, active filters have the following limitations in comparison with passive *LCR* filters:

1. Requirements for power supplies.
2. A dynamic range of the signal which is limited by the active device and the power supply.
3. A reduced frequency range: the upper limit is determined by the active device. Typically, a low-cost operational amplifier limits the filter passband to within the audio range. Although operation at higher frequencies, up to say 10 MHz, can be achieved, the amplifiers become progressively more expensive.
4. Increased sensitivity and possible instability: the sensitivity of a network is a measure of how the response or singularity locations change for a given change in any component value. An active network, in general, has greater sensitivity than its passive counterpart. For a passive network the poles cannot move out of the left-half plane, whereas for an active network no such restriction applies. In active network design it is necessary to ensure that instability does not arise because of additional right-half plane poles that can be introduced by the non-ideal characteristic of the active device. This problem can be difficult to overcome where higher frequency active devices are used.

Some of the above properties are considered in more detail in this and the following chapter, where we describe various synthesis methods for active *RC* networks that use the operational amplifier as the active element.

11.2 Principles of negative feedback

The operational amplifier is a device that is used in conjunction with negative feedback and we first look at some basic principles of negative feedback. A system that employs negative feedback can also be referred to as a control system and an elementary type is shown in block diagram form in Fig. 11.1. This block diagram is applicable to a wide variety of systems for the control of various physical quantities. Here, the controlled variable is assumed to be a voltage, but the theory is applicable to any other physical variable.

A negative feedback system operates on the basis of a difference signal being formed between the input signal V_i and some function of the output signal. Initially we assume that the function is βV_o where β is a constant whose magnitude

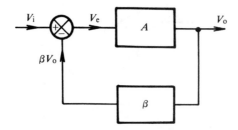

Figure 11.1 *Block diagram of feedback system.*

is less than or equal to unity. More generally, β can be a function of s and is known as the transfer function in the feedback path.

The difference signal V_e is

$$V_e = V_i - \beta V_o \tag{11.1}$$

V_e is referred to as the error signal and is the input to the block in the forward path. For the present, we assume that this block represents a voltage amplifier with a gain A, where A is a constant whose magnitude is very much greater than unity.

Since V_o is the output of the block A, we have

$$V_o = A(V_i - \beta V_o) \tag{11.2}$$

hence

$$\frac{V_o}{V_i} = \frac{A}{1 + A\beta} \tag{11.3}$$

The function V_o/V_i is known as the closed-loop transfer function.

If $A\beta \gg 1$ then (11.3) approximates to

$$\frac{V_o}{V_i} = \frac{1}{\beta} \tag{11.4}$$

that is, if the magnitude of the gain in the forward path is sufficiently large, the transfer function is determined only by β. This demonstrates a basic principle of a negative feedback system. It can be seen that a consequence of the magnitude of A being sufficiently large is that the error signal V_e is small. In the limit when $A = \infty$, V_e is zero. By putting $V_e = 0$ in (11.1) we obtain the result of (11.4) more easily than by the previous method. For more complex feedback arrangements, the initial assumption that the error signal is zero can lead to significant simplification in the analysis. The concept of zero error signal is known as the principle of 'virtual earth'.

The block diagram of Fig. 11.1 can be implemented using a voltage amplifier and two resistors R_1 and R_2 which form a potential divider as shown in Fig. 11.2. Clearly, we have

$$\beta = \frac{R_1}{R_1 + R_2} \tag{11.5}$$

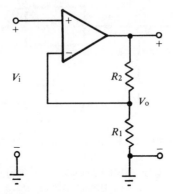

Figure 11.2 *Implementation of block diagram of Fig. 11.1 using operational amplifier with resistive feedback.*

and for $A\beta \gg 1$ we have from (11.3) and (11.5)

$$\frac{V_o}{V_i} = \frac{1}{\beta} = 1 + \frac{R_2}{R_1} \tag{11.6}$$

Thus for A sufficiently large, the closed-loop gain is determined only by the ratio of the resistor values. Note also that the condition $A\beta \gg 1$ can be written $A \gg 1/\beta$, which implies that the amplifier gain must be very much greater than the required closed-loop gain.

It is clear from the above that the amplifier is required to have the following properties:

1. A large magnitude of voltage gain A which extends down to zero frequency: typically, A is of the order of 10^5 at d.c.
2. Differential inputs: that is, if V_1 is the signal at the non-inverting input and V_2 is the signal at the inverting input, then $V_o = A(V_1 - V_2)$.
3. A high input impedance and a low output impedance: this ensures that the function of the output voltage fed back is determined only by the feedback network which, in the above case, comprises R_1 and R_2.

The above three properties are basic requirements for an operational amplifier. Further requirements to ensure stability are investigated in Chapter 12. We assume that the above requirements are satisfied in the synthesis methods described subsequently.

11.3 Resistive feedback

11.3.1 Voltage follower

A special case of the circuit of Fig. 11.2 occurs for $\beta = 1$. This is achieved by making $R_2/R_1 = 0$. This can be satisfied more easily by replacing R_2 by a short

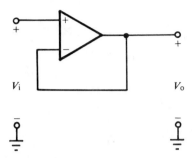

Figure 11.3 *Voltage follower.*

circuit and R_1 by an open circuit as shown in Fig. 11.3. From (11.3) we have

$$\frac{V_o}{V_i} = \frac{1}{1 + 1/A} \tag{11.7}$$

Since typically $A = 10^5$ at d.c., the closed-loop gain is very close to unity. The circuit has a high output impedance and a low output impedance and behaves as a high-grade emitter follower. It is known as a *voltage follower*.

11.3.2 Inverter

The arrangement of Fig. 11.2 can be redrawn as shown in Fig. 11.4. If we now modify the circuit in order to apply the input voltage source to the inverting terminal through the resistor R_1, and replace the voltage source at the non-inverting input with a short-circuit to ground, we obtain the circuit of Fig. 11.5.

To analyze the above case we observe that the voltage at the inverting input terminal is $-V_o/A$. We can then equate the currents through the two resistors

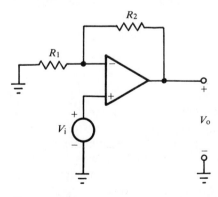

Figure 11.4 *Alternative form of network of Fig. 11.2.*

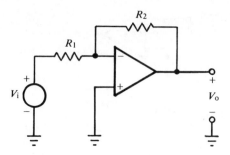

Figure 11.5 *Simple inverter arrangement.*

giving

$$\frac{V_i + V_o/A}{R_1} = \frac{-V_o/A - V_o}{R_2}$$

(11.8)

From the above we obtain

$$\frac{V_o}{V_i} = \frac{-R_2}{(1 + 1/A)R_1 + R_2/A}$$

(11.9)

If $A \gg 1$ then (11.9) becomes

$$\frac{V_o}{V_i} = \frac{-R_2}{R_1 + R_2/A}$$

(11.10)

If $A \gg R_2/R_1$ then (11.10) reduces to

$$\frac{V_o}{V_i} = \frac{-R_2}{R_1}$$

(11.11)

Thus the circuit is an inverter whose gain is determined by the ratio of the resistors. For equal resistor values we have a unity gain inverter.

(11.11) could have been obtained more easily by assuming the condition of virtual earth as follows: we equate the currents through the two resistors and obtain

$$\frac{V_i}{R_1} = \frac{-V_o}{R_2}$$

(11.12)

(11.11) follows directly.

The virtual-earth principle indicates directly that the input resistance of the network is equal to R_1. This can be compared to the non-inverting arrangement of Fig. 11.2 where the input resistance is very much higher, being determined by the input resistance of the operational amplifier.

A further comparison can be made between the non-inverting and inverting arrangements. It has been found that the magnitudes of the gains are different for each case. An explanation for this can be obtained as follows. Consider, in

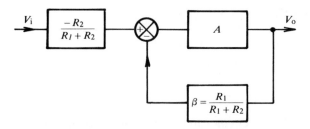

Figure 11.6 *Block diagram of inverter arrangement of Fig. 11.5.*

the case of the inverter, the potential divider formed by the two resistors with voltages V_o and V_i at the respective ends. We can readily determine the voltage V_2 at the amplifier inverting input as

$$V_2 = \frac{R_2}{R_1 + R_2} V_i + \frac{R_1}{R_1 + R_2} V_o \qquad (11.13)$$

Since the non-inverting input is grounded, the differential input signal to the amplifier is $-V_2$ and hence the block diagram is as shown in Fig. 11.6. A comparison of Figs. 11.1 and 11.6 indicates why the magnitude of the gain for the non-inverting circuit of Fig. 11.2 is different from that of the inverting circuit of Fig. 11.5.

11.3.3 Difference amplifier

The operations of Figs. 11.4 and 11.5 can be performed simultaneously to provide subtraction as shown in the circuit of Fig. 11.7. The voltage V_a is attenuated by the potential divider of R_3 and R_4.

We have that

$$V_o = \frac{R_4}{R_3 + R_4} \frac{R_1 + R_2}{R_1} V_a - \frac{R_2}{R_1} V_b \qquad (11.14)$$

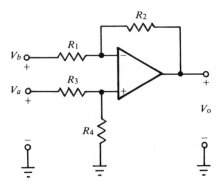

Figure 11.7 *Subtraction circuit.*

If $R_4 = R_2$ and $R_3 = R_1$ then (11.14) becomes

$$V_o = \frac{R_2}{R_1}\,(V_a - V_b) \tag{11.15}$$

11.3.4　Summing amplifier

The inverting amplifier circuit can be extended to perform the summation of any number of signals. This is illustrated in Fig. 11.8 for the case of three inputs. Applying the virtual-earth principle, we can express the relationship that the sum of the currents flowing into the node at the inverting terminal is zero as

$$\frac{V_1}{R_1} + \frac{V_2}{R_2} + \frac{V_3}{R_3} + \frac{V_o}{R_f} = 0 \tag{11.16}$$

Hence

$$V_o = -\frac{R_f}{R_1}\,V_1 - \frac{R_f}{R_2}\,V_2 - \frac{R_f}{R_3}\,V_3 \tag{11.17}$$

If all the resistor values are equal then V_o is the sum of all the inputs with sign inversion.

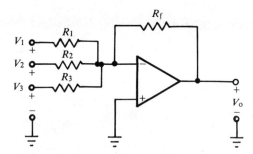

Figure 11.8 *Summing amplifier.*

11.4　Transfer function synthesis

The circuits described so far have used purely resistive networks for feedback, and have provided positive and negative fixed gain as well as the operations of summation and subtraction. We next consider the introduction of capacitors to provide methods of transfer function synthesis.

Theoretically, we can take any of the previous active networks and replace any resistor R_n by an RC impedance Z_n to obtain a network whose transfer function is a function of s. However, where capacitors are introduced, it must be borne

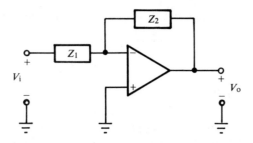

Figure 11.9 *Realization of transfer function* $-Z_2/Z_1$.

in mind that an operational amplifier requires a d.c. bias path to ground from each input. The requirement for input bias current, which is in the range of picoamps to microamps, depending upon the device type, imposes a restriction on the choice of RC impedances for the forward and feedback paths, and this is illustrated in a specific example later in the section.

The simplest arrangement for active RC synthesis is the inverter circuit of Fig. 11.5 with R_1 and R_2 replaced by Z_1 and Z_2 respectively as shown in

Table 11.1

	Elements	Impedance function
(i)	R	R
(ii)	C	$\dfrac{1}{Cs}$
(iii)	R / C	$\dfrac{R}{1 + CRs}$
(iv)	R C	$\dfrac{1 + CRs}{Cs}$
(v)	R_A R_B C	$(R_A + R_B)\dfrac{1 + Crs}{1 + CR_Bs}$ where $r = \dfrac{R_A R_B}{R_A + R_B}$

Fig. 11.9. Assuming a virtual earth, the transfer function is given by

$$\frac{V_o}{V_i} = -\frac{Z_2}{Z_1} \tag{11.18}$$

Thus the zeros of Z_2 and the poles of Z_1 become the zeros of the transfer function. Similarly, the zeros of Z_1 and the poles of Z_2 become the poles of the transfer function.

Since the singularities of an RC driving-point immittance are restricted to the origin or the negative real axis, the arrangement of Fig. 11.9 is suitable only for minimum-phase transfer functions whose singularities are real. Although this is a serious restriction, it is shown later that the arrangement is nevertheless an important one, since it can be used as a basic building-block in an arrangement with additional feedback paths to provide complex singularities.

To synthesize a specified transfer function with real singularities, we partition the singularities such that they can be assigned to lead to RC realizable impedances Z_1 and Z_2.

To facilitate the partitioning and selection of appropriate impedances for a specified transfer function, some simple RC combinations, together with their respective driving-point impedance functions, are shown in Table 11.1 on p. 213.

11.4.1 First-order lowpass function

For the first example we will realize a first-order lowpass function $F(s)$ given by

$$F(s) = \frac{-1}{Ts + 1} \tag{11.19}$$

This can be achieved by choosing Z_2 as a parallel RC section (entry (iii) in Table 11.1) and Z_1 as a resistor R as shown in Fig. 11.10. With the two resistor values equal, the transfer function of (11.19) is obtained where $T = RC$.

The arrangement of Fig. 11.10 satisfies the requirement for a resistive d.c. path from input to ground and, in general, is a satisfactory method of realizing a first-

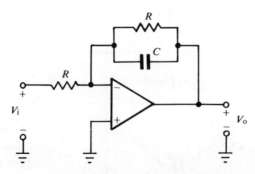

Figure 11.10 *Realization of transfer function of (11.19).*

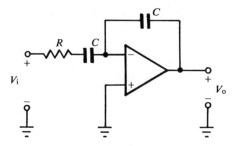

Figure 11.11 *Incorrect choice of impedances leading to violation of conditions for biasing.*

order transfer function. However, to demonstrate how it is possible to violate the above condition for biasing, consider an alternative choice of impedances where Z_1 is a series RC impedance (entry (iv) in Table 11.1) and Z_2 is a capacitor C as shown in Fig. 11.11. Substitution of the appropriate expressions for Z_1 and Z_2 in (11.18) yields the transfer function of (11.19). However, it can be observed that there is no d.c. path from the inverting input to ground, therefore the amplifier would not operate correctly. It should also be observed that at zero frequency, although theoretically the transfer function magnitude is unity, both Z_1 and Z_2 have infinite magnitude. The finite magnitude of the transfer function arises from cancellation of a pole and a zero at the origin. Therefore, even if the amplifier were correctly biased, the arrangement could not operate down to zero frequency and is an unsatisfactory method.

11.4.2 First-order lead or lag network

Consider next the transfer function $F(s)$ given by

$$F(s) = \frac{T_1 s + 1}{T_2 s + 1} \tag{11.20}$$

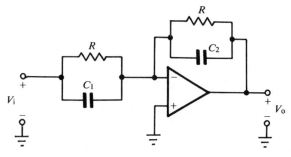

Figure 11.12 *Realization of transfer function of (11.20).*

This represents a lead network for $T_1 > T_2$ and a lag network for $T_1 < T_2$. (See also Sections 6.9 to 6.11.)

The transfer function of (11.20) can be realized as shown in Fig. 11.12 by choosing Z_1 and Z_2 as parallel RC impedances, and this satisfies the condition for biasing. Note that theoretically the transfer function can be obtained by choosing Z_1 and Z_2 as series RC impedances, but such an arrangement would have the same limitations as the circuit of Fig. 11.11.

11.4.3 Lead–lag network

Consider next the transfer function which is equivalent to a cascade of a lead and a lag network. Such a network has applications in feedback control systems in improving the stability and reducing low frequency errors. The transfer function $F(s)$ can be written

$$F(s) = -H \frac{(T_2s + 1)(T_3s + 1)}{(T_1s + 1)(T_4s + 1)} \tag{11.21}$$

where $T_1 > T_2 > T_3 > T_4$.

The segmented Bode diagram is shown in Fig. 11.13.

This transfer function can be realized by choosing both Z_1 and Z_2 as the series parallel combination of entry (v) of Table 11.1 as shown in Fig. 11.14. Note that for each impedance the pole is closer to the origin than is the respective zero, and this must be taken into account when assigning the singularities of $F(s)$ to those of the impedances. If, for example, we assign the zero at $-1/T_2$ as the zero of Z_2 then the pole at $-1/T_4$ cannot be assigned to Z_2. That is, it must be assigned

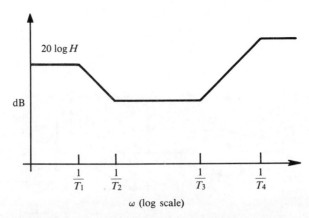

Figure 11.13 *Segmented Bode diagram for transfer function of (11.21).*

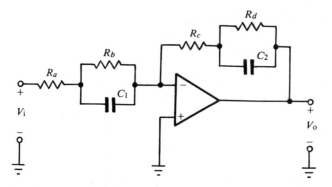

Figure 11.14 *Lead–lag network.*

as the zero of Z_1. We can then assign the pole at $-1/T_1$ as the pole of Z_2 and the zero at $-1/T_3$ as the pole of Z_1.

Writing

$$\left.\begin{aligned}
Z_1 &= (R_a + R_b)\,\frac{C_1 R_a R_b s/(R_a + R_b) + 1}{C_1 R_b s + 1} \\[2mm]
Z_2 &= (R_c + R_d)\,\frac{C_2 R_c R_d s/(R_c + R_d) + 1}{C_2 R_d s + 1}
\end{aligned}\right\} \tag{11.22}$$

and assigning the singularities as above, we obtain the following set of equations:

$$\left.\begin{aligned}
C_1\,\frac{R_a R_b}{R_a + R_b} &= T_4 \\[2mm]
C_1 R_b &= T_3 \\[2mm]
C_2\,\frac{R_c R_d}{R_c + R_d} &= T_2 \\[2mm]
C_2 R_d &= T_1
\end{aligned}\right\} \tag{11.23}$$

We have also that the d.c. input resistance R_0 is given by

$$R_0 = R_a + R_b \tag{11.24}$$

and the d.c. gain is $-H$ where

$$H = \frac{R_c + R_d}{R_a + R_b} \tag{11.25}$$

From (11.23), (11.24) and (11.25) we obtain the following design equations for the component values:

$$R_a = \frac{T_4 R_0}{T_3}$$

$$R_b = R_0 - R_a$$

$$C_1 = \frac{T_3}{R_b}$$

$$R_c = \frac{H R_0 T_2}{T_1}$$

$$R_d = H R_0 - R_c$$

$$C_2 = \frac{T_1}{R_d}$$

$$\left. \right\} \tag{11.26}$$

11.4.4 Integrator

One of the most widely used configurations for an operational amplifier is that which provides integration. As will be shown subsequently, the integrator can be used as a basic building-block in an arrangement with additional feedback loops to realize any transfer function.

The transfer function $F(s)$ of an ideal integrator with a time constant T is given by

$$F(s) = \frac{-1}{Ts} \tag{11.27}$$

The negative sign is included in anticipation of the inversion by the circuit of Fig. 11.15 which has the transfer function of (11.27) with $T = RC$.

Consider the steady-state frequency response. The theoretical magnitude function is given by

$$|F(\mathrm{j}\omega)| = \frac{1}{\omega T} \tag{11.28}$$

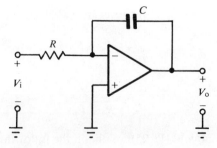

Figure 11.15 *Integrator with sign inversion.*

and we observe that the magnitude is infinite at zero frequency. This, of course, cannot be realized in practice, and the circuit of Fig. 11.15 has a magnitude at d.c. equal to the gain of the operational amplifier, i.e at zero frequency the capacitor behaves as an infinite impedance and hence there is no feedback. The effect of finite amplifier gain is considered in more detail subsequently in Section 12.3.

11.4.5 Differentiator

If the R and C in the circuit of Fig. 11.15 are interchanged, we obtain a differentiator circuit, as shown in Fig. 11.16, which has a theoretical transfer function $F(s)$ given by

$$F(s) = -Ts \tag{11.29}$$

where $T = RC$.

The differentiator, however, has a number of practical limitations. These include (a) a frequency-selective input impedance which becomes low at high frequencies, and (b) a high gain at high frequencies which can result in amplification of noise. Also, differentiators can be difficult to stabilize; this is considered in more detail in Section 12.2. For the above reasons, differentiators are used less frequently than integrators.

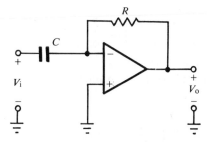

Figure 11.16 *Differentiator with sign inversion.*

11.4.6 Elimination of sign inversion

Although the sign inversion of the previous circuits can be eliminated by means of an additional inverter stage, the requirement for an additional operational amplifier can be avoided by using the circuit of Fig. 11.2 with R_1 and R_2 replaced with Z_1 and Z_2 respectively, as shown in Fig. 11.17. From (11.6) it follows that the transfer function $F(s)$ of the above circuit is given by

$$F(s) = \frac{Z_1 + Z_2}{Z_1} \tag{11.30}$$

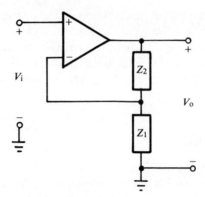

Figure 11.17 *Transfer function realization without sign inversion.*

Consider an inverted-L section interposed between the input of the network and the non-inverting terminal of the amplifier as shown in Fig. 11.18. The transfer function of the inverted-L section is

$$\frac{V_a}{V_i} = \frac{Z_2}{Z_1 + Z_2} \tag{11.31}$$

The overall transfer function is the product of the transfer functions of (11.30) and (11.31) giving

$$\frac{V_o}{V_i} = \frac{Z_2}{Z_1} \tag{11.32}$$

Thus the transfer function of (11.18) is obtained without sign inversion. Fig. 11.19 shows an example of how an integrator can be realized with no sign inversion using a single operational amplifier.

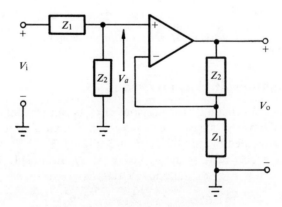

Figure 11.18 *Realization of transfer function Z_2/Z_1.*

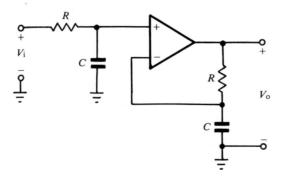

Figure 11.19 *Integrator with no sign inversion.*

11.4.7 Cascaded networks

As previously stated, an important advantage of active networks compared to passive networks is the simplification that can be achieved by breaking down the design of an active network into a cascade of unloaded first-order and second-order blocks.

An operational amplifier has an output resistance typically of the order of 100 Ω on open loop. However, the output impedance of a network whose output is at the amplifier output is determined also by the feedback. Consider, for example, the arrangement of Fig. 11.20 where the amplifier has a gain A and an output resistance R_a. We can determine the output impedance by applying a voltage V at the network output with the input voltage V_i set to zero. The output impedance Z_0 of the network is given by $Z_0 = V/I$.

The voltage V_a at the inverting input of the amplifier is given by

$$V_a = V/F(s) \tag{11.33}$$

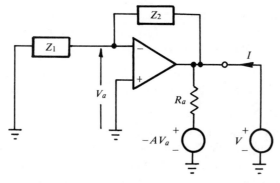

Figure 11.20 *Determination of output impedance.*

where

$$F(s) = \frac{Z_1 + Z_2}{Z_1}$$

The current I is given by

$$I = \frac{V}{Z_1 + Z_2} + \frac{V + AV_a}{R_a} \qquad (11.34)$$

Substituting for V_a from (11.33) we have

$$I = \frac{V}{Z_1 + Z_2} + \frac{V[1 + A/F(s)]}{R_a} \qquad (11.35)$$

Thus the output admittance is a parallel combination of Y_a and Y_b, i.e.

$$Y = Y_a + Y_b \qquad (11.36)$$

where

$$Y_a = \frac{1 + A/F(s)}{R_a}$$

$$Y_b = \frac{1}{Z_1 + Z_2}$$

Note that where the input is applied at the non-inverting terminal, as in the arrangement of Fig. 11.4, the expression for output impedance is identical to that of the above case.

It is clear from (11.36) that the magnitude of the output admittance cannot be less than $1/R_a$ and therefore the magnitude of the output impedance cannot be greater than R_a. In some cases, the output impedance approximates to a resistance whose value is very much less than R_a. For example, for the unity-gain inverter ($R_1 = R_2 = R$), we have $F(s) = 2$ and hence the output impedance comprises a shunt resistor $R_a/(1 + A/2)$ across a resistor $2R$. On the other hand, for the case of an integrator with a time constant T we have $F(s) = (1 + Ts)/Ts$, and at d.c. the shunt resistance has a value R_a.

From the above it can be concluded that the loading in a cascade arrangement can be neglected if the following conditions are met:

1. The output of each stage is taken from the output of an operational amplifier.
2. The input resistance of each stage is very much greater than R_a.

Where the input to the stage includes a series resistor R to a virtual earth, then a resistor value of, say, 10 kΩ is normally sufficient. Where the input is applied at the non-inverting terminal, as in the arrangement of Fig. 11.17, the input impedance is that of the operational amplifier which typically is 1 MΩ for a 741 but can be of the order of 10^{12} Ω or even greater for amplifiers which have FET input circuits.

Thus it is a relatively straightforward procedure to design cascade circuits with negligible loading. The transfer function of the cascade arrangement is then the product of the individual open-circuit transfer functions of the separate stages. Although, theoretically, it is possible to realize a transfer function of any order using a single operational amplifier, even for the case of complex poles, in practice it is usual to realize the transfer function as a cascade of second-order blocks, together with a first-order block if the overall order is odd. This approach has the following advantages:

1. Design simplification.
2. Improved stability.
3. Reduced error due to finite amplifier gain and bandwidth.
4. Reduced sensitivity to component changes and tolerances.

We therefore need to consider the realization of transfer functions up to second order only, in order to develop a general method of synthesis.

11.4.8 Realization of complex poles using a single operational amplifier

The methods described so far are suitable only for those cases where the poles are purely real. To obtain complex poles an additional feedback path or a path to ground is required. The two most popular techniques for realizing complex poles using single operational amplifiers, usually known as the *multiple-feedback method* and the *Sallen–Key method* are described here.

11.5 Multiple-feedback method

The term 'multiple feedback' can describe a number of arrangements but usually refers to the network of Fig. 11.21, which consists of a single operational amplifier together with five immittances, and with the non-inverting input grounded. Each immittance normally consists of a single resistor or a single capacitor.

The analysis of the network is facilitated by denoting each immittance in admittance form. If we assume a virtual earth at the inverting input, then the transfer function relating the output voltage V_o to the voltage V_2 at node 2 as shown is given by

$$\frac{V_o}{V_2} = \frac{-Y_4}{Y_5} \tag{11.37}$$

Hence

$$V_2 = \frac{-Y_5}{Y_4} V_o \tag{11.38}$$

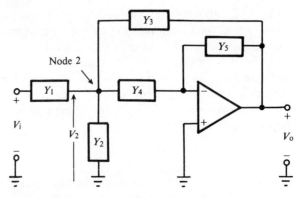

Figure 11.21 *Multiple-feedback network.*

Since the voltage at each node can be expressed in terms of V_i and V_o it is possible to express the current through each immittance in terms of these voltages and the admittances. If we equate the sum of the currents flowing into node 2 to zero, this leads to the following expression for the transfer function:

$$\frac{V_o}{V_i} = \frac{-Y_1 Y_4}{Y_5(Y_1 + Y_2 + Y_3 + Y_4) + Y_3 Y_4} \tag{11.39}$$

11.5.1 Lowpass case

For a lowpass realization, we require that there be no zeros at the origin. It is clear from the numerator of the above expression that Y_1 and Y_4 must both be resistive.

Consider next the denominator, which consists of the sum of products of pairs of admittances, and which is required to have a constant term, a term in s and a term in s^2. Taking the requirement for an s^2 term first, we observe that since Y_4 is resistive, the product $Y_3 Y_4$ cannot provide the s^2 term, and therefore we must have Y_5, which is a factor in all the other products, as capacitive. Consider next the requirement for a constant term. With Y_5 capacitive, the only product that can provide a constant is $Y_3 Y_4$ and therefore Y_3 must be resistive. With Y_3 resistive, the only product that can provide the s^2 term is $Y_2 Y_5$ and hence Y_2 must be capacitive. Thus the lowpass form is unique and is shown in Fig. 11.22 for the equal resistor case with the conductance values normalized to unity and with $Y_2 = C_1 s$ and $Y_5 = C_2 s$.

By substituting the above admittance values into (11.39) we obtain the normalized lowpass transfer function

$$\frac{V_o}{V_i} = \frac{-1}{C_1 C_2 s^2 + 3 C_2 s + 1} \tag{11.40}$$

The standard second-order lowpass form with the d.c. gain and ω_0 both nor-

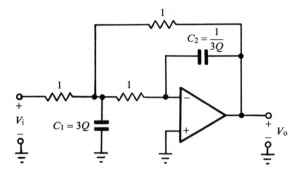

Figure 11.22 *Normalized lowpass multiple-feedback network.*

malized to unity is

$$\frac{V_o}{V_i} = \frac{-1}{s^2 + s/Q + 1} \tag{11.41}$$

Comparing (11.40) and (11.41), we obtain the following design equations for C_1 and C_2:

$$\left.\begin{array}{l} C_1 = 3Q \\[2mm] C_2 = \dfrac{1}{3Q} \end{array}\right\} \tag{11.42}$$

(11.42) indicates that the above circuit can theoretically be used for any finite value of Q.

For a resistor value R and an undamped natural angular frequency ω_0, we can apply impedance and frequency scaling to obtain the denormalized design equations for C_1 and C_2 as

$$\left.\begin{array}{l} C_1 = \dfrac{3Q}{R\omega_0} \\[3mm] C_2 = \dfrac{1}{3QR\omega_0} \end{array}\right\} \tag{11.43}$$

EXAMPLE 11.1

Design a fourth-order Butterworth lowpass filter with a 3 dB cut-off frequency of 2 kHz by using the multiple feedback technique. Use a resistor value of 10 kΩ.

SOLUTION

As a first step we will design a Butterworth filter with the resistor value and the angular cut-off frequency normalized to unity.

From Option E6.1 of ENTIS, the normalized values of Q and ω_0 for the two individual stages are as follows:

Stage	ω_0	Q
1	1	0.5412
2	1	1.3066

Hence from (11.43) with $R = 1$ we obtain the following normalized values for the capacitors:

Stage	C_1	C_2
1	1.6236	0.6159
2	3.9197	0.2551

The normalized filter is shown in Fig. 11.23.

We can impedance scale to obtain the denormalized values for a resistor value R of 10 kΩ by dividing every capacitor value by 10^4. To frequency scale to obtain a cut-off frequency f_c of 2 kHz, we divide every capacitor value by $4\pi \times 10^3$. Applying the two scalings we obtain the following capacitor values:

Stage	C_1/nF	C_2/nF
1	19.920	4.9011
2	31.192	2.0300

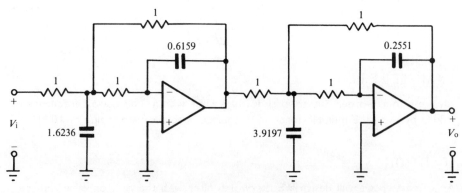

Figure 11.23 *Normalized fourth-order Butterworth lowpass filter.*

Computer Exercise 11.1

Design various Butterworth, Bessel and Chebyshev lowpass filters using the method of the above example, and check the results using Option F1.1 of ENTIS.

11.5.2 Highpass case

We can derive the highpass realization of the multiple feedback case using a similar procedure to that of the lowpass case. That is, since we require two zeros at the origin, inspection of the numerator of (11.39) indicates that Y_1 and Y_4 must both be capacitive. We can then use a procedure similar to that used for the lowpass case to obtain a unique choice of the remaining immittances. However, we can obtain the same result more simply by applying the RC lowpass-to-highpass transformation of Section 8.4.4 to the network of Fig. 11.22 to obtain the equal-capacitor realization with unity gain at high frequencies.

For convenience we can normalize the capacitor values to 1 F. Then, with

$$Y_1 = Y_3 = Y_4 = s \qquad Y_2 = 1/R_1 \qquad Y_5 = 1/R_2$$

(11.39) becomes

$$\frac{V_o}{V_i} = \frac{-R_1 R_2 s^2}{R_1 R_2 s^2 + 3R_1 s + 1} \tag{11.44}$$

The standard second-order highpass form with high frequency gain and ω_0 both normalized to unity is

$$\frac{V_o}{V_i} = \frac{-s^2}{s^2 + s/Q + 1} \tag{11.45}$$

The negative sign is included to enable compatibility with (11.44). By comparing (11.44) and (11.45), we obtain the following design equations for R_1 and R_2:

$$\left. \begin{aligned} R_1 &= \frac{1}{3Q} \\ R_2 &= 3Q \end{aligned} \right\} \tag{11.46}$$

Fig. 11.24 shows the normalized circuit.

For a capacitor value C and an undamped natural angular frequency ω_0 we can apply impedance and frequency scaling to obtain the denormalized design equations for R_1 and R_2 as

$$\left. \begin{aligned} R_1 &= \frac{1}{3QC\omega_0} \\ R_2 &= \frac{3Q}{C\omega_0} \end{aligned} \right\} \tag{11.47}$$

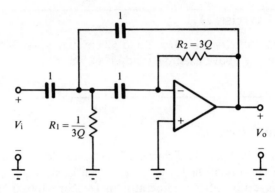

Figure 11.24 *Normalized highpass multiple-feedback network.*

EXAMPLE 11.2

Design a fourth-order Butterworth highpass filter with 3 dB cut-off frequency of 5 kHz by using the multiple feedback technique. Use a resistor value of 10 kΩ.

SOLUTION

We can use the normalized lowpass filter of Fig. 11.23 as a prototype and transform about $\omega = 1$ to a normalized highpass RC network (see Section 8.4.4). Each 1 Ω resistor transforms to a 1 F capacitor and each capacitor C_n *transforms to a resistor* $R_n = 1/C_n$.

This leads to the following normalized values for the resistors with $C = 1$ F:

Stage	R_1	R_2
1	0.6159	1.6236
2	0.2551	3.9197

The normalized filter is shown in Fig. 11.25.

We can impedance scale to obtain the denormalized values for a capacitor value C of 1 nF by dividing every resistor value by 10^{-9}. To frequency scale to obtain a cut-off frequency f_c of 10 kHz, we divide every resistor value by $2\pi \times 10^4$. Applying the two scalings we obtain the following resistor values:

Stage	$R_1/k\Omega$	$R_2/k\Omega$
1	9.802	25.84
2	4.060	62.38

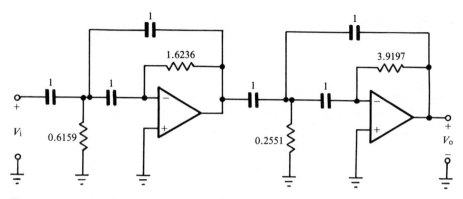

Figure 11.25 *Normalized fourth-order Butterworth highpass filter.*

Computer Exercise 11.2

Design various Butterworth and Chebyshev highpass filters by using the method of the above example and then check the results using Option F1.2 of ENTIS.

11.5.3 Bandpass filters using cascade arrangement

A bandpass filter, obtained by transforming an nth-order lowpass filter with all zeros at infinity, has $2n$ poles and n zeros at the origin. For n even, the filter can be realized by a cascade of $n/2$ lowpass and $n/2$ highpass second-order sections, the highpass sections providing the n zeros at the origin. Alternatively, we can use a cascade of n second-order bandpass sections. For n odd, we require at least one bandpass second-order section.

For a cascade arrangement, the relationship between the passband magnitude and the scaling factors of the individual sections needs to be considered. We define the scaling factor as the constant H in the second-order transfer function expressed in the following standard form:

$$\frac{V_o}{V_i} = \frac{\pm H(s/\omega_o)^r}{(s/\omega_o)^2 + s/(\omega_0 Q) + 1} \tag{11.48}$$

where $r = 0, 1, 2$ for the lowpass, bandpass and highpass cases respectively.

For the lowpass case, H is the d.c. gain, and for the highpass case H is the high-frequency gain. For the bandpass case the gain at $\omega = \omega_0$ is HQ. The frequency ω_0 is known as the midband frequency and the gain at ω_0 is known as the midband gain. Thus we have that H is the midband gain divided by Q.

Suppose we require a filter to have unity gain in the passband. For a lowpass or highpass filter this is achieved simply by having $H = 1$ for each section. For a bandpass filter, however, the situation is not quite so straightforward. Consider a first-order lowpass section with unity d.c. gain and a transfer function

$$\frac{V_o}{V_i} = \frac{\alpha}{s + \alpha} \qquad (11.49)$$

By applying the transformation $P_3(s)$, given by (8.57), to a lowpass filter whose d.c. gain is unity we obtain a bandpass transfer function whose midband gain is unity. Transforming (11.49) we have

$$\frac{V_o}{V_i} = \frac{\alpha}{(s + 1/s)/B + \alpha}$$

$$= \frac{\alpha B s}{s^2 + \alpha B s + 1} \qquad (11.50)$$

Therefore the bandpass section requires a scaling factor $H = \alpha B$ to provide unity gain in the passband.

Consider next a second-order section of the lowpass prototype with unity d.c. gain and a transfer function

$$\frac{V_o}{V_i} = \frac{\omega_0^2}{s^2 + s\omega_0/Q + \omega_0^2} \qquad (11.51)$$

By transforming (11.51), and after some manipulation, we obtain the bandpass transfer function

$$\frac{V_o}{V_i} = \frac{B^2 \omega_0^2 s^2}{s^4 + \ldots + 1} \qquad (11.52)$$

The denominator of (11.52) can be factorized into two quadratic factors which have been shown to have the same Q values and whose ω_0 values ω_{0_1} and ω_{0_2} are related by $\omega_{0_1}\omega_{0_2} = 1$ (see (8.60c)).

Hence (11.52) can be written

$$\frac{V_o}{V_i} = \frac{B\omega_0(s/\omega_{0_1})}{(s/\omega_{0_1})^2 + (s/Q\omega_{0_1}) + 1} \cdot \frac{B\omega_0(s/\omega_{0_2})}{(s/\omega_{0_2})^2 + (s/Q\omega_{0_2}) + 1} \qquad (11.53)$$

From (11.53) we deduce that the gain at the centre frequency of the bandpass filter is unity if the product of the magnitude scale factors of the second-order bandpass sections is equal to $(B\omega_0)^2$. For example, we can make the scale factor of each section equal to $B\omega_0$. Note that ω_0 is the value for the pole-pair of the prototype lowpass. Note also that the midband frequency of each separate section is not equal to the centre frequency of the overall filter.

If a passband gain value greater than unity is required then the scale factors can be increased accordingly. However, as will be shown in Chapter 12, an increase in the scale factor of a section results in a corresponding increase in the required gain for the operational amplifier. Where sufficient additional gain is not available then the increase in magnitude scaling is best provided by an extra operational amplifier with resistive feedback in either the inverting or non-inverting mode.

11.5.4 Multiple-feedback bandpass

To obtain the bandpass realization of the multiple feedback arrangement of Fig. 11.21 we require to choose the admittance in the transfer function of (11.39) to obtain one zero at the origin. Consideration of the numerator indicates that one of the elements of the product $Y_1 Y_4$ must be a resistor and the other must be a capacitor. That is, there are two possible choices for the numerator, and it can be shown that both can lead to complex poles. Thus for the bandpass case the selection is not unique. Here we consider the case where Y_1 is resistive and Y_4 is capacitive.

Consider the denominator and the requirement for a constant term. Since Y_4 is capacitive the product $Y_3 Y_4$ cannot provide the constant term. Therefore Y_5, which is a factor in every other product, must be resistive. With Y_5 resistive the only product that can provide the s^2 term is the product $Y_3 Y_4$. Hence Y_3 must be capacitive.

The remaining admittance Y_2 can be chosen to be either resistive or capacitive, or can be omitted from the circuit. If Y_2 is resistive then the admittances Y_1 and Y_2 form an inverted-L attenuator which can be replaced by the Thevenin equivalent of a single resistor together with a voltage source equivalent to the attenuation input signal. If Y_2 is capacitive, this will contribute to the s term in the denominator of the transfer function and hence reduce the value of Q.

Here we consider the equal-capacitor case with Y_2 omitted. With the capacitor values normalized to unity and $Y_1 = G_1$ and $Y_5 = G_2$ the transfer function is

$$\frac{V_o}{V_i} = \frac{-G_1 s}{s^2 + 2G_2 s + G_1 G_2} \tag{11.54}$$

Comparing (11.48) and (11.54), with ω_0 normalized to unity, gives the following design equations for the resistor values $R_1 = 1/G_1$ and $R_2 = 1/G_2$:

$$\left.\begin{aligned} R_1 &= \frac{1}{2Q} \\ R_2 &= 2Q \end{aligned}\right\} \tag{11.55}$$

The circuit of the normalized bandpass case is shown in Fig. 11.26. Since there are only two component values to be determined, it is not possible to specify H independently. Comparison of the numerators of (11.48) and (11.54) indicates that $H = 1/R_1$ and hence from (11.55)

$$H = 2Q \tag{11.56}$$

This gives a magnitude at $\omega = 1$ of $2Q^2$.

For a capacitor value C and an undamped natural angular frequency ω_0 we

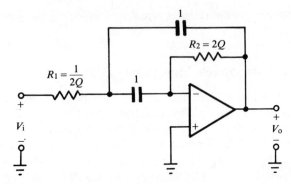

Figure 11.26 *Normalized bandpass multiple-feedback network using four immittances (H = 2Q).*

can apply impedance and frequency scaling to obtain the denormalized design equations for R_1 and R_2 as

$$\left. \begin{array}{c} R_1 = \dfrac{1}{2QC\omega_0} \\[4mm] R_2 = \dfrac{2Q}{C\omega_0} \end{array} \right\} \tag{11.57}$$

EXAMPLE 11.3

Design a multiple feedback fourth-order bandpass Butterworth filter whose 3 dB frequencies are 2 kHz and 8 kHz. Determine the midband gain of the final circuit.

SOLUTION

A fourth-order bandpass, which has two zeros at the origin and four poles, can be realized by either a cascade of a second-order lowpass and a second order highpass or a cascade of two second-order bandpass circuits. Here we use the latter approach to demonstrate the use of the second-order bandpass circuit. We will use a capacitor value of 1 nF.

We have that the centre frequency $\omega_m = 2\pi \times (2 \times 8)^{1/2} \times 10^3$. We first determine the normalized poles using the procedure of Example 8.6 or by means of Option E6.3 of ENTIS.

From Example 8.6, $B = 1.5$, and the poles are

$$\text{Pole-pair 1: } -0.8018 \pm j1.5665$$

$$\text{Pole-pair 2: } -0.2589 \pm j0.5059$$

Using the relationships of (3.19) we obtain the following values for ω_0 and Q:

Pole-pair	ω_0	Q
1	1.7596	1.0974
2	0.5683	1.0974

Using (11.51) with C normalized to unity we obtain the following values for the resistors:

Stage	R_1	R_2
1	0.2589	1.2471
2	0.8017	3.8623

To obtain a centre frequency of 4 kHz we can divide each resistor value by ω_m, and to obtain a capacitor value of 1 nF we divide each resistor value by 10^{-9}. By combining these two scalings, we obtain the following values for the resistors:

Stage	$R_1/k\Omega$	$R_2/k\Omega$
1	10.30	49.62
2	31.90	153.70

11.5.5 Midband gain

From (11.56), the scaling factor of each section of the equal-capacitor multiple feedback bandpass network is $2Q$. From (11.53), the required scaling factor to give unity gain at the centre frequency is $B\omega_0$. Since ω_0 refers to the normalized lowpass poles and is unity for the Butterworth case, the required scale factor for unity gain is therefore equal to B. Hence the overall gain at the centre frequency of the filter is $(2Q/B)^2 = 2.14$, i.e. 6.6 dB.

Computer Exercise 11.3

Design various Butterworth and Chebyshev bandpass filters by using the method of the above example and check the results using Option F1.3 of ENTIS.

11.6 Sallen and Key method

The Sallen and Key method is also referred to as kRC synthesis since it is based on the concept of an ideal active device with a fixed voltage gain k (i.e. a voltage-controlled voltage source) used in conjunction with RC feedback. In practice the gain k is usually achieved by using an operational amplifier in the non-inverting arrangement of Fig. 11.17. In many cases, the performance of the kRC circuit is similar to its counterpart in the multiple feedback arrangement, and there is little to choose between the two methods. For the kRC technique, realizations with $k = 1$ are possible; for these cases, if only moderate Q-values are required then a simple emitter–follower can be used to provide the voltage-controlled voltage source (VCVS).

11.6.1 Lowpass realization

Figure 11.27a shows the arrangement for a lowpass transfer function. To analyze the network we observe that the voltage at the input to the VCVS is V_o/k. The resistor R_2 and the capacitor C_2 form an inverted-L on open circuit which has a voltage transfer function $1/(1 + C_2R_2s)$. Hence the voltage V at node 2, the junction of R_1 and R_2, is determined in terms of V_o. All the currents flowing into node 2 can be expressed in terms of V_i and V_o and, by equating the sum of the currents to zero, the following transfer function can be obtained:

$$\frac{V_o}{V_i} = \frac{k}{R_1R_2C_1C_2s^2 + [R_2C_2 + R_1C_1(1 - k) + R_1C_2]s + 1} \tag{11.58}$$

The two following cases are of particular interest.

Equal resistors and equal capacitors
If we normalize the resistor values to unity and let $C_1 = C_2 = C$, the transfer function of (11.58) becomes

$$\frac{V_o}{V_i} = \frac{k}{C^2s^2 + (3 - k)Cs + 1} \tag{11.59}$$

By comparing (11.59) with the standard form of (11.41), we have that $C = 1$, and (11.59) becomes

$$\frac{V_o}{V_i} = \frac{k}{s^2 + (3 - k)s + 1} \tag{11.60}$$

where

$$k = 3 - \frac{1}{Q} \tag{11.61}$$

Note that the d.c. gain is k, which could be readily deduced by inspection of the network. We observe also that theoretically there is no restriction on the

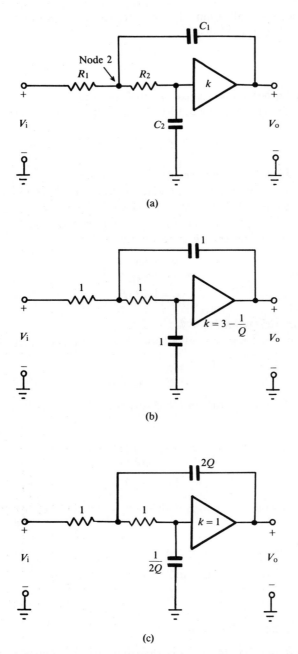

Figure 11.27 *Sallen–Key second-order lowpass circuit: (a) general form, (b) normalized, equal R, equal C, (c) normalized, equal R, k = 1.*

value of Q for this realization. The normalized equal-R, equal-C network is shown in Fig. 11.27b.

EXAMPLE 11.4

Design a second-order lowpass Butterworth filter whose 3 dB cut-off frequency is 1 kHz by using the above Sallen and Key circuit. Use a resistor value of 10 kΩ.

SOLUTION

We have that $Q = 0.7071$ and hence from (11.60), $k = 1.586$.

To obtain a cut-off frequency of 10 kHz we frequency scale by dividing the capacitor value by $2\pi \times 10^4$. To obtain a resistor value of 10 kΩ, we impedance scale by dividing the capacitor value by 10^4. This gives a capacitor value of 1.59 nF. Thus the parameters are as follows:

$$k = 1.586$$
$$R = 10 \text{ k}\Omega$$
$$C = 1.59 \text{ nF}$$

Equal resistor values and k = 1

For $k = 1$, with equal resistor values normalized to unity, (11.58) becomes

$$\frac{V_o}{V_i} = \frac{1}{C_1 C_2 s^2 + 2C_2 s + 1} \tag{11.62}$$

By comparing (11.62) with the standard form of (11.41), we obtain the following design equations:

$$\left. \begin{array}{l} C_2 = \dfrac{1}{2Q} \\[2mm] C_1 = 2Q \end{array} \right\} \tag{11.63}$$

The normalized equal-R network with $k = 1$ is shown in Fig. 11.27c.

11.6.2 Highpass realization

The highpass realizations of the above circuits can be obtained by the RC–CR transformation of Section 8.4.4.

11.6.3 Bandpass realization

As previously stated, bandpass filters that have an even number of zeros at the origin can be obtained by a cascade of lowpass and highpass second-order networks. Where there are an odd number of singularities at the origin, as would be obtained by transformation of an odd-order lowpass, then a second-order

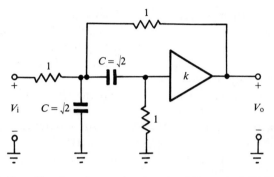

Figure 11.28 *Sallen–Key bandpass circuit: equal R, equal C, k = 4 − √2/Q.*

bandpass network is required. Figure 11.28 shows a kRC second-order bandpass realization for equal-R, equal-C with R normalized to unity. The transfer function, which can be obtained using the same method of analysis as applied to the lowpass case, is given by

$$\frac{V_o}{V_i} = \frac{kCs/2}{C^2s^2/2 + (2 - k/2)Cs + 1} \tag{11.64a}$$

By comparing (11.64a) with the standard form of (11.48), we have that $C = \sqrt{2}$ and (11.64a) becomes

$$\frac{V_o}{V_i} = \frac{ks/\sqrt{2}}{s^2 + (4 - k)s/\sqrt{2} + 1} \tag{11.64b}$$

Further comparison gives

$$Q = \frac{\sqrt{2}}{4 - k}$$

i.e.

$$k = 4 - \frac{\sqrt{2}}{Q} \tag{11.65}$$

Computer Exercise 11.4

Design various lowpass, highpass and bandpass filters using the kRC realizations and check the results using Option F2 of ENTIS.

11.7 State-variable method

The single operational amplifier networks described above provide simple methods of synthesis for transfer functions up to second order with zeros at infinity and/or the origin. In practice, amplifier imperfections in terms of finite gain and bandwidth limit the use of the above methods to moderate Q-values up to, say, 20. The techniques can be extended to provide zeros at other locations but, because of the interaction of circuit elements, difficulties can then arise in separate adjustment of the poles and zeros.

Where higher Q-values are required, or where the zeros are located at positions other than the origin or at infinity, then an alternative technique, known as the state-variable method, is preferable. This method requires more operational amplifiers but is less sensitive to amplifier imperfections than are the above methods. Also, it can simultaneously provide lowpass, highpass, bandpass and other outputs.

The state-variable method originates from the field of analogue computing, where integrators and summing amplifiers were employed as basic building-blocks for the solution of linear differential equations. The name is derived from state-space theory where the state equations lead to the state-variable form of simulation.

Any order of linear differential equation can be set up using the state-variable method but for filter synthesis, in the interests of reduced sensitivity of pole locations with respect to changes in component values, it is preferable to use a cascade of second-order networks.

11.7.1 Lowpass, highpass and bandpass realizations

To derive the second-order realization we start with the normalized lowpass transfer function. In anticipation of an arrangement with several outputs, we will denote the lowpass output as V_{o_1}. Also we anticipate sign inversion and write

$$\frac{V_{o_1}}{V_i} = \frac{-1}{s^2 + s/Q + 1} \tag{11.66}$$

We rearrange (11.66) to express the relationship in terms of operations of integration and summation. In the interests of minimizing component count, we use sign-inverting integrators and summing amplifiers and hence rearrange in the following steps:

$$-(s^2 + s/Q + 1)V_{o_1} = V_i \tag{11.67a}$$

$$s^2 V_{o_1} = -(V_i + V_{o_1} + sV_{o_1}/Q) \tag{11.67b}$$

$$V_{o_1} = \frac{-1}{s^2}(V_i + V_{o_1} + sV_{o_1}/Q) \tag{11.67c}$$

(11.67c) leads to the block diagram of Fig. 11.29a. For this diagram to lead to a practical realization, we must complete the paths that provide the signals V_{o_1} and sV_{o_1}/Q.

The path for V_{o_1} can be completed directly from node 1, the output of the second integrator. To complete the path for sV_{o_1}/Q we observe that the signal

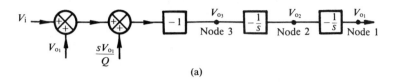

(a)

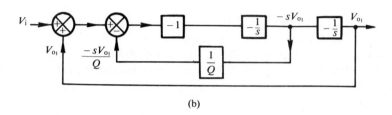

(b)

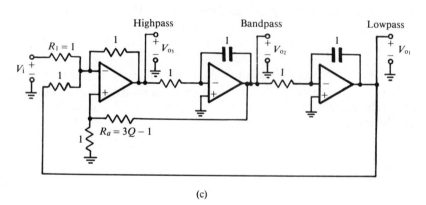

(c)

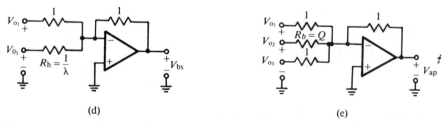

(d)   (e)

Figure 11.29 *State-variable realization of second-order transfer functions: (a) block diagram representation of (11.67c), (b) block diagram with closed paths, (c) practical realization of lowpass, bandpass and highpass outputs; (d) bandstop output, (e) allpass output.*

V_{o_2} at node 2, the input to the second integrator, is given by

$$\frac{V_{o_1}}{V_{o_2}} = \frac{-1}{s} \tag{11.68}$$

i.e.

$$V_{o_2} = -sV_{o_1} \tag{11.69}$$

Note also that

$$V_{o_3} = -sV_{o_2} = s^2 V_{o_1} \tag{11.70}$$

Hence the paths can be completed as shown in Fig. 11.29b.

We next replace the blocks with amplifiers, as shown in Fig. 11.29c, with the signal $V_{o_2} = -sV_{o_1}$ applied to the non-inverting input of the summing amplifier via an inverted-L resistive attenuator with the shunt resistor value normalized to unity. The resistor values for the summing amplifier and the integrator amplifiers are also normalized to unity.

We now determine the value of the series resistor R_a for the attenuator. Denoting the output signal of the attenuator as V_a we have

$$\frac{V_a}{V_{o_2}} = \frac{1}{1 + R_a} \tag{11.71}$$

We can apply the virtual-earth principle to the summing amplifier. This principle implies that the signals at the inverting and non-inverting inputs are equal. The sum of the currents flowing into the node at the inverting input is equal to zero, and therefore

$$(V_i - V_a) + (V_{o_1} - V_a) + (V_{o_3} - V_a) = 0 \tag{11.72}$$

which simplifies to

$$V_{o_3} = -(V_i + V_{o_1} - 3V_a) \tag{11.73}$$

From (11.69), (11.71) and (11.73) we have

$$V_{o_3} = -\left(V_i + V_{o_1} + \frac{3s}{1 + R_a} V_{o_1}\right) \tag{11.74}$$

Substituting from (11.70) for V_{o_3} in (11.74)

$$s^2 V_{o_1} = -\left(V_i + V_{o_1} + \frac{3s}{1 + R_a} V_{o_1}\right) \tag{11.75}$$

By comparing (11.75) and (11.67b) we have

$$R_a = 3Q - 1 \tag{11.76}$$

Magnitude scaling

The introduction of a magnitude scale factor in the numerator of (11.66) can be achieved simply by altering the value of the resistor R_1 in Fig. 11.29c. For a scale factor H we have $R_1 = 1/H$.

EXAMPLE 11.5

Design a second-order lowpass Butterworth filter whose 3 dB cut-off frequency is 10 kHz, using the state-variable method. Use a resistor value of 10 kΩ.

SOLUTION

We have that $Q = 0.7071$ and hence from (11.76) the normalized series resistor R_a of the attenuator is given by $R_a = 1.121$.

To obtain a cut-off frequency of 10 kHz we frequency scale by dividing the capacitor values by $2\pi \times 10^4$. To obtain a resistor value of 10 kΩ for all resistors except R_a, we impedance scale by dividing the capacitor value by 10^4. This gives a capacitor value of 1.59 nF. Thus the parameters are as follows:

$$R_a = 11.21 \text{ k}\Omega$$

$$R = 10 \text{ k}\Omega$$

$$C = 1.59 \text{ nF}$$

Computer Exercise 11.5

Design various Butterworth, Bessel and Chebyshev lowpass filters by using the state-variable method, and check the results using Option F3.1 of ENTIS.

From (11.66) and (11.69) we have that V_{o2} is given by

$$\frac{V_{o2}}{V_i} = \frac{s}{s^2 + s/Q + 1} \tag{11.77}$$

Similarly, from (11.66) and (11.70), we have that V_{o3} is given by

$$\frac{V_{o3}}{V_i} = \frac{-s^2}{s^2 + s/Q + 1} \tag{11.78}$$

Therefore the bandpass output V_{o2} and the highpass output V_{o3} are simultaneously available at nodes 2 and 3 respectively.

Computer Exercise 11.6

Design various highpass and bandpass filters using the state-variable method, and check the results using Options F3.2 and F3.3 of ENTIS.

11.7.2 Complex zeros

The lowpass, bandpass and highpass signals at nodes 1, 2 and 3, respectively, can be combined with appropriate scaling factors and sign inversion where necessary, using a summing amplifier to produce zeros anywhere in the s-plane. We demonstrate this by two examples, namely, the case of zeros on the real frequency axis for a bandstop response, and the case of zeros in the right-half plane for an allpass response.

11.7.3 Bandstop section

The normalized transfer function of a bandstop section can be written

$$\frac{V_{bs}}{V_i} = \frac{\lambda s^2 + 1}{s^2 + s/Q + 1} \tag{11.79}$$

Hence from (11.70) and (11.79)

$$V_{bs} = \lambda V_{o3} + V_{o1} \tag{11.80}$$

To realize the above transfer function we therefore require to scale the output from node 3 by a factor λ and add it to the output from node 1. This can be achieved as shown in Fig. 11.29d where the resistor R_h has a normalized value $1/\lambda$.

EXAMPLE 11.6

Realize, by means of the state-variable method, a second-order bandstop transfer function with the following specification:

> d.c. gain: unity
> Notch frequency: 1200 rad s^{-1}
> Pole parameters: $\omega_0 = 1000$ rad s^{-1}; $Q = 2$
> Input resistance $R = 10$ kΩ

SOLUTION

The transfer function of (11.79) in denormalized form can be written

$$\frac{V_o}{V_i} = \frac{\lambda(s^2/\omega_0^2) + 1}{(s/\omega_0)^2 + s/(\omega_0 Q) + 1} \tag{11.81}$$

From (11.76) with $Q = 2$ we have that in the circuit of Fig. 11.29c, the attenuator resistor $R_a = 5$ Ω.

We have that the zeros are at $\pm j\omega_0/\lambda^{1/2}$. From the specification for ω_0 and the zero locations we obtain

$$\frac{1000}{\lambda^{1/2}} = 1200 \tag{11.82}$$

Hence, in the circuit of Fig. 11.29d

$$R_h = 1/\lambda = 1.44 \qquad (11.83)$$

Using the circuits of Fig. 11.29c and Fig. 11.29d, we divide each capacitor by 1000 to frequency scale, and we divide each capacitor value by 10^4 to obtain a resistor value $R = 10$ kΩ. We obtain the following values:

$$C = 100 \text{ nF}$$
$$R_h = 14.4 \text{ k}\Omega$$
$$R_a = 50 \text{ k}\Omega$$

All other resistors values are 10 kΩ.

Computer Exercise 11.7

Design various bandstop second-order sections using the method of Example 11.7, and check the results using Option F3.4 of ENTIS.

11.7.4 Allpass section

The normalized transfer function of a second-order allpass section can be written

$$\frac{V_{\text{ap}}}{V_i} = \frac{s^2 - s/Q + 1}{s^2 + s/Q + 1} \qquad (11.84)$$

From (11.66), (11.69) and (11.70), (11.84) can be written

$$V_{\text{ap}} = - V_{o_3} - V_{o_2}/Q - V_{o_1} \qquad (11.85)$$

To realize the allpass transfer function we therefore require to scale the output V_{o_2} by $1/Q$ and add the signal to V_{o_1} and V_{o_3} using a summing amplifier with the resistor $R_b = Q$ as shown in Fig. 11.29e.

EXAMPLE 11.7

Realize, by means of the state-variable method, a second-order allpass transfer function with the following specification:

$$\text{Gain: unity}$$
$$\omega_0 = 1000 \text{ rad s}^{-1}$$
$$Q = 1.5$$
$$\text{Input resistance } R = 10 \text{ k}\Omega$$

SOLUTION

From (11.76) with $Q = 1.5$, we have that in the circuit of Fig. 11.29c, the attenuator resistor $R_a = 3.5$ Ω. Hence in the circuit of Fig. 11.29e $R_b = 1.5$ Ω.

Using the circuits of Fig. 11.29c and Fig. 11.29e, we divide each capacitor value by 1000 to frequency scale, and we divide each capacitor value by 10^4 to obtain a resistor value $R = 10$ kΩ. We obtain the following values:

$$C = 100 \text{ nF}$$
$$R_b = 15 \text{ k}\Omega$$
$$R_a = 35 \text{ k}\Omega$$

All other resistors values are 10 kΩ.

Computer Exercise 11.8

Design various allpass second-order sections using the method of Example 11.7 and check the results using Option F3.5 of ENTIS.

---

12 THE PRACTICAL OPERATIONAL AMPLIFIER

12.1 Introduction

The analyses of the previous chapter were based on the assumption of an ideal operational amplifier, with only brief reference as to how a practical operational amplifier differs from the ideal. Although the ideal and practical amplifier differ in many respects, the most important limitation of a practical amplifier in active *RC* synthesis is the finite gain characteristic. The practical operational amplifier has a frequency-selective lowpass transfer function $A(s)$ with finite magnitude at d.c. The effect of this departure from the ideal is twofold. Firstly, it causes the singularities of the overall network to be displaced from their desired locations, and secondly it results in the occurrence of additional poles. Unless precautions are taken in the design procedure, it is possible for the additional poles to occur in the right-half plane thus causing instability.

In the design of a practical active *RC* network, therefore, it is necessary to ensure that (a) the network is stable and (b) the errors introduced by the finite gain characteristic of the amplifier are tolerable. In this chapter we consider the problem of stability and show that for an amplifier with given singularities, there is a limit on the gain and bandwidth which can be used. We then investigate the effect of finite gain and bandwidth on the performance of the overall network.

12.2 General stability theory

There are many criteria that can be applied to determine the stability of a feedback system and the reader is referred to the many books on feedback control theory for a detailed treatment of the subject. Here we give a simplified treatment which is adequate for an understanding of the factors that affect operational amplifier design.

We start with the general feedback arrangement of Fig. 11.1 where the transfer function was shown to be (11.3)

$$\frac{V_o}{V_i} = \frac{A}{1 + A\beta} \tag{12.1}$$

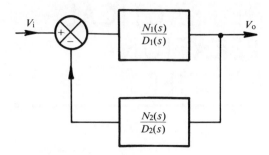

Figure 12.1 *Block diagram of feedback system.*

Here we will assume that the transfer functions in both the forward and feedback paths are rational functions of s as shown in Fig. 12.1. That is, the amplifier transfer function $A(s)$ is given by

$$A(s) = \frac{N_1(s)}{D_1(s)} \tag{12.2}$$

and the feedback transfer function $\beta(s)$ is given by

$$\beta(s) = \frac{N_2(s)}{D_2(s)} \tag{12.3}$$

where $N_1(s)$, $D_1(s)$, $N_2(s)$ and $D_2(s)$ are polynomials in s.

By substituting for $A(s)$ and $\beta(s)$ in (12.1), we obtain

$$\frac{V_o}{V_i} = \frac{N_1(s)D_2(s)}{N_1(s)N_2(s) + D_1(s)D_2(s)} \tag{12.4}$$

The poles of the transfer function are the zeros of the denominator polynomial $P(s) = N_1(s)N_2(s) + D_1(s)D_2(s)$. As discussed in Section 9.4, $P(s)$ is known as the characteristic polynomial, and for stability $P(s)$ must have all its zeros in the left-half plane, i.e. $P(s)$ must be a Hurwitz polynomial. Although, theoretically, the stability can be determined by application of the Routh–Hurwitz criterion, it is not particularly well suited to this application and does not easily lead to a useful design criterion. A better approach is through the steady-state frequency response as follows.

The zeros of the characteristic polynomial are the roots of the characteristic equation $P(s) = 0$ which is

$$N_1(s)N_2(s) + D_1(s)D_2(s) = 0 \tag{12.5}$$

which can be written

$$\frac{N_1(s)N_2(s)}{D_1(s)D_2(s)} = -1 \tag{12.6}$$

The left-hand side of (12.6) is the product of the transfer functions in the forward and feedback paths and is known as the loop transfer function which we can denote as $G(s)$. Thus the characteristic equation can be written

$$G(s) = -1 \qquad (12.7)$$

We next show how rearrangement of the characteristic equation into the form of (12.7) leads to a simple criterion based on the steady-state frequency response of the loop transfer function.

Consider the case where the singularities of the loop transfer function are fixed and the scaling factor or d.c. gain A_0 of the operational amplifier is varied. In control theory, the magnitude scaling factor in the loop is known as the gain factor. If the loop transfer function is itself stable, and the gain factor is sufficiently small, then the closed-loop system is stable. Suppose that the gain factor is increased and at some value the limit of stability is reached. For a system on the limit of stability the closed-loop transfer function has poles on the real frequency axis (see Section 3.6). Let us denote these pole positions as $\pm j\omega_1$. The poles are the roots of the characteristic equation and therefore satisfy (12.7). Hence

$$G(j\omega_1) = -1 \qquad (12.8)$$

The left-hand side of (12.8) is the steady-state frequency response function of the loop transfer function at the frequency ω_1. In terms of the magnitude and phase shift, (12.8) can be expressed as

$$\left. \begin{array}{l} |G(\omega_1)| = 1 \\ \angle G(\omega_1) = \pm\pi \end{array} \right\} \qquad (12.9)$$

That is, for a system on the limit of stability, the steady-state frequency response of the loop transfer function has a magnitude of unity and a phase shift of $180°$ at some frequency ω_1.

The significance of the above conditions can be readily appreciated by considering the system with a sinusoidal input signal $v_1 = V\sin(\omega_1 t + \theta)$ applied through the switch S_1 and with the loop broken by means of the switch S_2, as shown in Fig. 12.2. From the above conditions it follows that the steady-state signal at the input to S_2 is $v_2 = -v_1$. It is clear that if, simultaneously, S_1 is

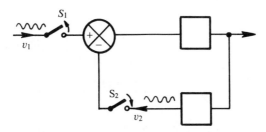

Figure 12.2 *Feedback system on limit of stability.*

opened and S₂ is closed then the output v_3 from the summing junction is unchanged and therefore the output signal remains. That is, with no input signal, the system sustains a continuous sinusoidal output, thus confirming that the system is on the limit of stability.

Suppose that with a system on the limit of stability, we introduce some additional gain into the loop without altering the phase characteristic. It would seem reasonable to expect that the additional gain would drive the system into instability. Similarly, if we could introduce some additional phase shift into the loop without altering the magnitude characteristic, we would expect instability to occur. It can be shown using a more rigorous mathematical treatment that the above suppositions are true subject to the restrictions that there is only one frequency ω_{ugf} at which the loop gain is unity and that there is only one frequency ω_{180} at which the loop phase shift is $180°$. Here it is sufficient to consider only those cases for which the above restrictions apply and this leads to the two following simplified stability criteria, either of which are sufficient to ensure stability:

1. The loop magnitude at ω_{180} must be less than unity.
2. The loop phase shift at ω_{ugf} must be less than $180°$.

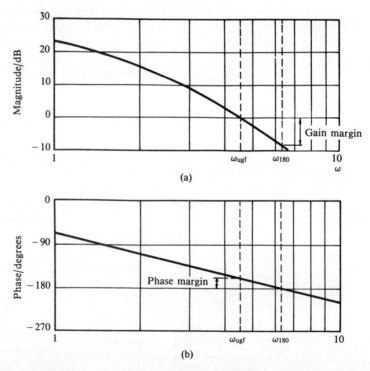

(a)

(b)

Figure 12.3 *Bode diagrams for loop transfer function of stable system: (a) magnitude, (b) phase.*

We can therefore investigate stability by means of the loop frequency response function. It should be emphasized that we are investigating the stability of the *closed-loop* network even though we are considering the *loop* frequency response. That is, the characteristic equation, whose roots are the closed-loop poles, is rearranged into a relationship involving the loop transfer function.

The loop frequency response function can be plotted in polar form in the complex plane known as the *Nyquist plane*. Alternatively, we can plot separate phase-versus-frequency and magnitude-versus-frequency characteristics. These are usually displayed as semilog plots, as described in Chapter 6, and are known as Bode diagrams. The mathematical derivation of the stability conditions expressed in terms of the loop frequency response function is best carried out on the basis of the polar plot. However, for practical purposes it is simpler to apply the conditions to the Bode diagrams and we will therefore base our theory of operational amplifier stability on Bode plots. Figure 12.3 shows an example of the Bode diagrams for a stable system.

Gain margin

In practice it is necessary to ensure that there is a sufficient margin of stability in order to provide a satisfactory amount of damping in the time domain, and also to allow for tolerances and drift in component values. The *gain margin* is a measure of relative stability and is defined as the factor by which the loop gain must be increased to bring the system to the limit of stability. It follows from condition 1 (p. 248) that the gain margin is the reciprocal of the gain at the frequency for which the loop phase shift is $180°$. Gain margin is usually expressed in dB. If, for example, the gain at ω_{180} is 0.1 then the gain margin is 20 dB. Gain margin can be readily determined from the Bode diagrams as shown in Fig. 12.3.

In practical design of feedback systems a gain margin between 10 dB and 20 dB is usually considered satisfactory. However, gain margin is not always a reliable guide to the degree of damping of the closed-loop system. If the phase characteristic of the loop is such that the phase lag is always less than $180°$ then the gain can theoretically be increased indefinitely without instability occurring. For such a case the gain margin is theoretically infinite. A second-order system is an example where the gain margin is infinite, even when the closed-loop poles are very close to the real-frequency axis.

Phase margin

An alternative measure of relative stability is the *phase margin*. This is defined as the amount of additional phase lag which must be introduced into the loop to bring the system to the limit of stability. It follows from condition 2 (p. 248) that the phase margin is the amount by which the phase lag at ω_{ugf} falls short of $180°$.

Evaluation of the expression for the phase margin of a second-order system yields the curve shown in Fig. 12.4. It is seen that a phase margin between $35°$ and $60°$ corresponds to a range of Q from 1.7 to 0.8 approximately which is

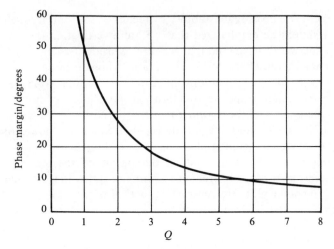

Figure 12.4 *Phase margin versus* Q *for a second-order system.*

usually considered satisfactory. For a system whose transient response is determined principally by a pair of dominant poles, the phase margin gives a reliable guide to the degree of damping.

Phase margin can be readily determined from the Bode diagrams as shown in Fig. 12.3. Note that it is not necessary to plot the phase characteristic; the unity gain frequency can be determined from the gain characteristic and then the phase shift at ω_{ugf} can be determined from the expression for the transfer function. This is demonstrated in the following example.

EXAMPLE 12.1

The loop transfer function $G(s)$ of a feedback system is given by

$$G(s) = \frac{5}{(s+1)(2s+1)(4s+1)} \tag{12.10}$$

Determine the phase margin.

SOLUTION

From (12.10), we have

$$F(j\omega) = \frac{5}{(1+j\omega)(1+j2\omega)(1+j4\omega)} \tag{12.11}$$

Hence the phase shift ϕ is given by

$$\phi = \angle F(j\omega) = -\tan^{-1}\omega - \tan^{-1}2\omega - \tan^{-1}4\omega \tag{12.12}$$

We can calculate the magnitude over a range of frequencies and plot the Bode diagram by hand or, using Option C of ENTIS, we can display the magnitude characteristic. We then find that $\omega_{ugf} = 0.6$.

From (12.12) we calculate the phase shift at ω_{ugf} as $149°$. Hence the phase margin is $31°$.

An approximate value of phase margin can be obtained by using the straight line approximation technique to determine the unity gain frequency, and then the phase shift can be calculated from the expression for the transfer function at the approximate unity gain frequency.

EXAMPLE 12.2

Repeat Example 12.1 but use the straight line approximation method to determine ω_{ugf}.

SOLUTION

Using Option C of ENTIS, we determine from the straight line approximation that $\omega_{ugf} = 0.8$. From (12.13) the phase shift ϕ is $169°$. Hence the phase margin is $11°$.

Further simplification in evaluation of the phase margin can be achieved using the Bode relationship between the semilog phase and magnitude plots. As discussed in Chapter 5, for a minimum phase system the phase characteristic is uniquely determined by the magnitude characteristic and vice versa. Rhodes (1976) gives the formula which relates the two. Except for some special cases, the evaluation of the formula can be achieved only by numerical methods. However, over regions of a magnitude characteristic which are not close to resonant peaks or troughs, the formula reduces to a very simple approximate relationship. This relationship is that the phase shift is proportional to the slope of the semilog magnitude characteristic. A slope of -20 dB/decade corresponds to a phase lag of $90°$, a slope of -40 dB/decade corresponds to a phase lag of $-180°$, etc.

The above approximate relationship is particularly suitable for the case where all the singularities of the loop transfer function are on the negative real axis. We can thus state the approximate criterion for stability as follows: the closed-loop system is stable if the semilog magnitude characteristic crosses the 0 dB line with a slope which is falling at less than 40 dB/decade. As will be shown, this criterion can be used in conjunction with the straight line approximation to the magnitude characteristic to provide a useful preliminary design procedure.

12.3 Stability of operational amplifier networks

A suitable starting point for the study of the stability of an operational amplifier with feedback is the voltage-follower arrangement which has unity feedback, i.e.

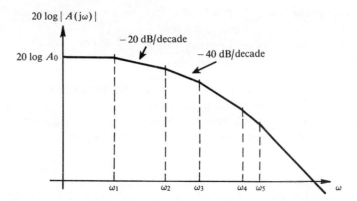

Figure 12.5 *Characteristic of uncompensated amplifier.*

$\beta(s) = 1$, and hence the loop transfer function $G(s) = A(s)$. Therefore, for this configuration, to determine stability we require to consider only the frequency response function of the amplifier and to investigate whether it satisfies the above conditions for stability.

An uncompensated operational amplifier is a complex device whose transfer function has many singularities arising out of the inevitable stray capacitances associated with active and passive components. Although an accurate model is not generally available, the frequency response is close to that of an all-pole transfer function with its poles $p_1, \ldots, p_n$ on the real axis.

Letting $p_1 = -\omega_1$, $p_2 = -\omega_2$, $\ldots$, $p_n = -\omega_n$, we can write the transfer function $A(s)$ as

$$A(s) = \frac{A_0}{(s/\omega_1 + 1)(s/\omega_2 + 1)(s/\omega_3 + 1) \ldots (s/\omega_n + 1)} \qquad (12.13)$$

where $\omega_1 < \omega_2 < \omega_3 \ldots < \omega_n$.

The segmented straight line approximation to the magnitude response is shown in Fig. 12.5.

As a consequence of the high value of d.c. gain A_0, typically 10^5, and the closeness of each corner frequency to the following one, it is readily observed from Fig. 12.5 that the rate of fall-off at the unity gain frequency is greater than 40 dB/decade and hence the phase shift exceeds $180°$. Therefore, the uncompensated amplifier is unstable in the voltage-follower configuration.

12.3.1 Lag compensation

A solution to the above problem is to introduce a compensating network that will shape the characteristic such that the rate of fall-off is less than 40 dB/decade at the unity gain frequency. The amplifier may be internally compensated, in which case the compensating network is part of the integrated circuit as in the 741 amplifier. Alternatively, an externally compensated amplifier will require external components to complete the compensating network, and this permits greater flexibility in that the compensation can be optimized to match the application.

Compensation using a single pole

Compensation is most easily achieved by the use of a first-order lowpass network which introduces a dominant pole at $-\omega_d$, where $\omega_d \ll \omega_1$. The transfer function, $A_{c_1}(s)$, of the compensated amplifier is then given by

$$A_{c_1}(s) = \frac{A_0}{(1 + s/\omega_d)(1 + s/\omega_1)(1 + s/\omega_2)\dots(1 + s/\omega_n)} \quad (12.14)$$

and the phase shift ϕ is given by

$$\phi = -(\tan^{-1}\omega/\omega_d + \tan^{-1}\omega/\omega_1 + \tan^{-1}\omega/\omega_2 + \dots + \tan^{-1}\omega/\omega_n) \quad (12.15)$$

Although the additional pole inevitably increases the overall phase shift, it can reduce the unity gain frequency to the point where the magnitude falls off at less than 40 dB/decade.

To demonstrate this we consider the case where ω_d is chosen to make the unity gain frequency on the straight line approximation diagram equal to ω_1 as shown in Fig. 12.6. We observe, using the theory of Chapter 6, that since the slope of the characteristic from ω_d to ω_1 is -20 dB/decade, which can also be expressed as -1, it follows that the ratio of the magnitudes at the two respective frequencies is ω_1/ω_d. Thus

$$\frac{\omega_1}{\omega_d} = A_0 \quad (12.16)$$

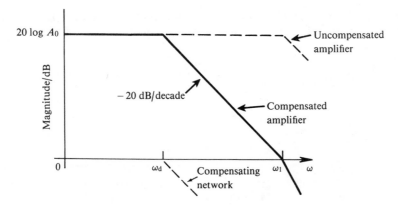

Figure 12.6 *Characteristic of amplifier compensated by addition of pole at* $-\omega_d$.

From (12.15) and (12.16) we determine the phase shift at $\omega = \omega_1$ as

$$\phi = -(\tan^{-1}A_0 + \tan^{-1}1 + \tan^{-1}\omega_1/\omega_2 + \tan^{-1}\omega_1/\omega_3 + \dots + \tan^{-1}\omega_1/\omega_n)$$

(12.17)

Since in practice A_0 is typically 10^5, we can assume that $\tan^{-1}A_0 = 90°$. Also, if $\omega_2 \gg \omega_1$ then the third and subsequent terms in the right-hand side of (12.17) are negligible. For such a case, ϕ approximates to $135°$ and consequently the phase margin is $45°$. If a greater phase margin is required, or if ω_2 is close to ω_1, then a lower value of ω_d is necessary.

Compensation using a pole and a zero

In the above example, the 3 dB bandwidth of the amplifier is reduced by a factor A_0 and this causes a significant reduction in the operating frequency range of the amplifier in filter synthesis. An improvement in bandwidth can be obtained by a form of compensation that uses the lag network described in Sections 6.9 and 6.10 and is illustrated again in Fig. 12.7. This network has unity d.c. gain and a pole and a zero on the negative real axis, with the pole closer to the origin than the zero.

Suppose that the zero is located at $-\omega_1$, thus cancelling the pole of the operational amplifier at ω_1. We again denote the location of the pole of the network as $-\omega_d$ but show that in this case a higher value of ω_d is possible. The compensated transfer function, $A_{c_2}(s)$, is given by

$$A_{c_2}(s) = \frac{A_0(1 + s/\omega_1)}{(1 + s/\omega_d)(1 + s/\omega_1)(1 + s/\omega_2)\dots(1 + s/\omega_n)}$$

$$= \frac{A_0}{(1 + s/\omega_d)(1 + s/\omega_2)\dots(1 + s/\omega_n)}$$

(12.18)

Using a similar procedure to that used to obtain (12.16), we can locate the pole of the compensating network to make the unity gain frequency equal to ω_2, i.e.

$$\frac{\omega_2}{\omega_d} = A_0$$

(12.19)

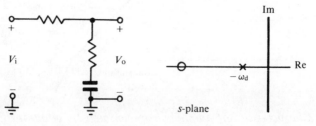

Figure 12.7 *Compensating network which introduces a pole and a zero.*

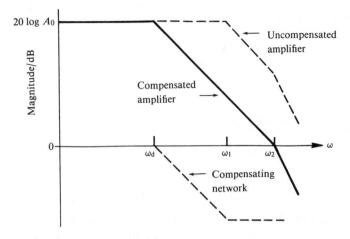

Figure 12.8 *Characteristic of amplifier compensated by network of Fig. 12.7.*

By comparing (12.16) and (12.19) we observe that, where the amplifier poles are widely separated, the effect of the zero in the compensating network is to permit a 3 dB bandwidth of ω_2/A_0 as opposed to a bandwidth of ω_1/A_0.

Figure 12.8 illustrates the Bode diagrams and Fig. 12.9 shows the s-plane diagrams for the above compensation technique. It can be seen that the technique effectively moves the most dominant pole of the uncompensated operational amplifier to a new position, closer to the origin.

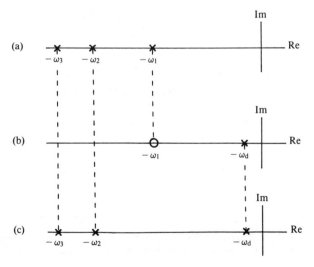

Figure 12.9 *s-plane diagrams for characteristics of Fig. 12.8: (a) uncompensated amplifier, (b) compensating network, (c) compensated amplifier.*

Computer Exercise 12.1

Use Option F4 of ENTIS to investigate the phase margin of an all-pole loop transfer function with a dominant pole. Use various values of A_0 and pole locations.

Computer Exercise 12.2

An operational amplifier has a d.c. gain of 80 dB and the following poles:

$$p_1 = -10^4 \qquad p_2 = p_3 = -10^5 \qquad p_4 = -3 \times 10^5$$

Show that the amplifier would be unstable in a voltage-follower arrangement. Determine the transfer function of a compensating network to provide a phase margin of approximately $45°$. Verify the solution using Option F4 of ENTIS

12.3.2 Stability with $\beta < 1$

We next consider the case where $\beta(s)$ is a constant and less than unity, i.e. the feedback is purely resistive.

In Section 11.2 it was shown (see (11.5)) that for both the non-inverting arrangement of Fig. 11.2 and the inverting arrangement of Fig. 11.5, $\beta(s)$ is a constant whose value β is given by

$$\beta = \frac{R_1}{R_1 + R_2} \tag{12.20}$$

For the non-inverter with a required gain K, we have that $\beta = 1/K$. For an inverter with a required gain $-K$, we have that $\beta = 1/(1 + K)$.

With $\beta(s)$ constant, the loop transfer function $\beta A(s)$ has a magnitude characteristic identical in shape to that of $A(s)$, but shifted down by $20\log(1/\beta)$ dB. This shift reduces the crossover frequency of the straight line approximation by a factor $1/\beta$ with a corresponding reduction in the loop phase shift at the unity gain frequency. We conclude therefore that if an amplifier is stable in the voltage-follower configuration then it is stable for all other cases of purely resistive feedback. We can also state that for a given compensated characteristic, the phase margin increases as β decreases. In the case of an externally compensated amplifier, we can design the compensating network specifically for the desired value of β. Using pole–zero compensation, from (12.18) we have that the compensated loop transfer function $G(s)$ is given by

$$G(s) = \frac{\beta A_0}{(1 + s/\omega_d)(1 + s/\omega_2)\dots(1 + s/\omega_n)} \tag{12.21}$$

By using the same argument that was applied to (12.18) we can make the unity gain frequency equal to ω_2, i.e.

$$\frac{\omega_2}{\omega_d} = A_0\beta \qquad (12.22)$$

Hence the 3 dB bandwidth of the compensated amplifier is

$$\omega_d = \frac{\omega_2}{A_0\beta} \qquad (12.23)$$

12.3.3 Frequency-selective feedback

To examine the stability for the case of a frequency-selective transfer function, we replace the resistors R_1 and R_2 by impedances Z_1 and Z_2 in the non-inverting and inverting circuits of Figs. 11.2 and 11.5 respectively. By a similar replacement in (12.20) we obtain the expression for $\beta(s)$ as

$$\beta(s) = \frac{Z_1}{Z_1 + Z_2} \qquad (12.24)$$

12.3.4 Integrator

We next examine the stability of the inverting integrator. We have $Z_1 = R$ and $Z_2 = 1/Cs$. Therefore (12.24) becomes

$$\beta(s) = \frac{Ts}{Ts + 1} \qquad (12.25)$$

where $T = CR$. That is, the feedback network used to provide integration constitutes a highpass first-order section.

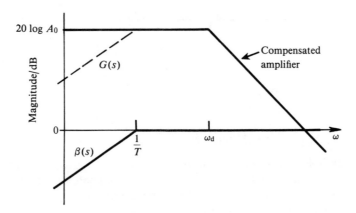

Figure 12.10 *Bode diagrams for integrator.*

The Bode diagram of the loop transfer function $G(s) = \beta(s)A(s)$ for the integrator using a compensated amplifier is shown in Fig. 12.10. It can be seen that the effect of $\beta(s)$ is to reduce the crossover frequency, although if the corner frequency $1/T$ is sufficiently small the reduction is negligible. The phase characteristic of $\beta(s)$ is a lead characteristic and therefore reduces the total phase lag. It follows that the phase margin of a given amplifier in the integrator arrangement is greater than the phase margin of the voltage follower.

12.3.5 Differentiator

We next examine the stability of the inverting differentiator. We have $Z_1 = 1/Cs$ and $Z_2 = R$. Therefore (12.24) becomes

$$\beta(s) = \frac{1}{Ts + 1} \qquad (12.26)$$

where $T = CR$. That is, the feedback network used to provide integration constitutes a lowpass first-order section within the loop and therefore introduces an extra pole at $-1/T$ into the loop transfer function. Depending upon the value of T, this additional pole can reduce the phase margin and even cause instability in an amplifier which has been compensated for use as a voltage follower. This is illustrated by the Bode diagram of Fig. 12.11. In such a case it is necessary to design the compensating network to take into account the extra pole at $-1/T$.

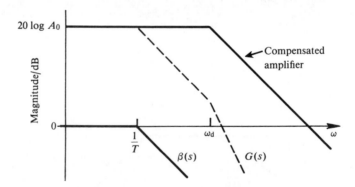

Figure 12.11 *Bode diagrams for differentiator.*

12.3.6 Practical considerations

It should be borne in mind that, in practice, the pole locations of an amplifier transfer function are not known and can only be estimated from the characteristic. Moreover, the parameters, including the d.c. gain, vary considerably from one sample to another. For example, according to the manufacturer's data sheet, the 741 has a typical value of d.c. gain of 200 000 but a minimum quoted value of 20 000. Thus compensation techniques that guarantee an adequate phase margin for the full production range of a device in, say, the voltage-follower arrangement will result in a bandwidth that is significantly less than that which could be often obtained by compensation for a specific application and device.

12.4 Errors due to finite amplifier gain

We next investigate the errors that occur because of the finite gain and frequency-selective response of the practical amplifier. For this analysis, we assume that the amplifier is compensated and can be represented by a lowpass transfer function with a dominant pole. This model is known as the *one-pole rolloff model*. We can write its transfer function $A(s)$ as

$$A(s) = \frac{A_0}{1 + s/\omega_d} \tag{12.27}$$

The magnitude characteristic is shown in semilog straight line approximation form in Fig. 12.12. We observe that the unity gain frequency is equal to $A_0\omega_d$ which is the product of the d.c. gain and the 3 dB bandwidth. The unity gain frequency is therefore also referred to as the gain bandwidth.

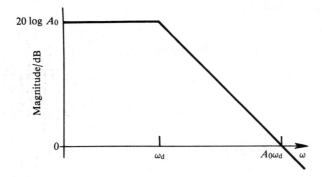

Figure 12.12 *Bode diagram for one-pole rolloff model of operational amplifier.*

12.4.1 Non-inverting amplifier

We analyze first the non-inverting amplifier that was shown in Fig. 11.2. For this arrangement a voltage βV_o is fed back by means of a resistor network and for an ideal operational amplifier the closed loop gain is $K = 1/\beta$. From (11.3), by replacing β by $1/K$ and A by $A(s)$, we obtain the transfer function $F(s)$ as

$$F(s) = \frac{A(s)}{1 + A(s)/K} \tag{12.28}$$

By substituting for $A(s)$ from (12.27) in the above, we obtain

$$F(s) = \frac{K}{(1 + K/A_0) + Ks/(A_0\omega_d)}$$

(12.29)

Therefore, the one-pole rolloff model for the amplifier results in a first-order lowpass characteristic for the non-inverting amplifier.

The closed-loop d.c. gain is $K/(1 + K/A_0)$, which is independent of the amplifier gain if $A_0 \gg K$. That is, the open-loop gain must be very much greater than the closed-loop gain, which is the virtual-earth condition at d.c. Note that a value of, say, $K = A_0/100$ would give an error at d.c. of 1%.

If the d.c. virtual-earth condition is satisfied then (12.29) becomes

$$F(s) = \frac{K}{1 + Ks/(A_0\omega_d)}$$

(12.30)

which shows that the 3 dB closed-loop bandwidth is given by the gain bandwidth of the amplifier divided by K. For the voltage follower ($K = 1$) the 3 dB bandwidth is equal to the gain bandwidth of the operational amplifier as shown in Fig. 12.13.

Computer Exercise 12.3

Option F5.1 of ENTIS displays the Bode diagrams for the non-inverting arrangement using a one-pole rolloff operational amplifier, i.e. the transfer function is given by (12.29). Investigate the response for various values of A_0, ω_d and K.

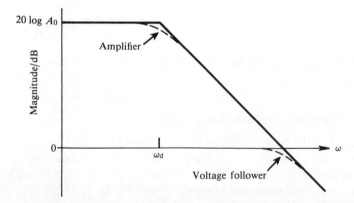

Figure 12.13 *Bode diagram for voltage follower with one-pole rolloff model for amplifier.*

12.4.2 Inverter

We analyze next the two-immittance inverter arrangement, but consider the more general case of frequency-selective feedback using impedances Z_1 and Z_2 as shown in Fig. 12.14. The transfer function $F(s)$ can be derived by means of the procedure used in the case of resistive feedback to obtain (11.9). If we replace R_1 and R_2 by Z_1 and Z_2 respectively, we have

$$F(s) = \frac{-A(s)}{1 + [A(s) + 1] Z_1/Z_2} \tag{12.31}$$

We can denote

$$F_1(s) = \frac{Z_2}{Z_1} \tag{12.32}$$

which is the theoretical closed-loop transfer function with altered sign for infinite operational amplified gain.

From (12.27), (12.31) and (12.32) we obtain

$$F(s) = \frac{-A_0 F_1(s)}{A_0 + 1 + F_1(s) + [1 + F_1(s)]s/\omega_d} \tag{12.33}$$

For the case of resistive feedback, $F_1(s)$ is a constant which we can denote as K. (12.33) then becomes

$$F(s) = \frac{-A_0 K}{(A_0 + 1 + K) + (1 + K)s/\omega_d} \tag{12.34}$$

The virtual-earth condition at d.c. can be expressed as $A_0 \gg K + 1$. If the condition is satisfied, (12.34) becomes

$$F(s) = \frac{-K}{1 + (K + 1)s/(A_0\omega_d)} \tag{12.35}$$

which shows that the 3 dB closed-loop bandwidth is given by the gain bandwidth of the amplifier divided by $K + 1$. Figure 12.15 shows the characteristic for the unity-gain inverter, for which the 3 dB bandwidth is equal to half the gain bandwidth.

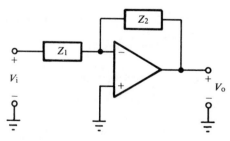

Figure 12.14 *Realization of transfer function* $-Z_2/Z_1$.

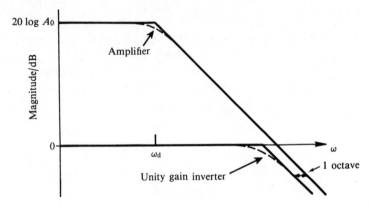

Figure 12.15 *Bode diagram for unity-gain inverter with one-pole rolloff model for operational amplifier.*

Computer Exercise 12.4

Use Option F.2 of ENTIS to display the Bode diagrams for the inverting amplifier using a one-pole rolloff operational amplifier, i.e. the transfer function is given by (12.34). Investigate the response for various values of A_0, ω_d and K.

12.4.3 Inverting integrator

We next consider the inverting integrator, for which $F_1(s) = Z_2/Z_1 = 1/Ts$. (12.33) becomes

$$F(s) = \frac{-A_0}{Ts^2/\omega_d + [(A_0 + 1)T + 1/\omega_d]s + 1} \tag{12.36}$$

Thus the one-pole rolloff model of the operational amplifier results, for the inverting integrator, in a closed-loop transfer function which has two poles and a d.c. gain A_0.

We can determine the locations of the poles for $A_0 \gg 1/T\omega_d$ as follows. Since $A_0 \gg 1$, (12.36) can be written

$$F(s) = \frac{-A_0}{Ts^2/\omega_d + A_0Ts + 1} \tag{12.37}$$

The poles p_1, p_2 are given by

$$p_1, p_2 = \frac{A_0\omega_d}{2} \pm \frac{A_0\omega_d}{2}\left(1 - \frac{4}{\omega_d A_0^2 T}\right)^{1/2} \tag{12.38}$$

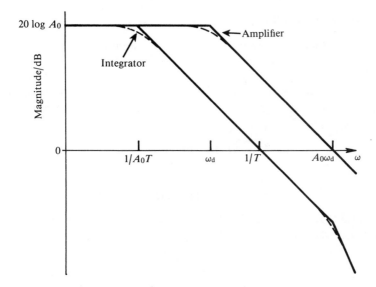

Figure 12.16 *Bode diagram for inverting integrator with one-pole rolloff model for amplifier.*

For $A_0^2 T \omega_d \gg 4$, which will normally be the case, the square root in the right-hand side of the above equation can be replaced by the first two terms of a binomial expansion which leads to

$$p_1, p_2 = -\frac{A_0 \omega_d}{2} \pm \frac{A_0 \omega_d}{2} \left(1 - \frac{2}{\omega_d A_0^2 T} \right) \qquad (12.39)$$

Again, noting that $A_0^2 T \omega_d \gg 1$ we obtain from (12.39)

$$\left.\begin{array}{l} p_1 = -\dfrac{1}{A_0 T} \\[2ex] p_2 = -A_0 \omega_d \end{array}\right\} \qquad (12.40)$$

Figure 12.16 shows the Bode diagram for the integrator with the poles given by (12.40).

Computer Exercise 12.5

Option F5.3 of ENTIS displays the Bode diagram for the inverting integrator using a one-pole rolloff operational amplifier, i.e. the transfer function is given by (12.36). Investigate the response for various values of A_0, ω_d and T.

12.4.4 Multiple feedback

As a final example, we analyze the effect of the amplifier one-pole rolloff model on the response of the multiple feedback network. The network is shown in Fig. 12.17 with the immittances expressed in admittance form. We start by determining the voltage transfer function $V_o/V_2 = F(s)$ from node 2 to the output. This is obtained in the same manner as (12.31) but with Y_5/Y_4 in place of Z_1/Z_2, i.e.

$$\frac{V_o}{V_2} = \frac{-1}{B(s) + [1 + B(s)] \, Y_5/Y_4} \tag{12.41}$$

where $B(s) = 1/A(s)$. Hence

$$V_2 = -\{B(s) + [1 + B(s)] \, Y_5/Y_4\} V_o \tag{12.42}$$

We have also that the voltage V_3 at node 3, the inverting input to the operational amplifier, is given by

$$V_3 = B(s)V_o \tag{12.43}$$

The relationship that the sum of the currents flowing into node 2 is zero can be expressed as

$$(V_i - V_2)Y_1 - V_2 Y_2 + (V_3 - V_2)Y_4 + (V_o - V_2)Y_3 = 0 \tag{12.44}$$

By substituting in the above for V_2 and V_3 from (12.42) and (12.43) respectively, we obtain, after some manipulation

$$\frac{V_o}{V_i} = \frac{-Y_1 Y_4}{Y_5(Y_1 + Y_2 + Y_3) + Y_4(Y_3 + Y_5) + B(s)[(Y_1 + Y_2 + Y_3)(Y_4 + Y_5) + Y_4 Y_5]} \tag{12.45}$$

We will take the three special cases of the normalized lowpass, highpass and bandpass realizations as considered in Section 11.5, with the component values

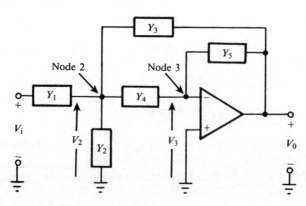

Figure 12.17 *Multiple-feedback network.*

determined as previously on the basis of infinite gain. Using the expressions previously derived for the normalized component values in terms of Q, we obtain the following transfer functions:

Lowpass: equal-resistor

$$\frac{V_o}{V_i} = \frac{-1}{s^2 + s/Q + 1 + B(s)[s^2 + (3Q + 1/Q)s + 2]} \tag{12.46}$$

Highpass: equal-capacitor

$$\frac{V_o}{V_i} = \frac{-s^2}{s^2 + s/Q + 1 + B(s)[2s^2 + (3Q + 1/Q)s + 1]} \tag{12.47}$$

Bandpass: equal capacitor

$$\frac{V_o}{V_i} = \frac{-2Qs}{s^2 + s/Q + 1 + B(s)[s^2 + (2Q + 1/Q)s + 1]} \tag{12.48}$$

It should be noted that $B(s)$ is unchanged when the above transfer functions are frequency scaled. That is, replacement of s by, say, s/ω_0 is not applicable to $B(s)$.

Computer Exercise 12.6

Options F5.4.1, F5.4.2 and F5.4.3 of ENTIS display the Bode diagrams for the multiple feedback lowpass, highpass and bandpass cases respectively, using a one-pole rolloff operational amplifier; the transfer functions are given by (12.46), (12.47) and (12.48) respectively, scaled by ω_0. Investigate the responses for various values of A_0, ω_d, ω_0 and Q.

13 DIGITAL FILTERS

13.1 Introduction

The rapid development of high-speed, low-cost microelectronic digital circuitry over the past decade has stimulated an ever-increasing use of signal representation in digital form for such purposes as transmission, control, measurement and storage. The conversion of a continuous analogue signal to digital form makes possible the numerical manipulation of the data by means of digital circuitry, and this procedure is known as digital signal processing (DSP).

The field of DSP can be divided into two main areas. The first is where the purpose of the numerical manipulation is to analyze the signal. A well-known example is the use of the discrete Fourier transform to determine the frequency spectrum. The second area of DSP concerns the techniques of processing the data to remove, for example, unwanted noise components, before the signal is reconstructed into analogue form. It is this area, known as digital filtering, which is of interest here.

Digital filtering can be applied to a stored signal as, for example, in the case of the reprocessing of a signal recovered from an old 78 r.p.m. audio recording. Alternatively, we can simultaneously have continuous analogue signals at the input and at the output as shown in block diagram form in Fig. 13.1 where the A/D and D/A conversions permit the signal processing to be applied to the digitized samples. In this case the filter is said to be operating in real time. For real-time operation, the complexity of the DSP algorithm is limited by the condition that the numerical manipulation to determine each output sample must be performed in less than the sample period. Thus design of a real-time filter generally involves a compromise between the conflicting requirements for a complex algorithm and a high sampling frequency.

The possibility of low-cost, real-time digital filtering first emerged in the 1970s when general-purpose microprocessors were introduced. The early devices, however, had limited speed and precision, which restricted their use to low-frequency applications and simple algorithms. In the 1980s, higher cost special-purpose devices known as DSP chips were introduced, which contained much faster arithmetic units and on-chip memory for storing filter coefficients and data. In some cases, on-chip A/D and D/A devices were included. Subsequently, further

266

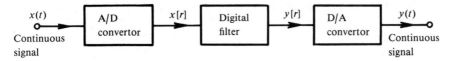

Figure 13.1 *Block diagram of digital signal processing in real time.*

improvements in speed and complexity were made possible by chips which contained additional hardware to utilize techniques of parallel processing.

The advantages of digital filters compared to analogue continuous filters include freedom from sensitivity to component value variations caused by drift, ageing and tolerances of practical component values. They can be operated at very low frequencies and can realize characteristics which cannot be achieved by continuous analogue filters; e.g. linear phase versus frequency. The cut-off frequency can be easily varied and the characteristic can be changed by software selection, without any change in hardware.

In some applications therefore, the advantages of digital processing can be sufficient to justify the A/D and D/A conversions solely for the purpose of filtering, whereas in other applications it may be convenient to use digital filtering because the signal is already in digital form.

The disadvantages of digital filters include (a) the additional hardware required, particularly in applications where the signal would otherwise be in analogue form, (b) their limited upper frequency range, (c) the errors caused by the quantization of the signal amplitude and (d) the errors caused by sampling.

This chapter describes some of the basic principles of sampled-data systems and linear digital filtering. The mathematical tool for analysis of sampled-data systems, namely the Z-transform, is introduced, and some methods of digital filter synthesis are described.

13.2 Sampling and quantization

13.2.1 Representation of sampled signal

Consider a continuous signal that is a function of time and is denoted by $x(t)$. Suppose this signal is sampled at instants $t = 0, \tau, 2\pi, \ldots$. We obtain a sequence of samples $x(0), x(\tau), x(2\tau) \ldots$. We can conveniently denote this sequence by $x[r]$ where the integer variable r denotes the sample number. An alternative representation of the sequence is in the form $\{x[0]\ x[1]\ x[2]\ \ldots\}$. Thus a sampled unit step would be written $\{1\ 1\ 1\ \ldots\}$.

13.2.2 Sampling frequency requirements

An important requirement in digital filtering is that of an adequate sampling frequency, in order to recover the continuous signal from the sequence of samples.

It can be shown that a sampled signal with values $x[0]$ $x[1]$ $x[2]$ ... at sample instants, and the value zero at all other times, has a frequency spectrum which is that of the continuous signal $x(t)$ but repeated at intervals of ω_s along the frequency axis where ω_s is the sampling frequency. This is illustrated in Fig. 13.2a, which shows a case where the highest frequency component ω_u of $x(t)$ is less than $\omega_s/2$. It is seen from the diagram that the frequency spectrum of $x(t)$ theoretically can be recovered from that of the sampled signal.

Fig. 13.2b shows an example where ω_u is greater than $\omega_s/2$, and it is seen that in this case overlapping of the repeated spectra occurs, preventing the recovery of the spectrum of $x(t)$. This effect is known as *aliasing* and leads to the requirement known as the Nyquist criterion, which states that the input signal must contain no frequency components greater than one half of the sampling frequency. The effect of aliasing can be readily seen from the diagram of Fig. 13.3 in which a sine wave of frequency ω_1 is sampled at a frequency ω_s where ω_1 is

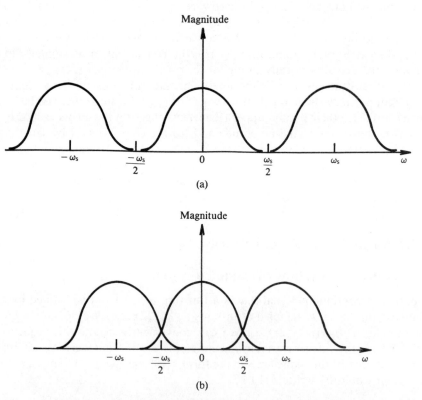

(a)

(b)

Figure 13.2 *Frequency spectra of continuous and sampled signals: (a) highest frequency component of continuous signal is less than half the sampling frequency, (b) highest frequency components of continuous signal is greater than half the sampling frequency.*

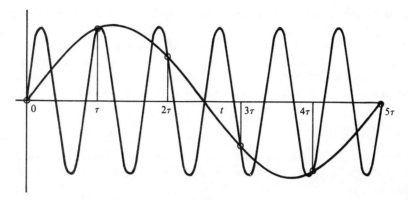

Figure 13.3 *Sampling of sine wave whose frequency is greater than half the sampling frequency.*

greater than $\omega_s/2$. The resulting samples are seen to be those of a sine wave of frequency $\omega_s - \omega_1$.

In theory, the Nyquist criterion can be satisfied by ensuring that ω_s is sufficiently high. However, if digital filtering takes place in real time then a lower limit to the sampling period (and hence an upper limit to the sampling frequency) is imposed by the time required to perform the arithmetic operations necessary to determine each output sample. In this case it may be necessary to prevent aliasing by means of an analogue filter, known as an anti-aliasing filter, operating on the input signal. Such a filter cannot entirely eliminate components above $\omega_s/2$ but can reduce them to an acceptable level. If the digital filtering does not take place in real time then, naturally, no such upper limit on the sampling rate applies.

13.2.3 Quantization errors

The representation of the signal magnitude by a finite word length results in quantization which introduces an error of one least significant bit. This quantization noise relative to the maximum signal amplitude is related to the number of bits used and can be expressed as a dynamic range in dB. For example, a 12-bit representation gives a dynamic range of $20 \log 2^{12}$ dB = 72 dB. Further analysis of the effect of quantization is beyond the scope of this treatment.

13.3 Simple filters

13.3.1 Basic operations

A fundamental operation in digital filters is that of storage or delay. For the unit delay, values are written to the storage location at sample instants and are read out one sample period later. That is, the unit delay stores a sample value for one sample period. Thus a signal $x[r] = \{x[0]\ x[1]\ x[2]\ ...\}$ applied to a unit delay would produce an output signal $y[r] = \{0\ x[0]\ x[1]\ x[2]\ ...\}$. Therefore we have that $y[r] = x[r-1]$. Other basic operations in linear digital filtering are addition/subtraction and multiplication by a constant. We will demonstrate how these operations can be combined to realize filters in the following section.

13.3.2 Integrator

We first consider an example of a simple digital filter, shown in block diagram form in Fig. 13.4, which utilizes a single unit delay and the operation of addition.

Consider the case where the input $x[r]$ is a sampled unit step $\{1\ 1\ 1\ ...\}$. The values of $y[r]$ and $w[r]$ are assumed to be zero for $r<0$. We have from the summation,

$$y[r] = x[r] + w[r] \tag{13.1}$$

and from the delay unit

$$w[r] = y[r-1] \tag{13.2}$$

Starting at $r = 0$ we can determine $y[0]$ from (13.1) and hence $w[1]$ from (13.2). Returning to (13.1) we determine $y[1]$. Continuing in this way, we find that the sequences $y[r]$ and $w[r]$ are as given in Table 13.1.

It is seen from the table that the sequence $w[r]$ is that of a sampled ramp which is the integral of a step, i.e. the filter behaves as an integrator.

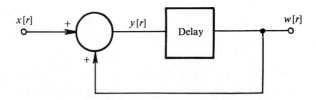

Figure 13.4 *Structure of a digital integrator.*

Table 13.1 *Sequence values of signals in structure of Fig. 13.4 with sampled step input*

r	-1	0	1	2	3	4
$x[r]$	0	1	1	1	1	1
$y[r]$	0	1	2	3	4	5
$w[r]$	0	0	1	2	3	4

Computer Exercise 13.1

Use Option G1 of ENTIS to demonstrate the behaviour of the filter of Fig. 13.4 in response to a unit step, a unit pulse and other input sequences.

13.3.3 Lowpass filter

Consider next the case where the structure of Fig. 13.4 is modified by the inclusion of a multiplier as shown in Fig. 13.5, i.e. the signal $w[r]$ is multiplied by a constant β before being fed back and summed with $x[r]$. We assume that $\beta < 1$. The equation for the summation becomes

$$y[r] = x[r] + \beta w[r] \tag{13.3}$$

As in the previous case we can evaluate the response to, say, a sampled unit step with zero initial conditions by evaluating $y[0]$, $w[1]$, $y[1]$, $w[2]$, etc., using alternately (13.3) and (13.2).

We find that for the above case, at the rth sample instant $w[r]$ is given by

$$w[r] = 1 + \beta + \beta^2 + \beta^3 + \dots + \beta^{r-1} \tag{13.4}$$

The right-hand side of (13.4) is a geometric series which sums to

$$w[r] = \frac{1 - \beta^r}{1 - \beta} \tag{13.5}$$

The right-hand side of (13.5) can be compared at sampling instants to the unit step response of a first-order lowpass continuous filter such as an *RC* section. The response $f(t)$ of such a system is given by

$$f(t) = 1 - e^{-t/T} \tag{13.6}$$

which at the rth sampling instant is given by

$$f(r\tau) = 1 - e^{-r\tau/T} \tag{13.7}$$

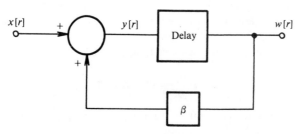

Figure 13.5 *Structure of a digital first-order lowpass filter.*

Comparing (13.5) and (13.7) it is seen that apart from the constant multiplier $1/(1 - \beta)$ in the right-hand side of (13.5), the two responses are identical if

$$\beta^r = e^{-rr/T} \tag{13.8}$$

i.e.

$$T = \frac{\tau}{\ln 1/\beta} \tag{13.9}$$

It is seen from (13.9) that the condition $\beta < 1$ ensures that T is positive. Thus the digital filter of Fig. 13.5 has a step response which is similar to the sampled response of a first-order lowpass section whose time constant is related to the sample period and multiplier constant of the digital filter by (13.9).

Computer Exercise 13.2

Use Option G1 of ENTIS to demonstrate the behaviour of the filter of Fig. 13.5 in response to a unit step, a unit pulse and other input sequences.

13.4 Linear difference equations

From (13.2) and (13.3), the relationship between x and y for the above filter can be expressed as

$$y[r] - \beta y[r - 1] = x[r] \tag{13.10}$$

(13.10) is an example of a linear difference equation; that is, the output is a weighted sum of the input and the previous value of output. The linear difference equation plays the part in sampled data theory that the ordinary linear differential equation plays in continuous signal theory.

One method of determining an equivalent linear difference equation from a differential equation is the method of backward differences. Although this method is not generally used in digital filter design, it is worth considering briefly in order to demonstrate very simply how a linear differential equation can lead to a related linear difference equation.

Consider, for example, the first-order differential equation

$$T \frac{dy}{dt} + y(t) = x(t) \tag{13.11}$$

where $x(t)$ and $y(t)$ are continuous functions of time and could represent, for example, the input and output voltages respectively of an RC section. If $x(t)$ and $y(t)$ are sampled then an approximation to dy/dt at sample instant r can be

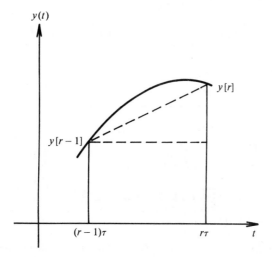

Figure 13.6 *Determination of an equivalent linear difference equation from a differential equation by the method of backward differences.*

obtained in terms of the sampled values as shown in Fig. 13.6, i.e.

$$\frac{dy}{dt} \simeq \frac{y[r] - y[r-1]}{\tau} \tag{13.12}$$

By substituting this expression into (13.11) and replacing $x(t)$ and $y(t)$ by their sampled values, we obtain

$$\left[\frac{T}{\tau} + 1\right] y[r] - \frac{T}{\tau} y[r-1] = x[r] \tag{13.13}$$

For higher order differential equations, approximations to higher order derivatives can be obtained in a similar manner. For example, the second derivative can be expressed in terms of the difference between the first derivatives at samples r and $r-1$ respectively.

$$\frac{d^2y}{dt^2} = \frac{1}{\tau}\left[\frac{(y[r] - y[r-1])}{\tau} - \frac{(y[r-1] - y[r-2])}{\tau}\right] \tag{13.14}$$

Thus a second-order differential equation leads to a second-order linear difference equation.

Consider next a differential equation which has right-hand side derivative terms involving dx/dt, d^2x/dt^2, etc.; in other words a system whose transfer function has finite zeros in the s-plane. Using a similar procedure to the above, it is clear that the method of backward differences can be applied to the input derivative terms to give a linear difference equation which has terms involving previous values of the input samples. Thus the general form of a linear difference

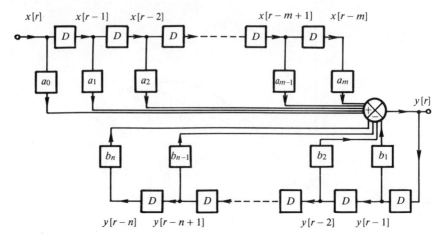

Figure 13.7 *Block diagram of a general digital filter whose linear difference equation is given by (13.15).*

equation can be written

$$y[r] + b_1 y[r-1] + b_2 y[r-2] + \ldots + b_n y[r-n]$$
$$= a_0 x[r] + a_1 x[r-1] + a_2 x[r-2] + \ldots + a_m x[r-m] \quad (13.15)$$

The form of (13.15) indicates the iterative nature of the equation. That is, the output is a weighted sum of the input, its m most recent values, and the n most recent values of the output.

A block diagram of a general digital filter is shown in Fig. 13.7 where the symbol D is used to denote the unit delay of one clock period τ. The arrangement, which uses m delays to store the previous values of the input and a further n delays to store the previous values of the output, is readily seen to correspond to (13.15). Other structures are possible but are more easily dealt with in terms of the Z-transformation and are therefore considered in a later section.

13.5 Recursive and nonrecursive filters

A special case of (13.15) occurs when all the coefficients $b_1 \ldots b_n$ are zero. In this case, the output is a function of the input and previous values of input only. Figure 13.8 shows the block diagram for this case. Because there is no feedback, there is no possibility of instability and the filter is known as *nonrecursive*.

The response to a sampled unit pulse $\{1\,0\,0\,0\ldots\}$ is readily determined since the value unity will propagate through the delays, i.e. at sample instant 1 the output of delay 1 is unity and all the rest are zero. Therefore the filter output is a_1. At the next sample instant the output of delay 2 is unity and all the rest are zero.

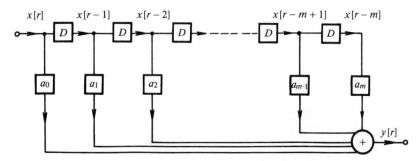

Figure 13.8 *Block diagram of a nonrecursive digital filter.*

Hence the filter output is a_2. Therefore the response of the filter can be written

$$\{a_0\,a_1\,a_2\ldots a_m\,000\ldots\}$$

After $m + 1$ sample instants all the inputs and outputs of the delays are zero and the filter output is zero. Therefore the filter is known as a *finite impulse response* (FIR) filter.

One particular example of an FIR filter is where all the coefficients $a_0\ldots a_m$ are equal, in which case the output is proportional to the 'moving average' of the input and its m most recent values.

A filter with any nonzero coefficients in the set b_1 to b_n is a recursive filter which has an infinite impulse response (IIR).

The distinction is made here between the two types of filters, namely recursive and nonrecursive. It will be shown later that given one type, an equivalent filter of the other type with the same characteristics can theoretically always be obtained. However, a given filter with a finite number of terms in its equation normally leads to an equivalent of the other type with an infinite number of terms.

Computer Exercise 13.3

Use Option G2 of ENTIS to demonstrate the behaviour of the FIR filter. Use various input sequences including the unit pulse. Investigate also the case where all the multiplying constants are equal.

13.6 Z-transforms

In general, the design of a linear digital filter consists of determining the coefficients of (13.15) to obtain or best approximate a specified response. The basic mathematical tool is the Z-transform calculus which is used for solving linear difference equations. In the strict sense, the linear difference equation and the Z-transform apply to sequences of numbers or to signals whose values are defined only at sample instants. However, a useful approach is one where the signal is assumed to remain constant for a short time at the sample instant and is otherwise zero between samples. This approach, described below, enables the Z-transform to be derived as an extension of the Laplace transform and leads to a simple relationship between the two transforms.

The sampling process of a continuous signal $f(t)$ can be represented by means of a switch which closes for a short time Δ at each sample instant as shown in Fig. 13.9. It is assumed that the sampled signal, which we denote by $f^*(t)$, does not change in the time Δ, and is zero at all other times. The sampled signal can then be considered as a form of modulation of the continuous signal by a sequence of pulses of unit height and duration Δ occurring at times $0, \tau, 2\tau, 3\tau \dots$ as shown. Let $\delta_1(t)$ be used to denote the pulse occurring at $t = 0$. Therefore the pulse occurring at the rth sample instant can be written $\delta_1(t - r\tau)$ and the complete sequence of pulses $h(t)$ can be expressed as

$$h(t) = \sum_{r=0}^{\infty} \delta_1(t - r\tau) \tag{13.16}$$

The sampled signal $f^*(t)$ is given by

$$f^*(t) = f(t)h(t) \tag{13.17}$$

If $f(t)$ has values $f[0], f[1], f[2] \dots$ at sample instants $0, 1, 2 \dots$ then (13.17) can be written

$$f^*(t) = \sum_{r=0}^{\infty} f[r]\delta_1(t - r\tau) \tag{13.18}$$

Consider next the Laplace transform of $f^*(t)$. The transform of $\delta_1(t)$ can be related to that of the unit impulse $\delta(t)$, used in continuous system theory. $\delta(t)$ is defined as the limit of a pulse of unit area whose magnitude tends to infinity and whose duration tends to zero. The Laplace transform of $\delta(t)$ is unity. The function $\delta_1(t)$ has unit height, width Δ and hence area Δ. Therefore, for Δ sufficiently small, the Laplace transform of $\delta_1(t)$ is Δ. A well-known theorem

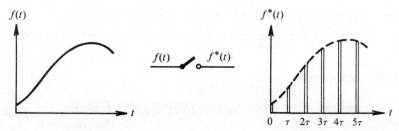

Figure 13.9 *Model of sampling process.*

states that if $F(s)$ is the transform of the function $f(t)$ then the transform of the delayed function $f(t - \tau)$ is $e^{-s\tau}F(s)$. It follows that the transform of $\delta_1(t - r\tau)$ is $\Delta e^{-rs\tau}$. We can therefore transform (13.18) and obtain

$$\mathscr{L}\{f^*(t)\} = \Delta(f[0] + f[1]e^{-s\tau} + f[2]e^{-2s\tau} + \ldots) \tag{13.19}$$

We now introduce the variable Z to denote $e^{s\tau}$ and (13.19) becomes

$$\mathscr{L}\{f^*(t)\} = \Delta(f[0] + f[1]Z^{-1} + f[2]Z^{-2} + \ldots) \tag{13.20}$$

The right-hand side of (13.20), excluding the multiplier Δ, is defined as the Z-transform $F(Z)$ of the sampled signal $f^*(t)$, i.e.

$$F(Z) = \sum_{r=0}^{\infty} f[r]e^{-rs\tau} \tag{13.21}$$

and the Laplace transform of $f^*(t)$ is related to the Z-transform by

$$\mathscr{L}\{f^*(t)\} = \Delta F(Z) \tag{13.22}$$

If we take the Laplace transform of a linear difference equation with the interpretation that each sampled function is a train of modulated pulses as described above, then each transform will contain a factor Δ which can be removed by dividing each side of the equation by Δ. This has the effect of replacing each Laplace transform by a Z-transform, and the overall result is the same as would be obtained by directly taking the Z-transform of the original equation.

For an arbitrarily varying function the Z-transform as given by (13.21) will be in the form of an infinite series. For some functions however, a closed form expression is obtained as demonstrated in the following examples.

13.6.1 Sampled unit pulse function

$$y[r] = \{1\,0\,0\,\ldots\}$$

We have that

$$Y(Z) = 1 \tag{13.23}$$

13.6.2 Sampled unit step function

$$y[r] = \{1\,1\,1\,\ldots\}$$

We have that

$$Y(Z) = 1 + Z^{-1} + Z^{-2} + \ldots$$

This is a geometric series which for $|Z| > 1$ can be summed as

$$Y(Z) = \frac{1}{1 - Z^{-1}} \tag{13.24}$$

13.6.3 Sampled exponential function

Let $y(t) = e^{-\beta t}$. We have that

$$y[r] = \{1 \, e^{-\beta\tau} e^{-2\beta\tau} e^{-3\beta\tau} ...\}$$

Hence

$$Y(Z) = 1 + e^{-\beta\tau} Z^{-1} + e^{-2\beta\tau} Z^{-2} + e^{-3\beta\tau} Z^{-3} + ...$$

This is a geometric series which for $|Z| > e^{-\beta\tau}$ can be summed as

$$Y(Z) = \frac{1}{1 - e^{-\beta\tau} Z^{-1}} \qquad (13.25)$$

13.6.4 Shifting right property

In order to show how the Z-transform can be applied to the solution of linear difference equations we first introduce a simple but fundamentally important property of Z-transforms known as the shifting right property.

Consider a sequence $x[r]$ which is zero for $t < 0$ and whose Z-transform by definition is

$$X(Z) = x[0] + x[1] Z^{-1} + x[2] Z^{-2} + x[3] Z^{-3} + ... \qquad (13.26)$$

Consider now a sequence $x_1[r]$ which is the signal $x[r]$ delayed by one sample period. We have

$$x_1[r] = \{0 \, x[0] \, x[1] \, x[2] ...\} \qquad (13.27)$$

The Z-transform of $x_1[r]$ is given by

$$\begin{aligned} X_1(Z) &= 0 + x[0] Z^{-1} + x[1] Z^{-2} + x[2] Z^{-3} + ... \\ &= Z^{-1}(x[0] + x[1] Z^{-1} + x[2] Z^{-2} + ...) \\ &= Z^{-1} X(Z) \end{aligned} \qquad (13.28)$$

Thus a delay of one clock period corresponds to a multiplication of the Z-transform by Z^{-1}. It follows that a delay of q clock periods corresponds to multiplication of the Z-transform by Z^{-q}.

13.6.5 *Z*-transfer functions

We can now undertake the transformation of the general linear difference equation. We write the equation in the general form given previously in (13.15):

$$y[r] + b_1 y[r - 1] + b_2 y[r - 2] + ... + b_n y[r - n]$$
$$= a_0 x[r] + a_1 x[r - 1] + a_2 x[r - 2] + ... + a_m x[r - m] \qquad (13.29)$$

Using the relationship of (13.28) we obtain

$$Y(Z) + b_1 Z^{-1} Y(Z) + b_2 Z^{-2} Y(Z) + \ldots + b_n Z^{-n} Y(Z)$$
$$= a_0 X(Z) + a_1 Z^{-1} X(Z) + a_2 Z^{-2} X(Z) + \ldots + a_m Z^{-m} X(Z) \qquad (13.30)$$

which can be written

$$(1 + b_1 Z^{-1} + b_2 Z^{-2} + \ldots + b_n Z^{-n}) Y(Z)$$
$$= (a_0 + a_1 Z^{-1} + a_2 Z^{-2} + \ldots + a_m Z^{-m}) X(Z) \qquad (13.31)$$

or

$$H(Z) = \frac{Y(Z)}{X(Z)} = \frac{(a_0 + a_1 Z^{-1} + a_2 Z^{-2} + \ldots + a_m Z^{-m})}{(1 + b_1 Z^{-1} + b_2 Z^{-2} + \ldots + b_n Z^{-n})} \qquad (13.32)$$

The function $H(Z)$ is known as the Z-transfer function and can be expressed either as the ratio of polynomials in Z or more usually as the ratio of polynomials in Z^{-1}, as is the case in (13.32).

In the Z-domain a unit delay has a transfer function of Z^{-1}. The block diagram of a linear difference equation such as that shown in Fig. 13.7 can be transformed into the Z-domain by representing each delay by Z^{-1}. As previously stated, other arrangements are possible and their derivation is facilitated by the use of the Z-domain. For example, $H(Z)$ can be factorized into the product of, say, second-order factors, leading to a serial form of realization. A partial fraction expansion into the sum of, say, second-order factors will lead to a parallel realization.

Another realization which, in general, is more economical in terms of storage requirements can be obtained as follows. Consider first the realization of the Z-transfer function $H_1(Z)$ given by

$$H_1(Z) = \frac{W(Z)}{X(Z)} = \frac{1}{1 + b_1 Z^{-1} + b_2 Z^{-2} + \ldots b_n Z^{-n}} \qquad (13.33)$$

That is, $W(Z)$ is the transform of the output sequence $w[r]$, which is the response of a filter for which the coefficients a_1 to a_m are zero and $a_0 = 1$.

$H_1(Z)$, as given by (13.33), can be realized using n delays and n multipliers b_1 to b_n as shown in the upper part of the structure of Fig. 13.10.

From (13.32) and (13.33) we have

$$Y(Z) = (a_0 + a_1 Z^{-1} + a_2 Z^{-2} + \ldots + a_m Z^{-m}) W(Z) \qquad (13.34)$$

$Y(Z)$ can then be derived from $W(Z)$ through the relationship of (13.34) using the additional $(m + 1)$ multipliers a_0 to a_m as shown in the remainder of the structure of Fig. 13.10.

In this arrangement, instead of storing m previous samples of input and n previous samples of output, we store only previous samples of $w(r)$. For $n \leqslant m$, no further unit delays are required. For $m > n$ a total of m unit delays is required. Thus the arrangement is more economical in delays or storage locations than that of Fig. 13.7.

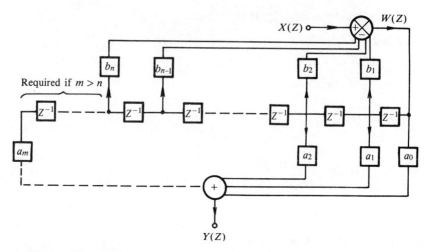

Figure 13.10 *Alternative realization of a general digital filter, using minimum number of delay units.*

13.6.6 Steady-state frequency response

We have shown that the Z-transform can be considered as an extension of the Laplace transform as related by (13.22), and therefore the steady-state response to a sine wave can be obtained in the same way as for a continuous system, by replacing s by $j\omega$ in the transfer function to obtain the frequency response function. Since $Z = e^{s\tau}$, a Z-transfer function $H(Z)$ will lead to a frequency response function $H(e^{j\omega\tau})$, and the magnitude and angle of $H(e^{j\omega\tau})$ determine the magnitude and phase characteristics of the digital filter. Since $e^{j\omega\tau}$ is a periodic function of frequency, it follows that the frequency response function is also periodic. It is important to avoid confusion here with the more familiar example of periodic functions of time. In this case the periodicity is with respect to frequency and the period along the angular frequency axis is $2\pi/\tau = \omega_s$. Reference was made to this property earlier in consideration of the effect of aliasing.

Two frequencies are of particular interest, namely d.c. and $\omega_s/2$. Since $\tau = 2\pi/\omega_s$, we have that the frequency response function is given by

$$H(e^{j\omega\tau}) = H(e^{j2\pi\omega/\omega_s}) \tag{13.35}$$

In particular, at d.c. or at any integer multiple of the sampling frequency, $e^{j2\pi\omega/\omega_s} = 1$. Hence, from (13.35) the frequency response function is given by

$$H(e^{j2\pi\omega/\omega_s}) = H(1) \tag{13.36}$$

Note that $H(1)$ is purely real but may be negative and hence the magnitude is given by the absolute value of $H(1)$. Note also that replacing Z by unity to determine the d.c. gain is equivalent in the *s*-domain to replacing *s* by zero in the transfer function of a continuous system.

Similarly, at half the sampling frequency and at frequencies spaced from it by an integer multiple of ω_s, $2\omega/\omega_s$ is an odd integer and the frequency response function is given by

$$H(e^{j2\pi\omega/\omega_s}) = H(-1) \tag{13.37}$$

Hence the magnitude at $\omega_s/2$ is given by the absolute value of $H(-1)$.

EXAMPLE 13.1

A digital filter has a transfer function $H(Z)$ given by

$$H(Z) = \frac{1}{1 + 0.2Z^{-1} - 0.48Z^{-2}}$$

Determine the magnitude at d.c. and at $\omega = \omega_s/2$.

SOLUTION

The magnitude at d.c. is given by

$$H(1) = \frac{1}{1 + 0.2 - 0.48} = 1.389$$

The magnitude at $\omega = \omega_s/2$ is given by

$$H(-1) = \frac{1}{1 - 0.2 - 0.48} = 3.125$$

13.7 Nonrecursive filter design

The methods of digital filter design can be divided into two categories; namely (a) the direct approach where no reference is made to known continuous designs, and (b) the indirect approach where the *Z*-transfer function is derived from a known *s*-transfer function such as that of the Butterworth. The first method to be described falls into the former category and is applicable to the nonrecursive-type filter. In this case the transfer function can be written

$$H(Z) = a_0 + a_1 Z^{-1} + a_2 Z^{-2} + \ldots + a_m Z^{-m} \tag{13.38}$$

and hence the frequency response function is given by

$$H(e^{j\omega\tau}) = a_0 + a_1 e^{-j\omega\tau} + a_2 e^{-2j\omega\tau} + \ldots + a_m^{-mj\omega\tau} \tag{13.39}$$

We examine first the phase response and show that it is possible to realize a linear phase–frequency relationship.

Consider the case where the right-hand side of (13.39) has an odd number of terms and therefore m is even. Let $a_M e^{-jM\omega\tau}$ be the middle term, i.e. $M = m/2$. If we take a factor $e^{-jM\omega\tau}$ out of the right-hand side of the equation we obtain

$$H(e^{j\omega\tau}) = e^{-jM\omega\tau} F(\omega) \tag{13.40}$$

where

$$F(\omega) = [a_0 e^{jM\omega\tau} + a_1 e^{j(M-1)\omega\tau} + a_2 e^{j(M-2)\omega\tau} + \ldots + a_M + \ldots$$
$$+ a_{m-2} e^{-j(M-2)\omega\tau} + a_{m-1} e^{-j(M-1)\omega\tau} + a_m e^{-jM\omega\tau}] \tag{13.40a}$$

There are two possible sets of conditions which make the phase a linear function of frequency as follows:

1. If the coefficients $a_0 \ldots a_m$ can be chosen to make $F(\omega)$ in (13.40a) purely real then the angle ϕ of the frequency response function is the angle of $e^{-jM\omega\tau}$ and is given by

$$\phi = -M\omega\tau \tag{13.41}$$

   which is a linear function of frequency.

2. If the coefficients can be chosen to make $F(\omega)$ purely imaginary then the angle of $F(\omega)$ is $\pi/2$ and ϕ is given by

$$\phi = \pi/2 - M\omega\tau \tag{13.42}$$

In this case the phase is again a linear function of frequency, but the characteristic does not pass though the origin.

To make $F(\omega)$ either purely real or purely imaginary, we observe that the first and last terms can be expanded as $a_0(\cos M\omega\tau + j \sin M\omega\tau)$ and $a_m(\cos M\omega\tau - j \sin M\omega\tau)$ respectively. Therefore if $a_0 = a_m$, the sum of the first and last terms is real. Alternatively if $a_0 = -a_m$, the sum of the first and last terms is purely imaginary. Similarly, we can match the other coefficients in pairs, i.e. a_1 with a_{m-1}, etc., in either of the following ways:

1. Symmetrical impulse response

$$\left. \begin{array}{l} a_0 = a_m,\ a_1 = a_{m-1},\ a_2 = a_{m-2}, \ldots \\[2mm] \phi = -M\omega\tau \end{array} \right\} \tag{13.43}$$

2. Antisymmetrical impulse response

$$\left. \begin{array}{l} a_0 = -a_m,\ a_1 = -a_{m-1},\ a_2 = -a_{m-2}, \ldots \\[2mm] \phi = \pi/2 - M\omega\tau \end{array} \right\} \tag{13.44}$$

We next consider the determination of the coefficients to approximate the ideal lowpass 'brick wall' magnitude response $G(\omega)$ together with a linear phase characteristic as shown in Fig. 13.11.

The frequency response function can be arranged in the form of (13.40), and to achieve a linear phase characteristic which passes through the origin the coeffi-

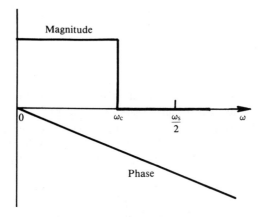

Figure 13.11 *Ideal 'brick wall' lowpass filter characteristic with linear phase.*

cients must satisfy the conditions of (13.43). If these conditions are satisfied, then $F(\omega)$ is purely real and since the magnitude of $e^{-jM\omega\tau}$ is unity it follows that

$$|H(e^{j\omega\tau})| = F(\omega) \tag{13.45}$$

We require therefore to determine the coefficients of $F(\omega)$ to satisfy

$$F(\omega) = G(\omega) \tag{13.46}$$

where $F(\omega)$ is given by (13.40a) and $G(\omega)$ is the specified magnitude character-istic. (13.40a) can be written in a more compact form as

$$F(\omega) = \sum_{q=0}^{m} a_q e^{j(M-q)\omega\tau} \tag{13.47}$$

Each term in $F(\omega)$ is periodic with respect to frequency. Since $\omega\tau = 2\pi\omega/\omega_s$, the period of each term is an integer multiple of ω_s. Therefore the coefficients can be determined by an inverse discrete Fourier transform. That is, each side of (13.46) is multiplied by $e^{j(q-M)\omega\tau}$ and integrated with respect to ω over a distance ω_s. All the terms in the expansion of $F(\omega)$, except the one containing a_q, are integrated over a whole number of cycles and therefore give a result of zero.

Taking the limits of integration as $-\omega_s/2$ to $\omega_s/2$ we have

$$\int_{-\omega_s/2}^{\omega_s/2} a_q \, d\omega = \int_{-\omega_s/2}^{\omega_s/2} G(\omega)e^{j(q-M)\omega\tau} \, d\omega \tag{13.48}$$

Observing that $G(\omega)$ is unity within the limits $-\omega_c$ to ω_c and is zero outside these limits, we can reduce the limits of integration to $-\omega_c$ to ω_c and (13.48) becomes

$$a_q\omega_s = \int_{-\omega_c}^{\omega_c} e^{j(q-M)\omega\tau} \, d\omega$$

$$= \frac{2 \sin[(q-M)\omega_c\tau]}{(q-M)\tau} \tag{13.49}$$

Substituting $\omega_s = 2\pi/\tau$ gives

$$a_q = \frac{\sin[(q - M)\omega_c\tau]}{\pi(q - M)} \qquad (13.50)$$

It is readily observed from (13.50) that the coefficients satisfy the conditions of (13.43) for a symmetrical impulse response. Naturally, the realization of the exact brick wall characteristic would require an infinite number of terms and implies an infinite phase lag. To determine the magnitude characteristic for a finite value of m we can simplify (13.47) using the fact that the imaginary part is zero and obtain

$$F(\omega) = \sum_{q=0}^{m} a_q \cos(M - q)\omega\tau \qquad (13.51)$$

where the coefficients a_q are given by (13.50).

Figure 13.12 shows a family of magnitude characteristics for the case $\omega_s = 5\omega_c$ and with different values of m. A linear frequency scale is used to show the response more clearly. It is seen that, as expected, the approximation improves as the number of terms, m, is increased.

Figure 13.13 demonstrates the effect of varying the ratio ω_s to ω_c with the number of terms, m, fixed. Here it is seen that the deviation between the actual characteristic and the brick wall function increases significantly as the ratio ω_s to ω_c increases.

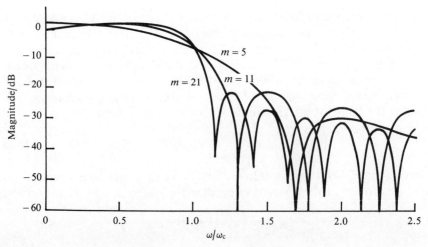

Figure 13.12 *Magnitude characteristics of FIR filter with $\omega_s/\omega_c = 5$ (number of terms = m).*

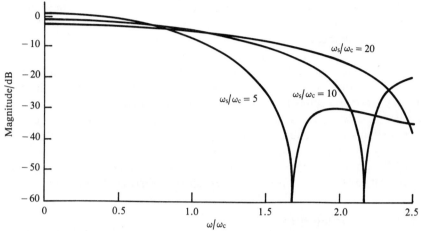

Figure 13.13 *Magnitude characteristics of FIR filters with five terms.*

Computer Exercise 13.4

Use Option G3 of ENTIS to investigate the magnitude characteristic of the FIR filter whose coefficients are given by (13.50). Use various values of m and ω_s/ω_c.

13.7.1 Window functions

The formula for the optimum coefficients, as given by (13.50), is based on the assumption that $m = \infty$. For a finite number of coefficients, the formula for the optimum values depends upon the criterion that is used to define the best approximation. The truncation of an infinite series can be regarded as the application of a rectangular window function to the series, where the magnitude of the window is unity up to the mth coefficient and is zero beyond the mth coefficient. Various other window functions, such as the Hamming and Kaiser windows, have been derived to improve the approximation, but these are beyond the scope of this treatment.

13.8 Impulse invariance method

The design method described above, applicable to nonrecursive filters, has the merit of providing a lowpass filter with an ideal phase characteristic. However, in order to obtain an adequate magnitude response for many purposes it is necessary to use a large number of terms, that is a high-order filter, together with a relatively low value of the ratio ω_s to ω_c. It will be shown that other methods, which lead to a recursive type of structure, can, for a given order, provide better magnitude characteristics.

The first such method to be described is known as the impulse invariance method. This is based on the property that the frequency response of a linear system is uniquely determined by its impulse response, and therefore if two systems have the same impulse response, i.e. they are impulse invariant, then they have the same frequency response. We therefore take a continuous prototype that has a satisfactory response in the frequency domain, such as the Butterworth or Chebyshev, and derive a Z-transfer function whose impulse response is identical to that of the continuous prototype. Since the impulse invariance between the continuous and digital filters can be at sample times only, the similarity between the frequency responses is restricted to a limited range.

13.8.1 First-order filter

We first take the example where the prototype continuous filter is a first-order lowpass. Suppose the voltage transfer function is written in terms of the pole p_1 and its residue A_1. In practice, the value of p_1 is real and negative. We have

$$\frac{V_o}{V_i} = \frac{A_1}{s - p_1} \tag{13.52}$$

For a unit impulse input $\delta(t)$, we have that $V_1 = 1$ and therefore $v_o(t)$ is given by the inverse transform of the right-hand side of (13.52). Hence

$$v_o(t) = A_1 e^{p_1 t} \tag{13.53}$$

Suppose that the response $v_o(t)$ is sampled at times $0, \tau, 2\tau, 3\tau$, etc. The values at the sample instants are $A_1, A_1 e^{p_1 \tau}, A_1 e^{2p_1 \tau}, A_1 e^{3p_1 \tau}$, etc. The Z-transfer function $H(Z)$ of a sampled-data system whose impulse response has the above values is

$$H(Z) = A_1 + A_1 e^{p_1 \tau} Z^{-1} + A_1 e^{2p_1 \tau} Z^{-2} + A_1 e^{3p_1 \tau} Z^{-3} + \dots \tag{13.54}$$

The right-hand side of (13.54) is a geometric series which can be summed as follows

$$H(Z) = \frac{A_1}{1 - e^{p_1 \tau} Z^{-1}} \tag{13.55}$$

Hence the Z-transfer function of a digital filter can be determined in terms of the s-transfer function of a continuous prototype.

The above example can be readily extended to the general case. The transfer function of a continuous lowpass filter with n distinct poles can be expressed as

$$\frac{V_o}{V_i} = \sum_{r=1}^{r=n} \frac{A_r}{s - p_r} \tag{13.56}$$

Proceeding as above we obtain an impulse invariant Z-transfer function $H(Z)$

given by

$$H(Z) = \sum_{r=1}^{r=n} \frac{A_r}{1 - e^{p_r \tau} Z^{-1}} \tag{13.57}$$

To demonstrate the properties and shortcomings of the impulse invariance method, we consider the first-order lowpass transfer function $F(s)$ as in (13.52) but written in the form

$$F(s) = \frac{1}{1 + s/\omega_c} \tag{13.58}$$

By substituting $A_1 = \omega_c$ and $p_1 = -\omega_c$ in (13.55) we obtain the impulse invariant Z-transfer function $H(Z)$ as

$$H(Z) = \frac{\omega_c}{1 - e^{-\omega_c \tau} Z^{-1}} \tag{13.59}$$

The frequency response function is given by

$$H(e^{j\omega\tau}) = \frac{\omega_c}{1 - e^{-\omega_c \tau} e^{-j\omega\tau}} \tag{13.60}$$

The first property to be observed is that the magnitude at d.c., $H(1)$, is in general not unity and thus differs from that of the continuous prototype. It might at first appear that this does not present any problems, since the transfer function of (13.59) can be modified by the introduction of any constant multiplier, i.e. we can write a modified transfer function as

$$H_1(Z) = \frac{K}{1 + b_1 Z^{-1}} \tag{13.61}$$

where

$$b_1 = -e^{-\omega_c \tau}$$

and where K can be chosen to have any convenient value.

The frequency response function is then

$$H_1(e^{j\omega\tau}) = \frac{K}{1 + b_1 \cos \omega\tau - jb_1 \sin \omega\tau} \tag{13.62}$$

the magnitude-squared function is

$$|H_1(e^{j\omega\tau})|^2 = \frac{K^2}{1 + b_1^2 + 2b_1 \cos \omega\tau} \tag{13.63}$$

and the phase is

$$\angle H_1(e^{j\omega\tau}) = -\tan^{-1} \frac{-b_1 \sin \omega\tau}{1 + b_1 \cos \omega\tau} \tag{13.64}$$

However, if we consider the structure of Fig. 13.5 we see that this requires the

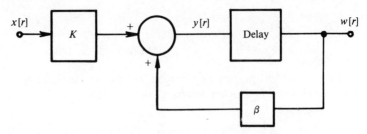

Figure 13.14 *Structure for a first-order lowpass filter modified by introduction of a multiplier* K *directly after input.*

numerator constant K to be unity. The structure can be modified by inserting a multiplier K directly following the input as shown in Fig. 13.14. It is clear, however, that for values of K less than unity the word length must be increased to prevent loss of dynamic range. If K is greater than unity, the word length must be increased to prevent overflow. An alternative realization could have the multiplier K directly preceding the output, but the above problems would still arise. For the above reasons, therefore, a value of K close to unity is advantageous.

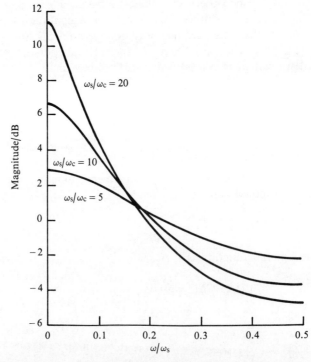

Figure 13.15 *Magnitude characteristics of IIR filters determined by application of impulse invariance method to a first-order lowpass filter.*

For the purpose of comparison, Fig. 13.15 shows a set of magnitude characteristics plotted against ω/ω_s on a linear scale with different values of ω_s/ω_c. In each case K has the value of unity. This demonstrates a shortcoming of the impulse invariance method, namely that in general it leads to a structure which gives a high value of d.c. gain. Moreover, it is seen that this value increases as the value of ω_s/ω_c is increased to obtain a more selective response. Therefore care must be taken to prevent overflow and/or loss of accuracy in the arithmetic operations.

The reason why the structure of Fig. 13.5 leads to a high value of d.c. gain can be appreciated by observing that the frequency response of the unit delay is that of a varying phase shift with constant unity gain. At d.c. the phase shift is zero and therefore the structure is that of positive feedback with a loop gain of β where $\beta < 1$. As β tends to unity, the d.c. gain $1/(1 - \beta)$ tends to infinity. At $\omega = \omega_s/2$ the phase shift is π and hence at this frequency the loop gain is $-\beta$. Thus the lowpass characteristic is achieved basically by means of a high gain $1/(1 - \beta)$ at d.c. which falls to a value of $1/(1 + \beta)$ at $\omega_s/2$.

Figure 13.16 shows the magnitude characteristics plotted against ω/ω_c on a

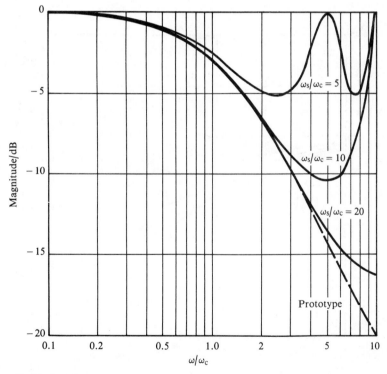

Figure 13.16 *Semilog magnitude characteristics normalized to unity d.c. gain for IIR filters determined by application of impulse invariance method to a first-order lowpass filter.*

logarithmic scale with K chosen, in each case, to make the d.c. gain unity. The magnitude of the continuous prototype is shown also. The curves demonstrate the second property of the impulse invariance method, namely that with proper adjustment of the multiplying factor, the curves coincide at low frequencies but as $\omega \rightarrow \omega_s/2$ they exhibit increasing deviation.

In general, the magnitude at $\omega_s/2$ relative to the d.c. value is given from (13.61) as

$$\frac{H_1(-1)}{H_1(1)} = \frac{1 - e^{-\omega_c T}}{1 + e^{-\omega_c T}} \tag{13.65}$$

This confirms that the attenuation can be increased by increasing the sampling rate.

Figure 13.17 shows the phase-versus-frequency characteristics for the cases considered in Fig. 13.16. It is seen that, as expected, the phase tends to that of the continuous prototype at low frequencies and the range of the correspondence increases as ω_s/ω_c increases.

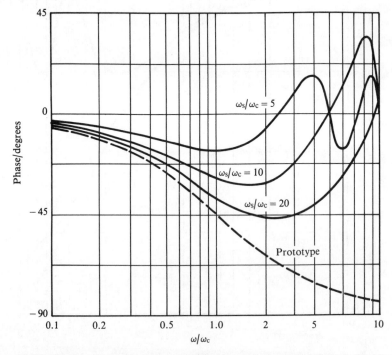

Figure 13.17 *Phase characteristics of IIR filters determined by application of impulse invariance method to a first-order lowpass filter.*

Computer Exercise 13.5

Use Option G4 of ENTIS to investigate the magnitude and phase characteristics of the first-order IIR filter whose Z-transfer function is given by (13.61). Compare the characteristics with those of the continuous prototype. Use various values of ω_s/ω_c.

13.8.2 Second-order lowpass filter

We consider next the application of the impulse invariance method to the case of the second-order lowpass transfer function $F(s)$ with complex poles, written in the form

$$F(s) = \frac{\omega_0^2}{s^2 + Q\omega_0 s + \omega_0^2} \tag{13.66}$$

which can be expressed as

$$F(s) = \frac{A_1}{s - p_1} + \frac{A_2}{s - p_2} \tag{13.67}$$

where

$$p_1 = \frac{-\omega_0}{2Q} + j\omega_0\mu$$

$$p_2 = \frac{-\omega_0}{2Q} - j\omega_0\mu$$

$$A_1 = \frac{-j\omega_0}{2\mu}$$

$$A_2 = -A_1$$

and

$$\mu = \left[1 - \frac{1}{4Q^2}\right]^{1/2}$$

By substituting into (13.54) we finally obtain

$$H(Z) = \frac{a_1 Z^{-1}}{1 + b_1 Z^{-1} + b_2 Z^{-2}} \tag{13.68}$$

where

$$a_1 = \frac{-\omega_0}{\mu} e^{-\lambda} \sin 2Q\lambda\mu$$

$$b_1 = -2e^{-\lambda} \cos 2Q\lambda\mu$$

$$b_2 = e^{-2\lambda}$$

and

$$\lambda = \omega_0 \tau / 2Q$$

The factor Z^{-1} in the numerator of $H(Z)$ in (13.68) provides an additional phase shift $-\omega\tau$ but does not affect the magnitude characteristic. The same magnitude characteristic can therefore be obtained more simply if the factor Z^{-1} is removed. Also if, as in the previous case, a multiplying factor K is introduced to replace the numerator constant, we obtain a modified transfer function $H_1(Z)$ given by

$$H_1(Z) = \frac{K}{1 + b_1 Z^{-1} + b_2 Z^{-2}} \tag{13.69}$$

The frequency response function is

$$H_1(e^{j\omega\tau}) = \frac{K}{1 + b_1(\cos \omega\tau - j \sin \omega\tau) + b_2(\cos 2\omega\tau - j \sin 2\omega\tau)} \tag{13.70}$$

the magnitude-squared is

$$|H_1(e^{j\omega\tau})|^2 = \frac{K^2}{(1 + b_1 \cos \omega\tau + b_2 \cos 2\omega\tau)^2 + (b_1 \sin \omega\tau + b_2 \sin 2\omega\tau)^2} \tag{13.71}$$

and the phase is

$$\angle H_1(e^{j\omega\tau}) = -\tan^{-1} \frac{-b_1 \sin \omega\tau - b_2 \sin 2\omega\tau}{1 + b_1 \cos \omega\tau + b_2 \cos 2\omega\tau} \tag{13.72}$$

13.8.3 Butterworth filter

As an example of the design of a second-order filter we take the Butterworth filter with a cut-off frequency ω_c. For this case $Q = 1/\sqrt{2}$ and $\omega_0 = \omega_c$. Figure 13.18 shows the characteristics for $\omega_s/\omega_c = 10$ and 20 respectively. The characteristic for the continuous prototype is also shown. For the purposes of comparison the magnitudes are in each case normalized to unity d.c. gain. However, it should be noted that with $K = 1$ the actual d.c. gains for the two cases $\omega_s/\omega_c = 10$ and 20 are 12 dB and 22 dB respectively. It is thus concluded that, as in the case of the first-order filter, to obtain significant attenuation in the stopband relative to that at d.c., a relatively high ratio ω_s/ω_c is required, and this results in a large value of d.c. gain with $K = 1$.

Computer Exercise 13.6

Use Option G5 of ENTIS to investigate the magnitude and phase characteristics of the second-order IIR filter whose Z-transfer function is given by (13.69). Compare the characteristics with those of the continuous prototype. Use various values of ω_s/ω_c.

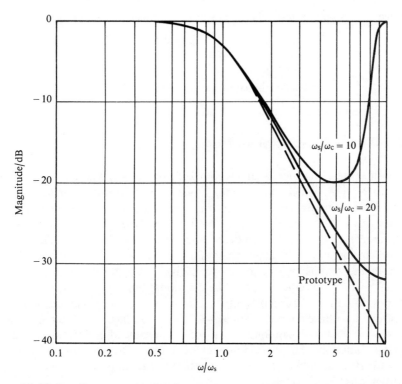

Figure 13.18 *Semilog magnitude characteristics normalized to unity d.c. gain for IIR filters determined by application of impulse invariance method to second-order lowpass Butterworth filter.*

EXAMPLE 13.2

Determine a digital filter to realize a fourth-order lowpass Butterworth characteristic with $\omega_s = 10\omega_c$. Determine the attenuation at $\omega_s/2$ relative to that at d.c.

SOLUTION

It has been shown that the poles of a Butterworth filter lie on a circle, radius ω_c, and for the fourth-order case the arguments of the pole-pairs are $\pm\pi/8$ and $\pm3\pi/8$ respectively. Since the Q-value for a pole-pair is related to the argument ϕ by $Q = 1/(2\cos\phi)$ this gives Q values of 1.307 and 0.541 respectively. Hence the transfer function can be expressed as the product of two second-order transfer functions with their respective Q-values as above and each with $\omega_0 = \omega_c$. The expression of the transfer function in product form leads to a serial form of structure for the digital filter. From (13.68) we obtain the following values:

> Section 1 $b_1 = -1.315$, $b_2 = 0.618$, $K = 0.303$
> Relative attenuation at $\omega_s/2 = 19.7$ dB
> Section 2 $b_1 = -1.087$, $b_2 = 0.313$, $K = 0.226$
> Relative attenuation at $\omega_s/2 = 20.5$ dB

Hence total attenuation at $\omega_s/2 = 40.2$ dB.

13.9 Bilinear Z-transformation

We consider next another indirect approach to design, known as the bilinear Z-transformation, which has several advantages over the impulse invariance method. With this approach the Z-transfer function $H(Z)$ is determined by replacing s in the prototype s-transfer function $F(s)$ by a suitable function $G(Z)$, i.e. $H(Z) = F(G(Z))$. To determine the function $G(Z)$, we first consider the problem in reverse. That is, given a Z-transfer function $H(Z)$ determine a corresponding s-transfer function by replacing Z^{-1} by a suitable function $P(s)$. Since $Z^{-1} = e^{-s\tau}$ we require $P(s)$ to be a rational approximation to $e^{-s\tau}$. In the frequency domain $e^{-s\tau}$ has a magnitude characteristic which is constant at all frequencies and a phase characteristic $\phi_1 = -\omega\tau$. The phase characteristic tends to infinity as $\omega \to \infty$ and cannot be realized by means of a finite-order rational s-transfer function. The magnitude characteristic, however, can be realized exactly by using an allpass function. The simplest form of such a function is the first-order case:

$$P(s) = \frac{1 - sT}{1 + sT} \tag{13.73}$$

which has a frequency response function

$$P(j\omega) = \frac{1 - j\omega T}{1 + j\omega T} \tag{13.74}$$

The magnitude is unity and the phase ϕ_2 is given by

$$\phi_2 = -2\tan^{-1}\omega T \tag{13.75}$$

To optimize the approximation we can define the error ε between the two phase characteristics as

$$\varepsilon = \phi_1 - \phi_2 = -\omega\tau + 2\tan^{-1}\omega T \tag{13.76}$$

Since ε is zero at $\omega = 0$ we can minimize ε in the maximally flat sense at $\omega = 0$ by making the derivative of ε zero at $\omega = 0$.

We have

$$\frac{d\varepsilon}{d\omega} = -\tau + \frac{2T}{1 + \omega^2 T^2} \tag{13.77}$$

which is zero at $\omega = 0$ if $T = \tau/2$. Hence

$$P(s) = \frac{1 - s\tau/2}{1 + s\tau/2} \tag{13.78}$$

(13.78) is a particular case of a set or table of rational approximations to the exponential function known as the Padé table, which gives approximations for all orders of numerator and denominator polynomials. The well-known Taylor series is another particular case of the Padé approximation.

We can now determine the inverse relationship. Since

$$Z^{-1} \simeq \frac{1 - s\tau/2}{1 + s\tau/2} \tag{13.79}$$

rearranging (13.79) gives

$$s \simeq G(Z) = \frac{2}{\tau} \frac{1 - Z^{-1}}{1 + Z^{-1}} \tag{13.80}$$

The relationship in the frequency domain between the two transfer functions $F(s)$ and $H(Z)$ can be determined by comparison of the frequency responses of $P(s)$ and $e^{-s\tau}$. As previously discussed, $P(s)$ and $e^{-s\tau}$ have the same magnitude but have phases $-2 \tan^{-1} \omega\tau/2$ and $-\omega\tau$ respectively. These characteristics are shown in Fig. 13.19. It can be seen that for any specified point on the phase characteristic of $P(s)$ at, say, $\omega = \omega_a$ there will be a corresponding point on the characteristic of $e^{-s\tau}$ at, say, $\omega = \omega_d$ such that the phases at the two points are equal. Since the magnitudes of the two functions are equal at all frequencies, we have that the frequency response function of $P(s)$ at $\omega = \omega_a$ must be equal to the frequency response function of $e^{-s\tau}$ at $\omega = \omega_d$. Thus

$$P(j\omega_a) = e^{-j\omega_d\tau} \tag{13.81}$$

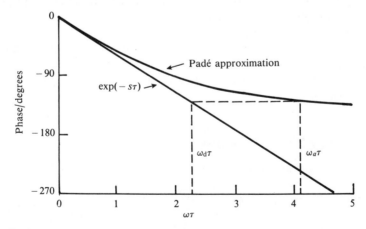

Figure 13.19 *Comparison of phase characteristics of exp(−sτ) and first-order allpass Padé approximant P(s).*

and therefore

$$F(j\omega_a) = H(e^{j\omega_d}) \tag{13.82}$$

That is, for every frequency ω_a the frequency response function of the prototype maps to a corresponding point at ω_d on the characteristic of the digital filter. The relationship between ω_a and ω_d is given by

$$2 \tan^{-1}\omega_a\tau/2 - \omega_d\tau = 0 \tag{13.83}$$

i.e.

$$\omega_a = \frac{2}{\tau} \tan \frac{\omega_d\tau}{2} \tag{13.84}$$

From (13.84) it is seen that as ω_a varies from 0 to ∞, ω_d varies from 0 to a finite frequency ω_u given by

$$\frac{\omega_u\tau}{2} = \frac{\pi}{2} \tag{13.85}$$

i.e.

$$\omega_u = \frac{\pi}{\tau} = \frac{\omega_s}{2} \tag{13.86}$$

Therefore the whole frequency response of $F(s)$ from d.c. to infinity is compressed into a finite range from d.c. to $\omega_s/2$.

For a given value of ω_a, (13.84) has an infinite number of solutions for ω_d spaced at intervals of ω_s, and hence the spectrum of $H(Z)$ consists of the compressed spectrum of $F(s)$ repeated with period ω_s. The compression of the spectrum of $F(s)$ eliminates the problem of reduced attenuation that occurs with the impulse invariance method, but causes a distortion of the frequency scale. This latter effect is known as frequency warping and must be taken into account in the design procedure, since the cut-off frequencies of $F(s)$ and $H(Z)$ will be different. (13.83) can be used to determine the cut-off frequency of $F(s)$ for a specified value of cut-off frequency of the digital filter. This is demonstrated in the subsequent examples.

13.9.1   First-order lowpass filter

We first consider the application of the bilinear Z-transformation to a first-order transfer function given by

$$F(s) = \frac{1}{1 + s/\omega_1} \tag{13.87}$$

where ω_1 is the 3 dB frequency of the prototype.

By applying the transformation of (13.76), we obtain

$$H(Z) = \frac{1 + Z^{-1}}{1 + \alpha + (1 - \alpha)Z^{-1}} \tag{13.88}$$

where

$$a = \frac{2}{\tau \omega_1} \tag{13.89}$$

To allow for frequency warping, we determine ω_1 in terms of the specified 3 dB frequency ω_c of the digital filter according to (13.84), i.e.

$$\omega_1 = \frac{2}{\tau} \tan \frac{\omega_c \tau}{2} \tag{13.90}$$

From (13.89) and (13.90) we obtain

$$\alpha = \cot \pi \frac{\omega_c}{\omega_s} \tag{13.91}$$

The frequency response function is given by

$$H(e^{j\omega\tau}) = \frac{1 + \cos \omega\tau - j \sin \omega\tau}{1 + \alpha + (1 - \alpha)\cos \omega\tau - j(1 - \alpha)\sin \omega\tau} \tag{13.92}$$

the magnitude-squared is

$$|H(e^{j\omega\tau})|^2 = \frac{1 + \cos \omega\tau}{1 + \alpha^2 + (1 - \alpha^2)\cos \omega\tau} \tag{13.93}$$

and the phase is

$$\angle H(e^{j\omega\tau}) = \tan^{-1} \frac{-\sin \omega\tau}{1 + \cos \omega\tau} - \tan^{-1} \frac{-(1 - \alpha)\sin \omega\tau}{(1 + \alpha) + (1 - \alpha)\cos \omega\tau} \tag{13.94}$$

The magnitude and phase characteristics of the above filter are shown in Figs. 13.20 and 13.21 respectively for two values of the ratio ω_s/ω_c. The results verify the foregoing theory that the whole of the frequency spectrum of the proto-type is compressed into the finite band from d.c. to $\omega_s/2$.

Computer Exercise 13.7

Use Option G6 of ENTIS to investigate the magnitude and phase characteristics of the filter obtained by means of the bilinear transformation applied to a first-order continuous lowpass filter. Compare the characteristics with those of the prototype. Use various values of ω_s/ω_c.

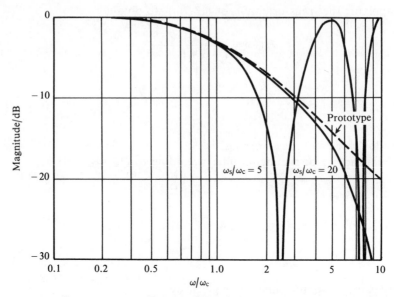

Figure 13.20 *Semilog magnitude characteristics for IIR filters determined by application of bilinear Z-transform to a first-order lowpass filter.*

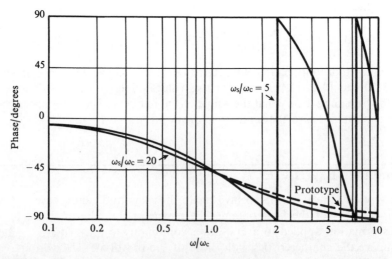

Figure 13.21 *Phase characteristics for IIR filters determined by application of bilinear Z-transform to a first-order lowpass filter.*

13.9.2 Second-order lowpass filter

We next apply the bilinear transformation to the second-order lowpass transfer function in the standard form

$$F(s) = \frac{\omega_0^2}{s^2 + Q\omega_0 s + \omega_0^2} \tag{13.95}$$

We obtain

$$H(Z) = \frac{1 + 2Z^{-1} + Z^{-2}}{b_0 + b_1 Z^{-1} + b_2 Z^{-2}} \tag{13.96}$$

where

$$b_0 = \alpha^2 + \alpha/Q + 1$$
$$b_1 = 2(1 - \alpha^2)$$
$$b_2 = \alpha^2 - \alpha/Q + 1$$

and

$$\alpha = \frac{2}{\tau\omega_0}$$

As in the previous section, to allow for frequency warping we relate ω_0 to its corresponding specified frequency ω_c of the digital filter according to (13.84) and obtain

$$\alpha = \cot \pi \frac{\omega_c}{\omega_s} \tag{13.97}$$

The frequency response function is

$$H(e^{j\omega\tau}) = \frac{1 + 2 \cos \omega\tau + \cos 2\omega\tau + j(2 \sin \omega\tau + \sin 2\omega\tau)}{b_0 + b_1 \cos \omega\tau + b_2 \cos 2\omega\tau - j(b_1 \sin \omega\tau + b_2 \sin 2\omega\tau)} \tag{13.98}$$

the phase is

$$\angle H(e^{j\omega\tau}) = \tan^{-1} \frac{-2 \sin \omega\tau - \sin 2\omega\tau}{1 + 2 \cos \omega\tau + \cos 2\omega\tau} - \tan^{-1} \frac{-b_1 \sin \omega\tau - b_2 \sin 2\omega\tau}{b_0 + b_1 \cos \omega\tau + b_2 \cos 2\omega\tau} \tag{13.99}$$

and the magnitude-squared is

$$|H(e^{j\omega\tau})|^2 = \frac{6 + 2 \cos 2\omega\tau + 8 \cos \omega\tau}{c_0 + c_1 \cos \omega\tau + c_2 \cos 2\omega\tau} \tag{13.100}$$

where

$$c_0 = 6\alpha^4 + \left[\frac{2}{Q^2} - 4\right]\alpha^2 + 6$$

$$c_1 = 8(1 - \alpha^4)$$

$$c_2 = 2\alpha^4 - \left[\frac{2}{Q^2} - 4\right]\alpha^2 + 2$$

13.9.3 Butterworth filter

As an example of the design of a second-order filter we take the same prototype as in Section 13.8.3, that is, a Butterworth filter ($Q = 1/\sqrt{2}$) with a 3 dB frequency ω_0. Taking a value of $\omega_s/\omega_c = 10$, where ω_c is the specified 3 dB frequency of the digital filter, we obtain from (13.96) and (13.97)

$$\alpha = 3.078 \qquad b_0 = 14.825 \qquad b_1 = 16.944 \qquad b_2 = 6.1190$$

Figure 13.22 shows the magnitude characteristic for the above case. The characteristic for the continuous filter is shown also. Again it is seen how the bilinear transformation compresses the response into the band from d.c. to $\omega_s/2$.

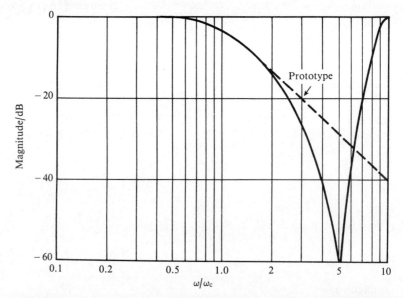

Figure 13.22 *Semilog magnitude characteristic for IIR filter determined by application of bilinear Z-transform to a second-order lowpass Butterworth filter ($\omega_s/\omega_c = 10$).*

Computer Exercise 13.8

Use Option G7 of ENTIS to investigate the magnitude and phase characteristics of the filter obtained by means of the bilinear transformation applied to a second-order lowpass continuous filter. Compare the characteristics with those of the prototype. Use various values of Q and ω_s/ω_c.

EXAMPLE 13.3

Design a digital filter by application of the bilinear transformation to a fourth-order Butterworth filter with $\omega_s/\omega_c = 5$, where ω_c is the required 3 dB frequency of the digital filter.

SOLUTION

As in Example 13.1, the transfer function can be expressed as the product of two second-order sections leading to a serial form of structure. The Q-values of the pole-pairs are 1.307 and 0.541 respectively, and the values of ω_{od} for each section are both equal to the specified 3 dB frequency, ω_c, of the overall response.

From (13.95) and (13.96) we obtain the following values for the coefficients:

$$\text{Section 1 } b_0 = 3.948, \ b_1 = -1.789, \ b_2 = 1.841$$
$$\text{Section 2 } b_0 = 5.439, \ b_1 = -1.789, \ b_2 = 0.350$$

14 SWITCHED-CAPACITOR NETWORKS

14.1 Introduction

In the early 1980s a new type of filter technology was developed which facilitated the realization of active filters in integrated circuit form. This method is based on the use of switched capacitors to produce a type of sampled-data filter, often referred to as an SC filter. The topology is basically that of a conventional active RC filter using the operational amplifier as the active device, but with the feedback resistors replaced by switched capacitors. These devices are now widely available as integrated circuits, and are finding an ever-increasing range of applications. In this chapter, a brief description of the basic principles and properties of switched-capacitor filters is given.

The manufacture of integrated circuits containing conventional active RC filters with no external components presents problems due to the fact that the area required on the chip for the feedback resistors and capacitors can be impractically large for the values of R and C normally used. Although, theoretically, impedance scaling can be applied to reduce, say, the required values of capacitors, this would result in a corresponding increase in the required resistor values, since the RC product values are unaltered by impedance scaling.

The solution to the problem of incorporating the feedback components in an integrated circuit arises from the property that the voltage–current relationship of a switched capacitor can approximate to that of a resistor, and the value of the simulated resistor is inversely proportional to the capacitor value. Thus small capacitors can be used to realize large resistor values, enabling the required RC product values to be achieved with reduced values for the nonswitched capacitors. In this way the area required for the feedback components on the chip can be significantly reduced.

As well as overcoming the problem of integration of large resistor and/or capacitor values, the switched-capacitor filter has additional advantages over conventional active RC filters.

Firstly, because the simulated resistor values are inversely proportional to the capacitor values of the switched capacitors, the effective RC values are determined by the ratios of capacitor values. In integrated-circuit manufacture of capacitors, it is difficult to control the density of the dielectric accurately and

302

hence ensure absolute capacitor values to a high degree of precision. However, photolithographic techniques used in manufacture can accurately control the areas of the capacitor plates. It is thus possible to control accurately the ratios of capacitor values. Therefore the effective RC values are accurately established. Moreover, changes due to temperature affect all the capacitor values in the same proportion, thereby maintaining the effective RC values and resulting in a low sensitivity to temperature variations.

Another advantage arises out of the property that the simulated resistor value is inversely proportional to the switching frequency. By having a single clock which controls the switching frequency, all the effective resistor values can be simultaneously varied by the same factor. This corresponds to frequency scaling and hence enables the cut-off frequency of the filter to be varied by means of the clock frequency.

The principal limitations of switched-capacitor filters arise because switching is effectively a sampling process. This gives rise to the same problems that were discussed in relation to the effects of sampling in a digital filter, namely the additional noise and aliasing problems. To avoid aliasing, any component of the input signal whose frequency exceeds one half of the clock frequency must be removed or attenuated to an acceptably low level. This is usually achieved by an anti-aliasing filter at the input. To eliminate the noise due to the switching, a further filter is required at the output to provide smoothing by removal of the clock frequency and its harmonics.

The need for pre-filtering and post-filtering might appear to defeat the principle advantage of the SC filter, since both the above functions require conventional networks. However, provided that the ratio of clock frequency to cut-off frequency of the SC filter is sufficiently high, the requirements for the input and output filters are not very demanding and often first-order lowpass RC sections will suffice. Values for the ratio of clock frequency to cut-off frequency of the main filter are typically in the range 30:1 to 100:1. Note, however, that in applications where the clock frequency is to be varied, the input and output filters must be designed on the basis of the lowest value of clock frequency.

14.2 Basic principles

The ability of a switched capacitor to simulate the behaviour of a resistor is demonstrated in Fig. 14.1. In Fig. 14.1a a resistor R is shown connected across nodes 1 and 2 with voltages v_1 and v_2, respectively, applied to the nodes. Figure 14.1b shows how the resistor R is replaced by a capacitor together with switches S_1 and S_2 as shown. In practice, S_1 and S_2 are solid-state switches such as MOS transistors. The switches are opened and closed in antiphase at a frequency determined by a clock. It is important that each switch opens before the other switch closes otherwise a short circuit appears across the two nodes.

We assume for the purpose of explanation that v_1 is greater than v_2. Consider

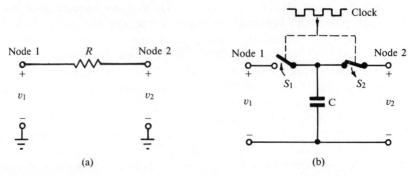

Figure 14.1 *Simulation of resistor by means of switched capacitor: (a) resistor, (b) switched capacitor.*

first the switch S_1 closed and the capacitor C charged to a voltage v_1. We have that the charge on C is $q_1 = Cv_1$. If S_1 is now opened and S_2 is closed, the capacitor discharges to a voltage v_2. The charge on C then becomes $q_2 = Cv_2$. Thus a charge $q_1 - q_2 = C(v_1 - v_2) = Cv$ is transferred during one clock cycle, where $v = v_1 - v_2$ is the voltage across the two nodes. If the clock frequency is f_s hertz then a charge of f_sCv coulombs is transferred each second. That is, the average current i_{av} in amperes is given by

$$i_{av} = f_sCv \tag{14.1}$$

The actual current waveform consists of a short burst into node 1 when S_1 closes followed by a short burst out of node 2 when S_2 closes. It therefore contains harmonics of the clock frequency f_s. However, provided that the voltage v does not change appreciably during one clock period, the high-frequency clock component can be removed at the output by a simple smoothing filter and the switched capacitor can be considered to obey the relationship $v = Ri_{av}$ where, from comparison with (14.1) we have

$$R = \frac{1}{f_sC} \tag{14.2}$$

Therefore, as previously stated, the simulated resistance is inversely proportional to both the capacitance and the clock frequency.

14.3 State-variable SC filters

SC filters are usually based on a cascade of second-order state-variable networks. They have a topology which is similar in most respects to that of their active *RC* counterparts. For example, the circuit of an SC inverting integrator in which the switched capacitor replaces the resistor of a conventional active *RC* inverting integrator is shown in Fig. 14.2.

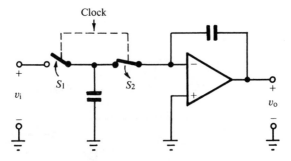

Figure 14.2 *Switched-capacitor inverting integrator.*

An interesting and useful feature of SC filter synthesis that does not have a direct counterpart in active *RC* filters is the possibility of elimination of the sign inversion which occurs in the two-immittance inverter, without the use of both inputs to the amplifier. This is demonstrated by the network shown in Fig. 14.3. As in the case of the inverting integrator of Fig. 14.2, the switched capacitor charges alternately to voltages v_1 and v_2 as the switches S_1 and S_2, respectively, close. However, the current flow into node 1B is in the opposite direction to the current flow into node 1A. Therefore, for v_1 greater than v_2, the nonswitched capacitor discharges and the voltage at the output of the amplifier increases. It is thus concluded that the network behaves as a non-inverting integrator.

The method used in Fig. 14.3 can be readily extended to provide a differential integrator as shown in Fig. 14.4.

It is clear therefore that all the standard active *RC* circuits have SC counterparts, and methods such as the state-variable technique can be readily applied.

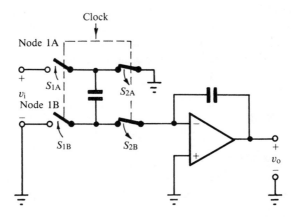

Figure 14.3 *Switched-capacitor non-inverting integrator.*

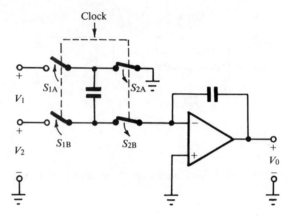

Figure 14.4 *Switched-capacitor differential integrator.*

14.4 Programmable filters

The use of switched-capacitor technology in integrated circuits leads to a further facility, namely that of digitally programmable filters.

The basic building-block for SC filters is the second-order state-variable filter, which is available on a single chip for use in a cascade arrangement for higher order filters. The Q-value and the ratio of ω_0 to clock frequency can be independently varied in discrete steps by the respective capacitors. Each capacitor value is changed by means of a parallel capacitor array on the chip, for which the capacitors can be switched in and out. External control of a capacitor value is achieved through, typically, a 5-bit input which would provide $2^5 = 32$ possible values. The inputs can be hard-wired or controlled by means of a microprocessor. The latter form of control permits the use of the SC filter in adaptive filter applications.

Higher cost SC filter integrated circuits contain several, typically four, second-order state-variable networks on a single chip. Other features which may be included on the chip are (a) uncommitted operational amplifiers for use in anti-aliasing and smoothing, and (b) volatile or nonvolatile memory for storage of the filter coefficients.

APPENDIX A

LAPLACE TRANSFORMATION

A.1 Introduction

Classical methods for the solution of linear differential equations with constant coefficients involve functions of time at every stage of the process and are therefore said to operate purely in the time domain. An alternative approach is a transformation in which the signals are expressed in terms of some variable other than time. A well-known example of a transformation is that of Fourier, in which the signals are represented as the sum of sine waves and cosine waves. For this case the transformed signals are functions of frequency and are said to be expressed in the frequency domain. The transform function determines the steady-state frequency spectrum of the signal.

For the solution of the transient behaviour of a system, a more suitable approach, which is closely related to the Fourier method, is the Laplace transformation. In this case, the new variable is complex frequency, referred to also as the Laplace complex variable, and is usually denoted by s. (In some texts the symbol p is used in preference to s.) We denote the real and imaginary parts of s by σ and ω respectively, i.e. $s = \sigma + j\omega$.

A complex frequency is a signal of the form $Ae^{\sigma t} \sin(\omega t + \theta)$. That is, the Laplace transformation expresses functions of time in terms of sinusoidal waveforms modulated by an exponential. The j-part of s is the angular frequency and the real part is the coefficient of t in the power of the exponential. Thus, whereas the Fourier method expresses the signal in terms of sinusoids with constant amplitude, the Laplace method introduces an exponential multiplier. Another important difference between the two is that in the case of Fourier the sinusoids are assumed to extend from $t = -\infty$ to $t = +\infty$, whereas the definition of the Laplace transform has limits of integration from $t = 0$ to $t = +\infty$ and the values of a function for $t < 0$ do not contribute to the Laplace transform. When the Laplace transformation is applied to a differential equation, the derivatives are replaced by powers of s. In this way differential equations become algebraic equations in s which are more easily manipulated than the differential equations. By manipulating the expression for the transform of the response into a form in which the inverse transformation can be performed, the response as a function of time can finally be obtained.

A.2 Derivation of Laplace transform pairs

The Laplace transform $F(s)$ of a function $f(t)$ is defined by

$$F(s) = \int_0^\infty f(t)e^{-st}\,dt \tag{A.1}$$

Not all functions possess a Laplace transform. The integral of (A.1) exists only if

$$\lim_{t \to \infty} e^{-\sigma t}f(t) = 0 \tag{A.2}$$

for some finite value of σ.

Most of the functions commonly encountered in network theory satisfy the above condition. An example of a function which does not satisfy (A.2) and therefore does not possess a Laplace transform is e^{t^2}.

To build up a table of Laplace transform pairs, we can use (A.1). For example, consider the unit step function $u(t)$. This has the same transform as $f(t) = 1$ since values of the function for $t < 0$ do not contribute to the integral. We have

$$F(s) = \int_0^\infty e^{-st}\,dt$$

$$= \frac{1}{s} \int_0^\infty e^{-st}\,d(st)$$

$$= \frac{1}{s} \left[-e^{-st} \right]_0^\infty$$

$$= \frac{1}{s} \tag{A.3}$$

This is shown as entry 1 in Table A.1.

While a table of Laplace transform pairs can be built up from first principles using (A.1) as in the above example, there are some useful theorems which can be applied to obtain the most commonly required transforms from one or two basic transforms. It is assumed in each case that the functions under consideration satisfy (A.2) and hence possess a Laplace transform. We denote the transform of $f(t)$ by $F(s)$. The theorems are given below without proof as follows:

Theorem 1
If α is not a function of time then $\alpha f(t)$ has the transform $\alpha F(s)$.

Theorem 2

If $f_1(t)$ and $f_2(t)$ have transforms $F_1(s)$ and $F_2(s)$ respectively then the transform of $f_1(t) + f_2(t)$ is $F_1(s) + F_2(s)$.

Theorem 3

The derivative $\mathrm{d}f(t)/\mathrm{d}t$ has the transform $sF(s) - f(0+)$ where $f(0+)$ is the value of $f(t)$ immediately after $t = 0$.

Theorem 4

The integral of $f(t')$ with respect to t' over the limits 0 to t has the transform $F(s)/s$.

Theorem 5

The function $\mathrm{e}^{-at}f(t)$ has the transform $F(s + a)$.

Unit impulse

As an example of the use of Theorem 3 we have that the unit impulse $\delta(t)$ is the derivative of the unit step and $\delta(0+) = 0$. Therefore the transform of $\delta(t)$ is $s \times 1/s = 1$ (see entry 2).

Unit ramp function

As an example of the use of Theorem 4 we have that the unit ramp function $f(t) = t$ is the integral of $u(t')$ with respect to t' over the limits 0 to t, where $u(t)$ is the unit step. Hence, from entry 1, we have that the transform of $f(t) = t$ is $1/s^2$ (see entry 3).

Exponential function

As an example of the use of Theorem 5 we have that the transform of e^{-at} is obtained from entry 1 in Table A.1 as $1/(s + a)$ (see entry 4).

Sinusoidal function

The transform of $\sin \omega t$ can be obtained from the relationship

$$\sin \omega t = \frac{1}{2\mathrm{j}} (\mathrm{e}^{\mathrm{j}\omega t} - \mathrm{e}^{-\mathrm{j}\omega t}) \tag{A.4}$$

From entry 4 we have that the transforms of $\mathrm{e}^{\mathrm{j}\omega t}$ and $\mathrm{e}^{-\mathrm{j}\omega t}$ are $1/(s - \mathrm{j}\omega)$ and $1/(s + \mathrm{j}\omega)$ respectively. Hence, using (A.4) and Theorems 1 and 2 we obtain the transform of $\sin \omega t$ as $\omega/(s^2 + \omega^2)$ (see entry 5).

The transform of $\cos \omega t$ can be obtained in a similar manner to the above, or by using Theorems 1 and 3 and observing that $\cos \omega t$ is a derivative of $(\sin \omega t)/\omega$ with respect to t. We obtain the transform of $\cos \omega t$ as $\omega/(s^2 + \omega^2)$ (see entry 6).

By applying Theorem 5 to entries 3, 5 and 6, we obtain entries 7, 8 and 9 respectively to complete the table.

	$F(t)$	$F(s)$
1	$u(t), 1$	$\dfrac{1}{s}$
2	$\delta(t)$	1
3	t	$\dfrac{1}{s^2}$
4	e^{-at}	$\dfrac{1}{s+a}$
5	$\sin \omega t$	$\dfrac{\omega}{s^2 + \omega^2}$
6	$\cos \omega t$	$\dfrac{s}{s^2 + \omega^2}$
7	te^{-at}	$\dfrac{1}{(s+a)^2}$
8	$e^{-at} \sin \omega t$	$\dfrac{\omega}{(s+a)^2 + \omega^2}$
9	$e^{-at} \cos \omega t$	$\dfrac{s+a}{(s+a)^2 + \omega^2}$

A.3 Inverse transformation

Determination of the inverse transform involves contour integration, and a simpler approach for rational functions is one in which a partial fraction expansion is performed and the inverse transforms are obtained by recognition from the table of Laplace transform pairs.

Consider a rational function $F(s)$ with the denominator expressed in factored form as follows:

$$F(s) = \frac{N(s)}{(s - p_1)(s - p_2) \dots (s - p_n)} \tag{A.5}$$

If the order m of the numerator is less than the order n of the denominator then $F(s)$ can be expressed in partial fraction form. If $m \geqslant n$, then we can divide the numerator by the denominator starting with the highest powers, until the remainder satisfies the condition $m < n$. We can then perform the partial fraction expansion of the remainder.

Assuming that in (A.5), $m < n$ and also that all the poles are simple, i.e. no poles are coincident, we can expand (A.5) as follows:

$$F(s) = \frac{A_1}{s - p_1} + \frac{A_2}{s - p_2} + \ldots + \frac{A_n}{s - p_n} \tag{A.6}$$

The constants $A_1, A_2, \ldots, A_n$ are known as the residues of the respective poles $p_1, p_2, \ldots, p_n$.

We can now apply an inverse transformation to (A.6) and we obtain

$$f(t) = A_1 e^{p_1 t} + A_2 e^{p_2 t} + \ldots + A_n e^{p_n t} \tag{A.7}$$

Note that (A.7) is valid even when some or all of the poles are complex.

A.4 Cover-up rule

We can determine each residue by a simple procedure known as the cover-up rule. We first assume that all the poles are simple. Suppose we require to determine the residue A_r of the pole p_r. We multiply each side of (A.6) by $(s - p_r)$ and let $s = p_r$. On the right-hand side of (A.7) all the terms become zero except the term A_r. On the left-hand side we remove the factor $(s - p_r)$ from the denominator and let $s = p_r$. That is, the cover-up rule states that to determine A_r we 'cover-up' the factor $(s - p_r)$ in the denominator of the function $F(s)$ and replace s by p_r.

EXAMPLE A.1

Perform a partial fraction expansion of the following function:

$$F(s) = \frac{(s + 2)(s + 4)}{(s + 3)(s + 5)(s + 10)} \tag{A.8}$$

SOLUTION

We have

$$F(s) = \frac{A_1}{s + 3} + \frac{A_2}{s + 5} + \frac{A_3}{s + 10} \tag{A.9}$$

To determine A_1 we 'cover up' the factor $(s + 3)$ in the right-hand side of (A.8) and replace s by -3. We obtain

$$A_1 = \frac{(-3 + 2)(-3 + 4)}{(-3 + 5)(-3 + 10)} = \frac{-1}{14} \tag{A.10}$$

Similarly we obtain

$$A_2 = \frac{(-5+2)(-5+4)}{(-5+3)(5+10)} = \frac{-3}{10}$$ (A.11)

and

$$A_3 = \frac{(-10+2)(-10+4)}{(-10+3)(-10+5)} = \frac{48}{35}$$ (A.12)

A.5 Multiple poles

The cover-up rule can still be used in the case of multiple poles. This is best demonstrated by means of an example.

EXAMPLE A.2

Perform a partial fraction expansion and determine the inverse transform of the following function:

$$F(s) = \frac{s+2}{(s+3)^2(s+4)}$$ (A.13)

SOLUTION

We can remove a factor $(s+3)$ from the denominator to leave a function with no multiple poles as follows:

$$F(s) = \frac{1}{s+3} \left[\frac{s+2}{(s+3)(s+4)} \right]$$ (A.14)

We can perform a partial fraction expansion of the function in the square brackets, using the cover-up rule, and obtain

$$F(s) = \frac{1}{s+3} \left(\frac{-1}{s+3} + \frac{2}{s+4} \right)$$ (A.15)

We next multiply by the denominator factor $(s+3)$ and perform a partial fraction expansion, again using the cover-up rule, of the new function in square brackets, i.e.

$$F(s) = \frac{-1}{(s+3)^2} + \left[\frac{2}{(s+3)(s+4)} \right]$$

$$= \frac{-1}{(s+3)^2} + \frac{2}{s+3} - \frac{2}{s+4}$$ (A.16)

We can now inverse transform to obtain

$$f(s) = -te^{-3t} + 2e^{-3t} - 2e^{-4t} \tag{A.17}$$

The above method can be used for any degree of multiplicity. That is, for a pole p_r with multiplicity q we start by removing a factor $(s - p_r)^{q-1}$ and use the above procedure to reduce the multiplicity to $q - 1$. Repeated application of this procedure enables the inverse transform to be finally obtained.

APPENDIX B
THE SUPPLEMENTARY DISK

All the computer exercises in this book utilize the program ENTIS: Electrical Network Theory Interactive Software. This fully interactive software package aids student learning and provides valuable class demonstration material for the lecturer. It is also of use for the practising engineer as an aid to filter design.

Contents

First-order network   Transient response to step, impulse and sine wave; magnitude and phase of steady-state frequency response on linear or log scales; simultaneous display of s-plane.

Second-order network   Transient response to step and impulse; magnitude and phase of steady-state frequency response on linear or log scales; simultaneous display of s-plane. Pole locations and relationship with ω_0 and Q; animated display of graphical relationship between singularities and frequency response for minimum and nonminimum phase networks; peaking circle construction. Comparison of step response of second-order function which has real poles with that of dominant pole; comparison of step response of fourth-order function which has complex poles with that of dominant pole-pair.

Bode diagrams   Semilog straight line approximations and actual characteristics of magnitude and phase for transfer functions with real singularities.

Steady-state frequency response   Magnitude and phase for transfer functions specified by pole locations; magnitude characteristics for transfer functions specified by coefficients of magnitude-squared function.

Standard filter tables and characteristics   Butterworth, Chebyshev and Bessel filters; lowpass magnitude, phase, delay and step response characteristics; s-plane diagrams; tables of singularity locations for lowpass, highpass, bandpass and bandstop.

Active networks   Design of Butterworth, Chebyshev and Bessel lowpass, highpass and bandpass filters using multiple feedback, Sallen–Key and state-variable networks; design of bandstop and allpass networks using state-variable network. Errors due to finite gain bandwidth of operational amplifier in the

314

following arrangements: inverting and non-inverting fixed gain, inverting integrator, multiple feedback lowpass, highpass and bandpass.

Digital filters   Time domain response of first-order recursive and third-order nonrecursive filters; frequency response of FIR filter designed using rectangular window; frequency response of first- and second-order IIR filters designed using impulse invariance and bilinear transformation.

Passive filters   Design of Butterworth and Chebyshev lowpass, highpass, bandpass and bandstop filters using double-terminated LC ladder networks.

Ordering information

ENTIS is distributed by Linton Software and is available on $3\frac{1}{2}$ inch or $5\frac{1}{4}$ inch floppy disk for the IBM PC AT and close compatibles. The program will operate with a CGA-compatible graphics card but for best results an EGA- or VGA-compatible graphics card with colour monitor is recommended.

The disk is priced at £19.95/$35.50 plus £1.50/$2.50 post and packing. Please write stating whether $3\frac{1}{2}$ inch or $5\frac{1}{4}$ inch disk is required and enclose cheque, postal or money order to

        Linton Software
        2 Danesway
        Prestwich
        Manchester M25 8FS
        Lancashire
        UK

Site licences are available for this software. Please address all orders and enquiries to Linton Software, not to Prentice Hall International.

REFERENCES

Budak, A. (1974), *Passive and Active Network Analysis and Synthesis*, Boston: Houghton Miflin.

Darlington, S. (1939), 'Synthesis of reactance 4-poles which produce prescribed insertion loss characteristics', *Jour. Math and Phys.*, **18**, 257–353.

Dorf, R. C. (1974), *Modern Control Systems*, Wokingham, England: Addison-Wesley.

Rhodes, J. D. (1976), *Theory of Electrical Filters*, London: John Wiley.

Temes, G. C. and LaPatra, J. W. (1977), *Introduction to Circuit Synthesis and Design*, London: McGraw-Hill.

Van Valkenburg, M. E. (1960), *Introduction to Modern Network Synthesis*, London: John Wiley.

Van Valkenburg, M. E. (1987), *Analog Filter Design*, London: Holt Rinehart and Winston.

INDEX

317